Songs of Love & Strength

An Anthology of Poems on Motherhood
Edited by Katharine Perry

**First published in Great Britain in 2021
by The Mum Poem Press**

**themumpoempress.com
themumpoempress@gmail.com**

Copyright © Katharine Perry t/a The Mum Poem Press.

All poems copyright © the individual poets.

The moral right of Katharine Perry to be identified as the
compiler of this work has been asserted in accordance with
the Copyrights, Designs and Patents Act of 1988.

A CIP catalogue record for this book is available from
the British Library.
ISBN 978-1-8382888-2-2

Typeset by Emma Dakeyne
madeyousomething@gmail.com

For my mum,
Karen Muldown

Foreword by Katharine Perry

During my first pregnancy I felt anxious and, as I'd always done, I turned to poetry to try and make sense of things. But it was hard to find poetry about pregnancy, birth and motherhood. And the anthologies I did find contained mostly verses written by men, about their wives and mothers.

I found this shocking. Creating and sustaining a new life felt like a huge and universal experience. Where was the poetry about it?

Once my daughter was born, the idea of reading a whole novel felt like an impossible dream. But the poets I'd sought out during my pregnancy gave me short bursts of truth and beauty to consume in the few minutes I had in between tending to the constant needs of my baby. Hollie McNish, Liz Berry, Kate Clanchy and Fiona Benson became my friends during night feeds – reassuring me that my feelings were valid and the overwhelming job of keeping my baby alive was important and beautiful.

When I had my second baby, I started writing poetry in a way I never had before. I couldn't stop myself, it poured out of me and into the Notes app of my phone while my son slept with his fat cheeks smushed against my chest.

I started posting it anonymously on Instagram and immediately found women from all over the world doing the same thing. The idea that having children stifles creativity turned out to be a myth: here were thousands of women inspired by the extraordinary experiences of motherhood to write and share poetry, many for the first time in their lives.

I loved reading other mums' poems. Their words would beam out of my phone in the middle of the night while I fed my baby and I immediately felt less alone. Women were capturing magic moments of joy and crushing days of struggle with such skill and honesty. They were distilling fragments of motherhood into little capsules of emotion, sending them out like messages in bottles, treasure maps secretly and carefully crafted and carried over the waves of the worldwide web to provide comfort to other mothers scrolling social media in the dark.

These poems helped me so much in processing the experience of motherhood, normalising the extraordinary roller-coaster of emotions involved and validating the constant round the clock care that had suddenly become my job.

Motherhood can feel so vast and overwhelming, I found that exploring it in tiny detailed portions of poetry made it feel manageable and helped me focus on the small moments in my own exhausted days.

I felt sure that other mothers would feel the same comfort if they read these poems, so I decided to publish this anthology of poetry on motherhood created by women writing today.

I started collecting favourite poems – some posted by the authors on social media, some found in anthologies such as 'Mothership Writers' and I put call-outs for submissions in as many places as I could.

I received hundreds of poems of all different styles and touching on all different themes and experiences. Some by established writers who happened to be mothers too and some by women who were compelled to write a poem for the first time in their lives by the incredible experience of motherhood. All were honest, all were beautiful.

There were poems about infertility, miscarriage, stillbirth, almost dying in labour, suffering mental illness, engorged breasts, loss of identity, boredom, the smell of babies' heads, tiny fingers, sleep deprivation, first shoes, parenting children with special needs, time spent in ICUs, home-schooling during the pandemic, having babies in lockdown, the bittersweet pain of babies growing up and becoming independent, how it feels when your children leave home – things that you don't often see written down, let alone read poetry about. But experiences that affect millions of people and are so important to share.

In putting together this anthology, I have tried to represent the range of poetry that was submitted in the hope that there is something for every mum in this collection, the ones that read and write poetry every day and the ones who don't usually like poetry. Poetry is a comfort that should be available to all.

I hope this anthology gives the reader a glimpse into the stories of these mother poets, so varied and unique but also relatable and universal.

Here is a collection of contemporary mothers singing of one of the most profound human experiences with humour, grace and beauty.

These are songs of love and strength.

CONTENTS

Chapter 4: *Early Days*

Chapter 5: *Feeding*

Chapter 6: *Sleep*

Chapter 7: *Strength*

Chapter 8: *Growing*

Chapter 9: *Grandparents*

Chapter 10: *2020*

Chapter 13: *Join the Mum Poet Club*

Chapter 1
Introduction

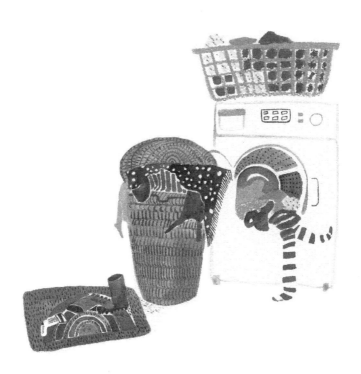

Loads of Love

Loads
But still there's more
Never a chore
Sometimes tumbling
Never shrinking
Not ever delicate
Absolutely infinite
Colourful but
Bright
White
My love for you
Is like laundry

Emma Dakeyne

Her Strength

I attempt to unravel
From the clutches
Of desperate sleep
Using all of my strength
To lift my eyelids
With an invisible force
Of what I hold in my arms
I look down
And I see her
For the first time
And her beauty
Takes my breath
The adrenaline
Pulses through me
Soothing the pain
In the space
You left behind
You are here
I am here
Two bodies
Put through hell
Emerging
Into the light
Harsh and bright
A steady warmth

On delicate skin
Oxygen flowing
In and out
We made it
We made it!
I look down
And her strength
Keeps me going
Two years later
It still does

Emily Way-Evans

When

When friends become mothers
for the first time
when
they realise
that those blue and pink soaked dreams are anything but,
and instead
bleed red
red birth, red heart,
filled with more love than can be expected.
I inwardly smile.
They ask:
"will it be ok?"
I just laugh, pretend I didn't hear, play with my phone.
How can you explain to someone
that something you wanted, for so long
signals the very end of your life as you know it?
That each moment of love,
each tiny bead of
milk, sweat and blood
is actually your very un-doing.
Instead, mothers lie.
"You will be fine,"
you say.
Far away, past women whisper a warning.
Her birth is also your re-birth.

Anna Woolf

To Me, Before I Entered

There is no time here,
a hundred tasks overlap
and intertwine, falling
in and around each other
in a maelstrom of un-doneness
that tugs at my clothes,
a tornado of stained drudgery.

Everything hurts, here
I am bleeding and torn
and I thought my mind was
twisted before but I would give
anything for what, then
was an untangled thought
because here,
that most unpicked of knitting
would be a beautiful tapestry
of sanity.

Here, the neighbours spy on me
report me to the police of motherhood
whose hands grasp out
of their door-knocking bureaucracy
to grab my baby's wrists
and pull.

The grass is not the green
that you imagined, here
when you peeked through the gate
with your nieces and nephews
in hand and pram and heart.
But, although it does not glitter
with the blooming heart-shaking shine
that you imagined all through youth
it is green,
and in that green grows life
and in that life blooms smiles
and wonder and play,
and love.

Ellen Uttley

6

Chapter 2
Expecting

Most Of The Weight I Gained During Pregnancy Was From Carrying Around Other People's Opinions

You watch me walk with a world inside me
Skin stretched ribs aching smile so wide
It could split the sky open.
I do not hide my happiness
(Isn't that beautiful?)
And yet you open your mouth and
Poison spills out:
How old are you?
Aren't you a bit young to have a baby?
Where's the dad?
You must've quit uni then?
Are you keeping it?
The stars fall from my eyes
My teeth sting with a string of answers
I shouldn't have to give:
Eighteen
At home
No, I haven't
Yes.
It takes all the strength in me

Not to scream:
My age is not a measure of my ability to be a good mother
I am a good mother.
I do not want your pity
Your sympathetic smiles have no place here
Replace them with joy.
Only joy.
Unfiltered joy.
Because the only thing that is wrong here
Is you.

Samantha Nimmo

Mumpa

Mother –
Yet another
      Identity that's just not me.

A misnomer for this baby grower
Who's over being proud owner of this
Swollen vulva,
      Breasts
           And areola
That blinds beholders
In perpetual gender comas
To assume that
I'm a
Mum.

Disclosure.

I'm not.

Let's pick this over.

Gender is a swelling sweep
Of Masculine,
      Feminine,
           In Betweens

And

            Set Aparts.
Not just "Boy" / "Girl", as society imparts.
A rainbow, vortex, symphony
Of ego, self-fuelled honesty.

I too bowed out of binaries
And declared that I had
None.

Hence, you see,
The problem posed by
"Mum".

Ward names honour flowers, pastel colours,
Precious stones,
Gift bags passed down "Mummy" before my first
Was even born.
Antenatal means "Maternal"
Challenging that question universal
(Am I really so abnormal?)

So, who am I now?

The distressed unrest of
Breast (not chest) is best,
Mum (not me) knows best,
And oppressed, compressed, and tensely stressed
As my forename and former names are dumped –
"So, how's Mum doing?"

I will not permit dysphoria
(Despite voices and torn clitoria)
To dampen my euphoria
Of growing, pushing, feeding, guiding
My little people. My radiant souls
Who call me "Mumpa" –
A portmanteau of their creation.
Because at ages two and three
Their communication and empathy
Already eclipse those two-tone expectations
                    In which past generations
                    Are steeped.

They know that I'm their parent.
And that is sheer perfection –
            For me.

Ash Bainbridge

Body

Your body was just a vessel,
Designed to bring your soul to me.
I loved you before it existed,
When you were connected only to me.
You were nothing but a thought,
A feeling in my heart.
Yet somehow you were everything,
Such a huge part.
Of our plans for the future,
Of all our hopes and dreams.
And what I mourn the most,
Is all that could have been.

Sarah Hardy

Belly

I miss the shape of us
Russian dolls
In motion
Our veins like
Heart-made
Paper chains
My belly full
Of ocean

I miss the tummy hour
Matinee of breathing
Our rise and fall
The velvet crawl
Your first home
In ovation

I miss the shape of two
The cast of me
And you

Lisa Perkins

Just Me

Just me
Solo with my dreams
Nonetheless starting
Researching it all

Just me
Saving the money
Finding a clinic
Choosing a donor

Just me
Getting more healthy
Scans and injections
Insemination

Just me
Finding two lines, then
Incredulous tears
Scared and elated

Just me
Telling my family
Telling my best friends
Yoga, deep breathing

Just me
Bigger and bigger
Alone with the kicks
Milestones ticking

Just me
Asleep to birth you
Waking. Bliss dawns – now
It will never be

Just me.

Jennifer Gill

The Ring of Expectation

Are you pregnant yet?

Four simple words
that struck fear into my heart
and a lurch in my tummy
every time I heard them

Those little glances
from my eyes to my belly
looking for any signs
of a new life

This new life
called marriage
aka wedded bliss
came with weighty expectations

Not from my beloved
but from the outside world
our closest family and friends
and random strangers

We were honest
as most couples are
that a family was on the cards
we wanted a baby

Simple!

From the moment we met
I knew that this was the man
I wanted to have
a baby with

What I didn't know
how can any of us know
what the future holds
what lay ahead of us

The rocky road
of infertility
spanning
15
tiring
years

Lucy Arden

Are you done?

Are you done?
3 benign syllables
Ready. Steady. Go!
ears ringing
motion sick
100m diversion sprint
leaping deflection hurdles on autopilot
like driving home and having no recollection
of the journey
I'm too old
3 sharp syllables
one's enough... to hide behind
one took a lifetime... and all my hope

I stumbled over the repetitive chorus...eventually
to a new verse
It's a girl
3 momentous syllables
I was old then
I'm older now
Are you done?
Have I satisfied your curiosity?
She is shouting tongue twisters
as butterflies are being chased by barking guard dogs
a cacophony of confusion as I wee on a stick

Hope lolly? Betrayal dipstick?
Is there a word for that deafening pause whilst nature
makes up her mind?

So, I guess it's good to ask.
After the ringing stops
rehearsed phrases cross the line
there is a momentary silence
space created
my complicated truth can be heard above the hubbub
such painful beauty
Yes... I am done.

Abi Coyle

A prayer for my son
before he enters the new world

I

you have chosen me as your
guardian – on a day soon
i'll lie
beside you
on warm grass watching

                    you gaze
at waving leaves

and you are not mine,
you are yours you are

                    life's longing
                    for itself

II

my son – men
in pain are roaring
about the world howling
from the lack

of love
when they were   small
                              gazing
                              at waving leaves

when they were
beaten told
to toughen
up to be

a killer

III

my son I will never
kick
away   your softness

as long as you need
i'll carry you – rock
you with my body as my body
rocks you now until
you step beyond

me to a new
world with open
eyes open hands knowing
what i was taught to forget
that

love
never leaves

IV

for now

my body
surrounds
your water globe

with warm
grass beneath i feel
your wriggles watch
the leaves wave
knowing

the earth
holds us both.

Ellie Nova

The Anxious Wait

The days and nights are long now,
it is an anxious wait.
I pause, breathe in, count to four,
breathe out and count to eight.

I know the time is getting close
to hold you in my arms,
but now I'm feeling frightened,
my mind cannot get calm.

You're safe and warm inside me,
we snuggle up in bed,
the strange confusing world out here
keeps filling me with dread.

Out here we're all imprisoned,
our human rights are stripped.
A deadly virus shakes the earth,
for which we're not equipped.

I'm trying to relax enough to
bring you to this world –
your little body resting there,
head down, bum up, back curled.

Your movements are so strong now,
your kicks have so much might,
I know you're ready to come out,
I must not feel this fright.

It's 6am, I step outside,
as sun begins to rise,
the birds are singing as dawn breaks,
you stretch at my insides.

I reconnect myself with earth,
the one thing that is true,
I fill my lungs with golden light
and send it down to you.

The air is cool, a gentle breeze
now skims across my face,
this natural world, the only thing
that's filling me with grace.

I want you here beside me now,
time is moving slow,
I'm longing for you in my arms,
but can't seem to let go.

I try to calm my mind again,
it is an anxious wait,
I pause, breathe in, count to four,
breathe out and count to eight.

Chloe Morgan

Chapter 3
Birth

Birthing

Smashed.
Like a plum
tumbled from the bough.
Ragged flesh spread wide,
glistening with love seeping sticky, sweet,
oozing from every crack.
Bruised,
tender, exposed to pain, beauty, terror. Feeding
the wasps and searching roots. Sucked
into deepest caring. Leaking tears through shredded skin.
Split
by needs, cries, outstretched hands. Nerves laid bare
to pounding rain, flayed by searing sun.
No sanctuary here. Broken, shattered, torn – BORN –
quivering,
sobbing, afraid.
Alive.
Pounded into mire by storms of want,
thrashed by hiccupping howling
wind. Wailing in darkness, dissolving
into earth. And at the centre:
a stone, a pit, a kernel.
A strength
unhidden.

Liz Proctor

When I Gave Birth

I still haven't said, "when I gave birth".
I fall clumsily around the words, trying to find a way
of telling
how you came to be in the world
that doesn't feel
like a falsehood.

I still haven't said, "when I gave birth".
It sounds deceitful –
too proactive –
for such a passive act.
The slicing open of my skin,
the tearing through muscle and sinew,
to rip out a baby
caught unawares.

I still haven't said "when I gave birth".
72 hours of labour is somehow not enough
to earn the right to say
"I birthed my baby"
when in reality,
someone else gave birth to you
tore you
from your warm cocoon.
I don't even know their name.

I still haven't said, "when I gave birth".
It seems misleading
when my first sight of you
was in a stranger's arms
instead of mine.
I tried to reach up to stroke your newborn foot
but found my limbs paralyzed.
"It's a girl", your dad sobbed
as you were both rushed away
from the developing emergency –
the heavy shock of adrenaline
delaying my screams to have my baby back
on my chest
where she belonged.

I still haven't said, "when I gave birth".
How can I have given birth to someone
when I was barely alive?
Heart in shutdown,
lungs collapsing.
Hurried talk of hysterectomy
and how to save my life
while all I could do was lie bleeding
and wonder,
where has it gone wrong?

before the theatre lights faded
and shut off
into darkness;
my long-held dreams of our serene first meeting
stolen, without remorse.

I still haven't said "when I gave birth".
Waking up in a room I've never seen,
a sea of blue pleated curtain,
my mother appears as a blur amongst the waves.
Unrelenting thuds of pain
and no sign of a baby,
only Star Trek screens and a deflated belly
covered by the cheap fabric of a hospital gown.
A deep sense of unease
spread over my limbs
like spilt oil;
the tube down my throat
suffocating any attempt to speak
or scream
or sob.

I still haven't said "when I gave birth".
After they told me you were safe,
my first question

was
'Do I still have my womb?'.
My fingers, heavy with sedation,
trying their best to move
across the laminated alphabet card,
to spell out questions
whose weight
I could not yet fully understand.

And then.

The sickening crack of comprehension
and a wrenching in my gut so powerful,
it reached up
and tore at my throat
when I realised
your first seconds, minutes, days
of life
had been lived without me.
After nine months of just us,
how could fifty strangers have known
the colour of your eyes
before I did.

But despite the fact

I've still not found the words to say
how you came to be in this world,
I can at least say
I gave birth to the wildest, fiercest, most potent love
I have ever known.

Imogen Schäfer

Birth Colours

Plucked from the water
and placed on my chest,
You didn't make a sound
for the first 30 seconds—
nothing. No breathing.
It felt like an eternity.
The moments rush back—
flashes of silvery, slippery
skin, our breath sucked in,
muscles tensed, waiting. I
remember the midwife's
confident hands gently
massaging your limp form,
limbs still curled and fists
balled, your little eyes
scrunched shut against
the light flooding the room.
I remember relaxing when
I sensed her calm, though
your Dad's knuckles
were clenched white in
mine.

Suddenly, a cough— a few
staccato splutters and your

airways cleared of mucus.
"There, he's pinking up"
the midwife said, smiling—
your tiny body blushing
before our eyes as you
began to squirm and
whimper. I've never been
so happy to see the colour
pink before— usually I avoid
it at all costs— but in this
moment, it stains everything
in this bland hospital room
with beauty and wonder,
heralding the beginning
of new life— YOUR life,
precious boy.

We let out a collective
sigh of relief as you drink
up oxygen and test your
lung capacity. Loud cries,
ecstatic smiles all round,
joy-filled tears spilling down
cheeks as we exchange
first words, mother and

son. "You're here!" I
murmur across your
flailing arms, hoping to
soothe you with the music
of my voice. I can feel the
umbilical tethering us,
its purplish-blue hue still
pulsing— pumping nourishment.
What a surreal moment
this is, cradling you in
my arms, no longer one,
yet still so inextricably
connected. We have a few
moments to take each
other in before the cord is
cut and we are separated
for a little while.

You briefly open your eyes,
and I am met with my own
reflection staring back from
the deep blue centre of them.

Micah Klassen

Bitter Taste

Baby's red sidekick,
Marshmallow soft under tiny feet,
Sitting high in my pelvis.
And suddenly, furiously, you're left behind
Our billowing airbag,
with the inextricable cord.
The fleshy tunnel
from his vital heart to mine.
Yet, you get away from us,
Abrupt disposal, through no fault of your own.
No cushioning words.
Delirious detachment from the undulating pulse
of our inner world.
Cut away, reeling.

Rachel Dickens

Cats

Babies sound like cats.
I didn't notice the first time,
So engrossed in my new love.
But the second time I lay there alone.
No baby to stare at.

"He's having some problems breathing," they said.
It's a boy? That day full of surprises.
I get a room to myself.
Spoilt because I don't have my baby.
I can hear mewing from everywhere.

A new day, a new hospital.
Breast pump whirring, the mechanical sound soothing me.
This I know I can do. Moo.
My baby cries, silently, in pain,
The noise eaten by the tubes coming out of his throat.

There is no mewing in the ICU.

Catherine Hamilton

Cornflakes at half past eight

New mum paraphernalia
Coconut water
And Snickers
Breast pump clamped
To my boob
Tena Lady knickers
Haven't showered
Since he was born
I'm scared of seeing the scar
If I can't see it
It never happened
Tuck it into my mason jar
I shuffle on
Down the ward
Pull the curtain
And chat to Jen
Bikini line
Underscored
My baby 7 weeks prem
I've become quite accustomed
To cornflakes at half past eight
I can't take my baby home
Until he puts on weight
It doesn't really matter
That this hospital's a joke

That I haven't been
Outside for weeks
For a Starbucks or a smoke
The way his jaw moves
Hearing him suck
My heart fixes and breaks
My whole body
Rearranged
My mind gathering keepsakes
Just me and him
In the dark
I hold him warm and near
My scar weeping
Birthmark scrawled
George woz 'ere

Ebony Gilbert

Blue Moon

October 2020 brings us a blue moon
two full moons within the month
and it reminds me of the time
I gave birth twice in less than a year
exactly eleven months apart
one dead, one alive, both fully and forever mine
because sometimes love comes knocking
and you cannot deny its bright face
blossomed in the skies above
and sometimes love comes crashing
into hard spaces, painful places
and sometimes we get to live with one foot
on the ground, and one foot on the moon.

Julia Marsiglio

Your Scar

Birthmarked
It sits at the top of your forehead.
A thumbprint of scar tissue.
Barely there except when I brush back your hair
or the sun darkens your skin.
Indenting slightly your skull.
A reminder of the violent pull and push,
contractions and forceps.

It was a reddish half-moon once, when you were
newer than you are now,
I touched it like a talisman during night feeds
and precarious naps,
it's slowly fading, never quite gone.
Your birthmark,
your ticket to ride.
Safely out of womb-world
and into my arms.

Sjanneke Farrell

Stitches

Susan says they fucked up her stitches.
I have an extra hole, she bellows,
in my vagina! We all laugh and continue
to compare episiotomy stories.

This is not what we were promised when
we did our active birth class. This is not
what Susan expected when she practised
hypnobirthing, religiously.

This is not what we were aiming at
when the lady in the red bikini
on One Born Every Minute, gave birth
immaculately, without a murmur.

Tara Wheeler

Chapter 4
Early Days

Don't Buy Her Flowers

For there is already too much
fragility between these walls
and it terrifies her.
She is learning to swim
in the moonlight and soft fog of these rooms,
made suddenly unfamiliar with sleeplessness
and the feathered cries of the new.

She is building palaces
from sofa cushions, rebuilding
herself from buttered crusts and cold tea.
She is exploring the sweet pain
of her heart expanding, her rib cage
more a cathedral of feeling
than she ever thought possible.

Don't buy her flowers.
For as time stretches like treacle
she will be powerless to do anything
but watch them die. As life contracts
to the tiny curves and hollows of his face,
his warm body, they will scatter pollen
into the hearth like golden soot,
their petals leached of colour –
papyrus with nothing to say.

Instead, show her the village of lanterns
you've left blazing in your windows.
Bring her star-crusted nights
as a balm to her itching eyes. Let her feel
the comforting weight and substance
of all your little anchors.
Neighbouring boats rocked by the same deep tide.

Jen Feroze

First-born

I liked the hospital clockwork. Meals at set times,
a trolley with stewed tea, Horlicks last thing.
Painkillers if you asked, a bell to press.

Now at night, the waking is endless,
the dozing and waking, the crying and crying,
sore nipples under hard gums, the rush of milk.

And cleaning bum; some startling colours.
First black tar stuff called mecony-something,
then yellow purée, and so much piss.

My time's no longer mine, but his,
I went in bulging but unattached
came out a mother, an appendage.

But oh his silkiness against my face,
his warm milk scent, heart tappity-fast,
enormous burps, and then he'll smile at last.

Ruth Aylett

Today

Today the baby slept in mid suck and fell away
milk in a thin arch streaming over her.

These words are all I have of time:
the hard crust of frost that blackened the nasturtiums,
the fog that hugged the ground white for a week.

The fat baby choking with pleasure
at a breast is six weeks old,
knows only the hours between feeds,
this round of flesh is her horizon.
Mine is the twilight of half opened eyes
cries tingling across nipples like small shocks.

Today the winter sun bleaches the clematis,
orange and filigree lanterns sprawl beneath.
The purple buds of a hellebore are rising.

Over everything there is a flutter of wings.
Snow drops open, the one winter
aconite is unfolding.

Jennifer Vuglar

Those Early Days of Mothering

Weighed down with expectations
Burdened by it all
What joy there should be
Flattened by chores
Must-urbation of the maternal kind.
Lonely but never fully alone
Held together with yet another cup of coffee
Unsure if any of this counts.
Attuned? Attached? Perhaps.
How and when would she know?
But then she smiles
And looks again
Pats her breast fondly,
Knowingly greets her like
An old friend.
Perhaps patience is its own reward
She thinks.
Her smile and gaze enough
To remind her why
She chose all of this.
The quiet knowing of it
Enough
To get her through
Another day.

Julianne Boutaleb

Unsolicited Advice

What about motherhood makes some people
around you backseat drivers?
Unsolicited advice, expert baby advisers.

The "I've had three kids, trust me" to the
"Let me tell you how it's done!"
The "In my day we did it like this", the
"Don't do that, you're doing it wrong!"

She's so tiny, is she breastfed?
She's being whiny, you should put her to bed.

Don't place her on the playmat, she's cold to the touch.
Don't carry her like that, don't pick her up too much.

Don't even think about co-sleeping, they'll get
too attached.
It's too cold for a dress and her socks don't match!

You should always let babies cry it out and exercise
those lungs!
If she's struggling to latch then there must be something
wrong with her tongue.

She's crying again, hasn't she been fed?
Your breast milk isn't enough, I told you to feed her
formula instead!

For the sake of sanity and a mother's mental health,
Please be considerate and keep your comments to yourself.

Nazia Hamidah

I've just had a baby

I've just had a baby –
don't expect too much of me.
Invite me, but don't be annoyed if I say no.
For days, weeks, months.
I'll come when I can; when we're ready.
If you ask to visit and I hesitate,
please take that as a polite "no" (not yet).
But if I'm indecisive, gentle persuasion might be
just what I need.
A quick visit, a cup of tea, talking about the world
outside of my cocoon.
Company is important but so is rest.
I might appear selfish but I need to be:
right now, it's about me, my baby and my body.
If I push myself to please other people
I'll break down in both body and mind.
I need time, love, care, nurturing, support, understanding.
No negativity, judgement or expectation.
I've just had a baby.

Annie Ridout

10pm

A nighttime bellow
Mournful sinking begins in my chest

Like weights in my pockets

For every new wail I wonder if I am doing the right thing

A teabag on the side
A ring around my finger
Eating blueberries and grapes

But I know you need me there
So I begin to crawl the stairs
Slow and endless

A cry pure and clean as a cut mushroom
Boiled garlic
A hand-pressed glove

I give myself labels to pass the time –
Tinker, tailor, Mother, failure

I'm doing fine
I'm doing fine

I hear your cry long after it has finished
The sound is seeping through the walls

Beth Talbot

The Field

We came home
to the high desert where
the moonlines around
the clouds are so
sharp they etch the sky
and the land is
turbulent with sagebrush
creased with pink arroyos
mottled by piñon,
each hill piebald under
the shadows of thunderheads.
I carried my four-month-old
through my father's field
along sunny mud walls.
At first I pointed,
saying the names of things –
bee, red willow, crab apple –
then I thought, what's the hurry
in naming the world?
How must it be now
in the wordless embrace
from which she has gathered
into form for a moment?
There is so short a time
when an olive branch is

a shoal of fish is
the edge of a dream.
We can save naming
part conquest and part romance
for a little while.
Let's not sunder ourselves
from this mother but
dip tiny fingers
in the honey of
the space between.

Sofia Greenberg

I Love You ITV4

Three o'clock, an idle Tuesday;
he rests his milk blot head
on my chest, swims to nod to the tune
of *Where the Heart Is.*

A blessed hour where
up and down
he rides
the waves of breath,
floats on his milk moon belly.

I swim too
on a deflated balloon
down streams of sweet tea
because today no one will see
the deck has not been scrubbed;

the hill high pile of washing
hasn't been scaled;
the treasure chest of pre-motherhood
muscle has not been found –
                    only a bounty of Milky Ways.

Just a phase,
a glorious, reflux ridden

phase where sleep
is induced
at three o'clock
on an idle Tuesday
to the tune
of *Where the Heart Is.*

Claire Hughes

Strawberry Hands

Your hands
Find my mouth
Smack my face
Grab my glasses
They smell like strawberries
And feel like pudgy little pillows
But grabbier
More curious
Clumsy
Grimy between the fingers
Sharp where I need to clip your nails
I love those mischievous hands
I bite them and kiss them
I watch how it makes you laugh
My glasses are always smudged now
But it's a small price
To smell those strawberry hands

Chelsy Meyer

Little Adventurer

I am neither trampoline nor climbing frame
Yet your small limbs scale my body
Using curves and rolls as footholds
You clamber up
Grasping on to breast, and then shoulders
Getting a good hold on flesh
As you pull yourself atop of my chest
Sitting there a while
Before descending to my lap
We sit cuddled together
In affectionate silence
My hair becoming the guide rope
Of which you hold for safety
Twisting it around your miniature fist
A quiet moment passes
The mischievous look returns to your eyes
Comfortable embraces end
Replaced by baby feet bouncing against supple thighs
I know that you will leave footprints on my skin
Body marked by my little adventurer
Too rough in play.

Leanne Cooper

That First Year

The year that two became three
No. More. Hot. Tea.

The year of not leaving your side
For more than an hour
And feeling revived
From a two minute shower

The year of white noise
Cuddles and baby slings
As you slowly adjust
To the outside things

The year of sleep regressions
Monkey impressions
Panicked Google searches
Too many to mention

That year I realised that women
Really do hold all the powers
Rocking and pacing
For hours and hours

Being more selective
Of the company I keep

And dreading that question
So, how does he sleep?

The year of building all the rods
For my own back
Binning the baby books
And not looking back

Endless walks with the pram
To help you to nap
Pounding the pavements
Looking like crap

One whole year to realise
That there's no wrong or right
There's what works
What you *need*
In the middle of the night

The year of doubts and fears
And bending the ears
Of family and friends
He'll sleep eventually
But *when?*

But you're more than
Your sleep struggles
So much more
You're that look of wonder
At a knock at the door

Your giggles
And protests
And that tiny roar

Beaming with pride
As you take in your stride
Learning to roll
Crawl
And stand
And wave your wee hand

A sudden respect for those
Who've done all this before
But with two
With three
With four
Or more

The year of grand plans and dreams
Of these homemade cuisines
But some days just called
For eggs, chips and beans

And yet somehow you thrived
And we just about survived
The hourly wake-ups
And some almost-breakups

You really did shake-up
These two kids

Karen McMillan

Chapter 5
Feeding

Hunger

That first time, your body
across my own under bulbs

brighter than day, you chirped
and bobbed your downy head

as my hands learned to hold you,
as the nurse pressed my flesh

so you could breathe and eat,
a primal determination

in your twiggy fingers, tiny O
of a mouth catching golden

beads in wild gulps: your hunger
alight, opening like wings.

Emily Patterson

Chronicles of a Breastfeeder

The natural has come unnaturally.
Am I then the only woman since Eden that cannot
do this?

Oh, the searing pain.

Only quietened by the substitute sounds of the
breast pump.
Re-amplified by the
"Breast is Bests" and the "Hang In Theres"
Always followed by the
"I Promise It Gets Betters"

Do I remain in pain until I'm not?
Do I grit through tears until I don't?

Mom Guilt trips me as my child rummages her face
into my bosom
screaming for what's rightfully hers yet pulled back
and met with the shove of a bottle between her gums.
She gives two unwillful sucks and looks back at me,
disapprovingly,
as her tongue assertively pushes the teat back out of
her pursed lips
and her face turns red ready to scream.

No choice.
I exhale and align her.
At parallel to the areola she sucks in sharply,
charged up from her previous frustration at the
Tommee Tippee attempt and the searing pain soars
this time causing my whole body to cave.
I desperately worm my little finger into the side of her
gummed mouth and unhook the latch.
She wails
with a blood rimmed mouth
Gingerly
I pick the nipple flesh off her bottom lip
My tears of shock fall on to her cheeks merging with
her own.
Oh, the searing pain.
The burning sensation shoots through my stomach
down to my toes that curl into arches seeking solace in
the grip of the carpet
as I,
exhausted,
bend over my newborn in agony.

We are stuck here.

Jessica Kaliisa

It's Milk

Soft little kitten pawing at my cheeks
Gentle strokes on my skin, melting me
Rough claws scratching and pinching
Please be gentle with Mummy

Two procedures to release your tongue
Over in seconds
But months before you relaxed
Me tense and worried
Logging data and tracking apps
Coughs and splutters; too much milk, Mummy!
Tears and pain and upset tummy
No one can prepare you
I didn't know what was coming

Distracted baby by day
Milk guzzler at night
No, don't look at the dog!
Ignore that sound!
Shh Daddy don't talk to me now!

It's my secret superpower
My clever magic trick
Your eyes flutter closed
So peaceful, so quick

But "don't feed to sleep, it's a rod for your back"
"She'll never sleep through if you keep doing that"
But she's just a baby
Can't she want her Mummy?
Makes me feel like I'm failing
Asleep now but awake 45 minutes later
7 months of sleep deprivation a form of torture
I should be sleeping but I'm staring at the monitor
I miss you
Addicted to you
Watching old videos back again and again

Daddy stands guard while I take a shower
I hear you downstairs getting louder and louder
I open my eyes to see you both
"I think it's milk..."
...And that's my free time over
I'm touched out and need some space
Sometimes I need a break
But I don't want to be replaced
By a piece of plastic

Dammit which side is next?
There's only 2 but I always forget!
We relax back in bed, phone at the ready

Then it slips...
Ahh don't land on her head!
Excited wide eyes
Big fat chubby thighs
Little gremlin sounds of appreciation
Stretching back and smacking your lips in satisfaction
It's all from me
It's all of me

Sleepy little body, heavy on my chest
Cocooned from it all
With my human hot water bottle
Intertwined like knotted rope around my heart
Your eyes look deep into my soul
I hope you think I'm good enough
You make me feel so whole
Rubbing your back
Cheeky bum tap
I close my eyes and thank my lucky stars
The good, the bad; nothing lasts forever

Daisy Bates

Last Orders at the Milk Bar

I notice tonight
as your little hand plays with my hair
twirls the strands between your fingers
unaware
that this is the last time I'll hold you this way.
The last time you'll find me in the dark
so easily
like you've done from that first day.

We won't speak of this day again
I know that now.
I'd like to remind you about how
we spent these nights and days and
I fed you again and again in so many ways.

But you won't want to hear that, it won't belong
in the stories we tell, in the photos we share
I can try and save this feeling,
gather it up,
but the moment has already gone.

And I feel it deeply,
more than your touch,
so deep within my heart,
in the bottom of my stomach,

the tears start.

I know it must come to an end
but I'm not quite ready to let go.
My body will return
and life will carry on
and you will forget
but I notice.
I notice everything tonight.
This is the last time I feed you, I know.

Nelly Bryce

Thank fuck for formula

Powdered power
Devoured
Our bottle bond
Just as strong
Science milk
Without guilt
Happy baby and happy mum
See just how far we've come –
We survived, and now we thrive
Formula kept us both alive

Emma Dakeyne

Anywhere

Yes, I'll feed her anywhere,
at a restaurant, in the park.
No, location does not matter,
be it daytime, be it dark.
For, wherever we may travel,
her food source ventures too.
To soothe her any time of day.
Drinks on tap, a dream come true.

Maria Tempany

Chapter 6
Sleep

Energy

You're tired, I'm tired,
You want to feed, I want to sleep,
I want to put you down, but you won't let me.
You cry, I cry,
You smile, I smile.
I'm exhausted, you're impatient,
We connect and we are joined,
You are me and I am you.

Kia Brown

The Dawn Chorus

As snuffles turn to cries
A slow stagger
Bleary eyed
Arms outstretched
Daring not to look at the clock
Babe tucked in arms
Chest rising and falling
Breath slowing
Drifting off whilst I sit
Patiently in the dusky shadows
My mind wondering and racing
Wondering and racing
Peace returns
Just as morning light streams through
But snuffles turn to cries

Ali Lewis

Four Month Sleep Regression

The night creeps in with dread
An insomniac;
Grasping with two hands; an hour
Between circadian rhythm.
An internal clock, once one
Mother and child;
Now, so out of sync.
You sleep.
Tick tock.

The shadows
My only witness,
My captive audience,
My only friends.
Fellow soldiers
March on with pride.
But this soldier is weary,
This lioness injured,
Pride clings on by the white tip of a brittle nail.
I must soothe, reassure, comfort you...
And me.
Who shall I turn to? Read.
Who will know the answer? Everyone.
I admire you once again
Peering through the dark haze

You little glorious thing
Life unknown in your short-lived hands.
I must feed you:
You fight with vengeance
The beast at my breast
Pulling back, writhing and riling in fury
Like a vulture
Devouring their own hunted prey.
I long to satisfy your needs.
Tick tock, tick tock.

I drift in and out of consciousness,
Random thoughts, memories, aspirations,
Satisfied, deeply content;
Frustrated; in need of sleep.

Prisoner to fatigue
My perfect puppeteer
Mosquito, my love
Like a bugle upon my ear you taunt me.

I glance again at the clock.

Finally, light with hope gradually rise
With the melatonin and cortisol

That builds in your perfect body.
The blanket of darkness
Lifts to start another day.
I drift around in a nebulous, blurry eyed state.
Nodding unknowing,
Unable to follow conversation
As I sip my coffee in the Honey Bee cafe at 11am
as you sleep.
'It's only a phase; it'll pass'
They said.
'Sleep when they sleep'
They said.
'Isn't motherhood the most glorious experience'
They said.
Tick tock, tick tock, tick tock.

Olivia Hall

The Smallest Hours

Half-light dawn. My son's hot breath
on my cheek: finally asleep.
I am resigned to my own wakefulness;
lost in the silence
– am I the   only   person
in the world awake?
A caul encloses the bed; echoing with
uncertainty. How lonely
it is to be a mother sometimes –
never alone but

separate

in the darkness. The weight of urgency
pressing – minutes ticking by – unused, wasted;
time's tangled strands knotting in my hands.
this is the burden: the shock
that they are no longer a part of   you.
They are not yours   they are their own.
Every day they grow
further

and

     further

        away.

His hand is curled in my hair;
Ariadne's tendrils.
For now, this is enough.

Karan Chambers

You Do Not Sleep

In the early hours you wake
You beckon
I go, I soothe
You do not sleep
You cling to me and I submit
You do not sleep
You wriggle, writhe, fart
You do not sleep
I stroke your head
I close my eyes to show you how
You do not sleep
I doze, you fidget
You appear to defy sleep
We lie suspended in the darkness

Not sleeping
Not sleeping
You finally roll over and settle
I creep away, retreat, retreat
Relax and collapse into slumber
You wake, I wake
We repeat
As twilight reveals a hopeful face we admit defeat
I absorb your enthusiasm and we begin the day together
Sleep can wait
Coffee
Cake
Repeat

Emily Way-Evans

Night Feed

Much of my night feeds
involved online shopping.
Pointless things I'd convince myself
I needed, things
that would absolutely
improve our lives.
I enjoyed the thrill
that accompanied the later deliveries;
purchases I'd forgotten about,
a little treat from
past sleep-drunk me.

I once spent £25
on an expanding shelf
for the spice cupboard.
It didn't even fit.

Lowri Ann

Nap Time

You curl up on my shoulder
From a busy morning bouncing and babbling,
Rolling and reaching.
Your ruffled blonde hair somehow reminds me
Of your great grandfather and my little brother
Your long eyelashes like feathers on silk velvet
Your warm body heavy and finally still.
I hold you and smell you
And all is calm.
Furrowed brow and tears all gone.
Twinkly lights and calming sleepy sounds,
The hustle and bustle of the outside world shut out.
Sleep, my love.
Sleep.

Sophie Blinstrub

In The Garden

In the garden, whilst you nap
Dark, like a refuge, is the crease in your neck.
To kiss you there is to become opaque.
I bleed into the air, nothing but nerves.
Like a small bird, you startle as I turn the pages.
I shall try to write more quietly.

Bronwen Wilson

Monster

Why won't she sleep?
Is it monsters under the bed?
No, too little, too small an imagination yet for that.
But I know one day she'll look up at me, small blue eyes
pleading for reassurance in the middle of the night –
"Will you keep me safe from the monsters mummy?"

What will I tell her?

My love, I've rocked you and held you, nursed you and
sung to you, paced up and down mountains of resistance at
3am each night, borne the brunt of scratches and kicks and
elbows in the throat, patted, placated, promised I'd stay
with you, night after night.
And not once have there been monsters under the bed.

But there have been nights I've wanted to walk away.
To just not be a mummy anymore.
To cry back at you, louder and longer.
To shout.
To scream.
To leave you.

So, what will I tell her?
Can I keep her safe from the monsters?
Can I keep her safe from me?

Kirsty Woods

A.M.

Mornings are the hardest,
when I am never ready,
when they are never pre-packed with warnings,
when they resemble a cynical smile,
when they think twice to ever serve me gleams of silence
to stop and breathe,
when they allow the sunlight to rush its way
to the most fragile sides of my skin,
when it feels nice yet somewhat in a hurry
as if reminding me that I cannot indulge in it
for too long; time's up –
the to-do lists are piling up,
the children are echoing each other,
debating the hesitations in my head
as if they can read through me
yet choose to tear these pages anyway,
no time for coffee nor contemplation
as society has promised,
when the only space allowed and given to me
is the only one I can ever remember –
the one for me to cry on
and that's probably not even on my own space,
my tears are busy finding their place
in between the clutter – the mismatched blocks,
the cookie crumbs, the half-folded clothes,

the strands of hair that dropped but never swept away,
the deluge of thoughts that belong in the night.

My tears; they tiptoe their way around this clutter
I wasn't prepared for,
but alas rest themselves at the edge of
too-much.
This is me, waking up
not into mornings,
but into postpartum anxiety.

And my children; maybe they are my mornings,
bringing light into my day.

Azalia Suhaimi

Tears and Lullabies

I wonder if my mother ever cried
As she sang me to sleep
Singing lullabies through tears is a strange melody
The trembling scales of those moments
Teeter on a figurative edge
As you both rock back and forth
Swish, shhh, swish, shhh
Unsure of who you're actually calming
How can so much love feel so sad too?
And after a while your voice fades
The baby rising and falling
To the rhythm of your breath
As you both sleep in the chair

Pamela Smith

I thought that was tiring...

I thought being a teenager was tiring –
angsty, in tiny panties, snogging in pantries,
pay as you go phone on loan from Mum
and mouth full of Hullabaloo bubble gum.
Cheap perfume, Charlie deodorant, Mizz, Cosmo,
staring at armpits, waiting for the occasional hair to grow,
smoking Marlboros without inhaling,
attempting school exams and failing.
Angry diary entries and dramatic love letters
to teenage boys interested only in weed and the odd
computer game,
each week the declaration of love addressed to a
different lad's name.
Disappointment, depression on the rejection of
each confession,
then the desperate suppression of feelings,
hours spent sleepless, staring at ceilings.
Absurdly self obsessed, crushingly insecure –
the constant feeling that I couldn't take any more...
I thought that was tiring...

I thought my first job was tiring...
After three lazy years at uni,
I was tied to a desk – desperate for approval,
eager to please and terrified of reproval.

Stuck in the web of lies formed in my CV disguise,
GCSE French forged as fluency.
Late nights in the office quickly turned
to later nights spending cash newly earned,
chasing around my first love – he was older and angry.
Trying to prove that I was rageful and worthy,
candle burning at all ends – seeking scurvy.
Mac and cheese for lunch and an afternoon
Apple Mac pass-out when nobody was about.
Stinking of booze, dehydrated and fixated on bed,
but on leaving the office, going for a 'few' drinks instead,
A vicious circle of contortion and exhaustion,
ignoring all bodily signs to take caution…
I thought that was tiring…

Feeding, burping, jiggling, playing,
watching every move and swaying,
Panicked, anxious or in utter bliss, googling –
What's that? What's this?
Up, down, up, up, up and down again,
take a deep breath and count to ten
2am, 4am, 6am and then awake –
that's it, the night has gone,
the day is even more full on:
Nappy change, breast, nappy change, breast,

or unable to move as someone is sleeping on my chest.
All plans out the window, going nowhere fast,
leaving the house now the most momentous task,
high on adrenaline and purpose
or tearful, scared and morose.
If not feeding or assisting in napping and crapping,
I'm in a state – marching about and flapping,
I have no control over time, it's not something I own,
and nor are my arms, "they're too weak" I moan
as they get caught in awkward positions and go dead
from weight,
I arrive at everything a milk drenched zombie who's
horribly late,
He's either in a sling, attached to my boob or rocking
in my arms
while I try desperately to keep him happy and calm,
dabbing my nipple as it squirts milk everywhere,
or trying to remove curdled spit-up from my hair.
I spend hours staring at his minuscule hands and feet,
or bouncing on the spot to get him to sleep,
But one thing is for sure:
I do not really sleep anymore.
My mouth is filled with ulcers and my eyes with styes,
and I realise all those times I thought I was tired
from merely staying up late,

That wasn't anything at all.
I knew rest was coming – it only ever lasted a night or two
and would eventually end in sleep – that I always knew.
No, I wasn't tired then,
Now I am tired,
Now I am tired.

Grace Pilkington

Chapter 7
Strength

The Circus

Roll up! Roll up!
The circus is in town.

Our star attraction this year is
The STRONGWOMAN!

Watch as she performs amazing feats
such as the bench press.

Witness the amazing strength,
her ability to cope.

See her walk the tightrope,
the high-wire.

Admire her levitation skills
as she fills her arms

and lifts everybody up, up, up.

Kate Phipps

A rod for my own back

I have made a fish out of my arm
where your weighty head has cut off the blood supply.
I have made a radiator out of my ribcage
where you nestle against me.
I have made a football ground out of my stomach
as you kick your way through your dreams.

I have made a bird's nest out of my hair
as your hands rake through it at night.
I have made a barrier out of my body
to stop you rolling to the ground.
I have made an island out of flesh
for you to cling to when you fret.

I have made a habit of comfort, yours and mine,
when you call for me;
I have a made a safety net of memories,
woven from your two arms criss-crossed around my neck.

I have made a bed we'll lie in,
and we haven't finished yet.

Vanessa Napolitano

The Fight

A thrash
A crash
Your frustrations freed as rage
Hitting hard like waves on my side
Tides turn within my chest

The tears
Leaving lines
Separating pictures on your face
Tired, confused, simply not amused
You're stuck in the mist of this haze

Gently, I consume
The air around us full of gloom
Lips stretched from frown to pout
And we're spiralling further down
Down and out

The screams lie inside me
You can feel it in my heartbeat
We are caught in each other's arms
And I know this is my chance to show
How deep my love will always go.

Nicola Dellard-Lyle

Cuddle

A child's stick arm
wrapped round her neck.
A full, raised dome
of apple cheek.
Clinging on to her,
a delicate spindled burr.

The shape of clothes
clutches at her hair;
entwines it round a fist
and fixes a tear-lapped stare.

Slowly, all is stroked away,
the desperate, clawing actions cease.
Sobs subside and one sticky eye peeps
up through a mass of sorrow
and matted hair.

Shames and hurts drain into
this open oasis of arms.

Sitting tight and just holding
did not change the streaked
and woe-encrusted face,
but it was soothed and
surely that was enough.

I know about this:
a warmth, a certain smell,
a contact, a love, are
all contained in the cradle
of her caring hands and eyes.

Ali Pember

Cracked

And then I cracked
Like furrows of dried plaster.
Before, immaculately seamless,
Now a silhouette of mountains,
Foreboding; fearful apprehension.

It doesn't weaken me.
My structural integrity is still unbroken,
But I see it every day.
I know it is there.
I anticipate its expansion.

But, this time others can see it.
Comforted to know that they can recognise it.
We're maintaining vigilance.

Leander Moore

Mother's Love

I'm broken today
An accumulation
Of
Sleep-deprived
Nights
The nights, the nights
Oh why
Won't you just sleep!
Memory
A shattered mess
Forgetting conversations
Had just yesterday
Not replying
To well-intended texts
Unable to fathom
Cooking
A gourmet dinner
Or
Even bangers and mash
While I lovingly prepare
Food for you that
Ends up on the floor
But...
I get up in the morning
And love you

A bit more than I did
Yesterday
And you fix my pieces
Back together.

Rachael Jowitt

A Mum Dancing

I'm a Mum, dancing,
But so much more
Feeling like the woman I was,
Before

Feet brush and shuffle
Across the dining room floor,
As collective minds
Drift back decades in time

Cracked hands punch and flail,
As three souls sail across the sea
Back to Ibiza,
Where we suddenly long to be

This kids' climbing frame
Bends and bows,
Melting into moves
Forgotten

Breasts that gave life
Bounce with the beat,
My brain now alive
With the sense of me

Three hearts yearn
For nights lived
On throbbing dancefloors,
Laughter making our faces sore

Lips that seal the day,
With love
On two little foreheads
Pass wine and whoop

Old stories
Pave pathways in my brain
To memories
Locked in its corners

Pause for a top up,
Pick a new tune,
Dance with the baby's rattle,
He'll probably wake up soon

I'm a Mum, dancing
But now so much more
I'm the woman I was,
Before

Rachel Watson-Steward

Steeped

Light translates   the brown water.
Coffee grounds turn   this liquid into wine
for the mind,
it's still dark,
the sun in sweet repose   won't be up for another hour,
 so I burn   the midnight oil,
                    every mother's superpower.

Kelsi Folsom

Strength

I remember
as a teenager
seeing my brother
eight years my senior
sitting
slumped
at the kitchen table...
weeping.

Heartbreak
a break-up
hopeless
his head bent over aged wood
features hidden.

And my mum
a tiny wisp,
even more so
in the shadow
of his tall, broad form.
Sat on his knee
and wrapped her arms
around his shaking shoulders.
His shaggy head shuddered into her neck
as she soothed him like a toddler.

Watching
this physical dichotomy
Her strength
shone through to me.

And now I feel my own son
leaning on my chest
Struggling in his infancy
with tears, frustrations, communication,
one year old anxieties.

I hope that when you're grown
even if you're twice my height
you know where to lay your hurting head.
You'll look down too
and feel the strength
rising up
from my arms, half the size of yours
my neck – soft and narrow,
my shoulders far below...

...still there
to hold, cradle, carry you.

Rachel Inman

Chapter 8
Growing

Nostalgia

Life goes on. Mostly.
And for those of us
Whose babies survive
They are gone.

Each version of you
Is my comforter
For the one I have lost.

I wrap us in warm
Stories of the baby you were.
You believe we can
Miss her together.

Zoe Gardner

Vulva

Use accurate anatomical language they said.
Minnie, Nunnie, Front Bottom, Privates and Pee Pees,
Progressive parents don't use words like these.
So, I tell him, when he asks.
"That's Mummy's vulva."
It hangs in the air. His eyes widen.
"V-U-L-V-A," he says.
"Ahmm," I say. Trying to move the topic on.
Ashamed to admit I thought it was a vagina anyway.
Apparently, that's just the passage...
Not the whole package?
I continue getting dressed. He is deep in thought.
"Mummy"
"Yes darling?"
"Does Captain Hook have a vulva?"

Daisy Phillips

Pigeons

She hurtles down the pavement.
No more than three years old,
bright in her red duffle coat, T-Bar shoes,
chasing High Street pigeons.
Her hair, feather-soft with mist,
bounces in curls as she runs.

She reminds me of my own girl,
her toddler days. Everything in haste
on unsteady, eager legs.

Now, we browse for make-up, Nikes,
waist-skimming tops; sit in cafes
where she sips hot chocolate,
teen song on her lips.

And this little girl who runs after pigeons,
who cries as they scatter at the rush of her,
calls after them and swamps the air with her words:
come back, come back, come back.

Claire Walker

Walking

Sometimes I dream of walking alone
In a straight line, illimitable
The destination uncharted
Taking giant, meaningful strides
With the sun baking my arms
Wind gently lifting my hair
No real purpose but to unfurl and unravel
Untethered
Free of backpack or school book bag or sticky wrappers
Unconstrained
I don't want it to end
No sudden scooter to the shin, no abrupt stop for sticks
or pebbles
No tugging of coat sleeve or pulling of arm
Where thoughts no longer flutter and whirl but collect
and can be still
Walking in dreamy reverie
On and on
Then a small hand wakes me from my daydream
Chubby and soft, clutching mine tightly
'Mummy, let's go!'
I look down and smile, ruffle strawberry blonde hair
Time is fleeting, walks with him evanescent
We stroll, hand in hand
I don't want it to end.

Nicola Greenbrook

Plaiting Rapunzel's Hair

I brush your tangles
grown so long now,
not the wild baby curls
so tightly wound they barely bounced,
tucked close round your ears.
They tumble down your back, longer
than they've ever been.

I brush as you bounce on the balls of your feet
never still.

I tease out each knot.
Brush to drown out my quiet thoughts.
Brush.
Capture.

I'm not quite ready to let you go yet.

I brush again
slick out the tiny tangles,
brush in the shine.

Brush.
Capture.
Plait.

Slide in bobby pins
(I never know which way up the smooth side should be).
Coil and catch your curls, secure in place,
watch the wispy bits escape — still my wild girl.

Soon I must teach you to brush your own hair.

Zoë Siobhan Howarth-Lowe

Hands

Stretching my fingers
As far as they will go
So that they will flex around
The feelings that you fling at me
Yet today my hands feel too small
To hold it all.

I want you to give me
All of your sadness
So that your hands are free
To do the things you love.

I want to hold
All of your fears
So you don't have to
Look through fingers
Over eyes too small
To understand this world.

The feelings that
Cannot yet be named
Are wrapped around my fingers
So that you no longer
Feel so trapped.

But my hands are too small
To carry it all,
So instead I'll cup
Your hands in mine
Let you hold those feelings still
While I just catch the over-spill.

Sally MacLeod

Milk-tooth

I blindly pat the mattress to claim your first tooth
till one fingertip catches
on a hollow root tapering to bluntness,
so big in your mouth, so small on my palm,
built with mother's milk, Calpol syringes
and soggy muslins.

Oh tears and blood, oh unbridged gap,
oh implacable loss, never to be returned;
my milk is gone now and my hair is grey,
I have wrapped the incisor in tissue
in a keepsake box with your hospital nametag
and the quilted elephant blanket
and the other tag, from our other stay,
the one you don't know about.

Jenny Pagdin

On A Walk

You run before me
yapping like little puppies
in the sharp winter air.
Your breath streams behind you
as you dart this way and that,
arms stretched to feel for the
invisible boundaries
that net our path.

Around the corner,
you stop with a start.
A tree stands strange as a question mark,
wine bottles hung from every branch
bodies weighed down with grief.
I think of Klan trees dropping
death on the gardens of black families.
We watch the bottles sway.
We note their number
their density.

Suddenly you're off again with a howl
I run to follow.
We don't know where we're going
a little lost
in each other, but I don't mind.
I thought I was your guide.
Yet you, my children
with your fierce
unlidded eyes, you show me
what needs to be seen.

Flora Cruft

Specialties

I have always felt
A little bit mediocre
Middle of the road, yet well-rounded
Like a cul-de-sac
Full of hat tricks and quick shticks
For instance, a pogo stick
And juggling balls
Fall sometimes, but mostly not
And my fingers tickle ivories
Quite — well... that song?
I can't play that.
And so on and so forth
My life has been
Not quite measuring
Up to the standards within.

Until within myself
I carried life itself

Now I long
To pass along
The wealth of
Mundane Specialties
To which I have come to hold on.
After all, the title, Mom --
I have clumsily
Mastered.

Leslie Yeary

Waterslide

Giddy
and dripping wet
from the splash at the bottom
you suck on the ends of your hair
and I taste the chlorine

You smile and run back up the hill
away from me
as I let out the breath I've been holding
since that morning

I squint against the sun to watch you
stand in line with strangers
who have no idea
they're witnessing a miracle

Here we both are
back from the dead

Corrie McCrea Nahimi

it isn't as light as it should be

i've more in common with the teddy bears
he leaves on the kitchen floor
after he's poured his cereal out
and turned heel (comic in hand)
to read and eat

when he comes home from his dad's
and finds Doggy in my bed
he doesn't like it –
'he moves there by himself he gets lonely!'
i protest

he makes me promise i'm telling the truth
i have to distract him
because in my house
a promise is an absolute

it isn't as light as it should be
it's only a cuddly toy
but sometimes it weighs as heavy as a boy

sunday morning i lie in
he watches television for hours too many
and, wild eyed, eats his cereal
from a small table near the floor

surrounded by the milk and the cereal packet
(in case he wants more)
the teddies strewn on the sofa
comfortably ignored

my boyfriend tidies them in amusing ways
setting up scenes on my son's bed
sometimes one has a hat on his head
or sunglasses
there's always laughter in response
(while he's heading out the back door
to do something more important)

it isn't as light as it should be
it's only a cuddly toy
but sometimes it weighs as heavy as a boy

Normal the bear came from santa
he's new
the others must be cross
put out by his rapid ascent
i say it's his fur (which is softer than soft)
and his demeanour (which is equally so)

his name changes with the world

Normal on normal days
Santa on christmas day
on my birthday he shared my name
it was nice to feel cuddled twice

but Doggy is the one
the oldest
the don

he and i share a secret we'll never tell
(we know him so well)

it isn't as light as it should be
it's only a cuddly toy
but sometimes it weighs as heavy as a boy

Natalie Thomas

Poem for a Daughter Leaving Home

In photo after photo you are a laughing girl
blue eyes scrunched shut, mouth wide
given over to giggles, that chaos
of blonde curls caught mid-air,
crazy hair fanning your child-pale face.
And all that time your body
was simply a vehicle:
you push the toy pram
you cling to the donkey's mane
you tug my hand.

Then it starts calling you, demanding
dexterity. Bicycles and letters are
hard to master. People are harder.
Their reactions require yours.
What do they want? You're elsewhere.

From then on, for years, I wonder
where you are, lovely? That girl
all synapses and squeals
whose body now is a shield
none of us would dare touch.

The not-sleeping the not-eating
The cutting, the truanting

The refusing, the overdose –

Gradually
quietly
you start asking for me
in the hidden early hours
I kneel by your bed
stroke your arm, your hair
3am 4am 5 finally
sleeping, your breathing
steady. I tiptoe away.

And this morning
your belongings boxed,
the car crammed, you are ready,
unafraid of the world beyond.
Dad drives you off
and you wave. You smile, you
make the effort
to turn in your seat to keep
waving. And I absolutely
know I did okay.
And you will do
just great.

Vicki Bertram

Son

He unwinds his adult arms from my neck,
steps away with a childlike grin and wave.
The woman peers over Polarised lenses,
sips her glass of wine, turns to me,
asks 'What's the matter with him?'

The summer's day drifts into slow motion:
boats float past, a Red Admiral settles on buddleia,
water continues to cascade over the weir.
Outside the pub, a man stumbles as he carries
a tray, steadies himself, not a drop spilled.

'I'm a professional,' she says. 'Special needs.'
as if to explain the directness of the question.
His kiss burns my cheek like a touch of sun
as I grope for an appropriate answer
somewhere along the autistic spectrum.

Angi Holden

Dents

We gently press his baby foot
into clay, let it harden
into a safer keepsake
than our sleep-deprived memories.

Age eighteen, the shape
of his full-pelt body's imprinted
in the side of a stranger's
white van. Heaven knows how

he survives this crash, shaken
but unbroken. I carry the dent
and his bruises for months,
limp in sync with his battered hip.

I'm not sure which aches most,
his pain, or the fear that love
stamps into my heart – something like
the impression of a baby foot

in a size ten boot, 'FRAGILE'
patterned across the sole.

Sarah James

On Swimming Pools

Standing aloft while your vertebrae pop,
Your water wings.
I watch them flex from the concrete gods above.
There seemed so little here to value at first.
Cavernous warehouse ceiling holding false aquamarine sea.
Tides of grime on the '80s tiled floor.
But within these sweltering breezeblock walls
You have become yourself.
Body so far from the slumping softness of babyhood.
Still more part of me than solo being when we first
slipped into the cool waters.
Now arms strong, lungs holding so much air,
You rise again and again from the swell.
When my womb swelled once more I too ploughed
those lanes, stomach breaking the water line.

I watched the overhead bulbs refract my skin beneath
the surface,
Harsh fluorescence rending me luminous.
My lungs gulped hot air and pushed me onwards,
and him – swimming
in his own amniotic pool – waiting for the other waves
to begin.
This chlorinated municipal sea has held us three so closely,
flowing into mouths, amongst toes, gently separating
strands of hair.
The place I will miss the most, now we are grown,
and leaving.

Eleanor Rose Shaw

October's End

Oh, don't leave me!
I can see you running headfirst into this dark
autumnal night
Hair streaming behind you framed in flight, like
something out of a
Story that has been cast a thousand times
The path you soar down is brimming with the possibility
of your everything
And yet I can only think in old-told cliches

My heart with you in its place, copper-spark curls
Well-summered freckles like stars across your face
The woman within you efflorescent in her blaze
Your wild-flower smile – a picture of the joy you
find in life
Oh, don't leave me by running from childhood into
that chasm of time
Don't go into that terrible space... Stay here in my arms

Where I could hold you so selfishly, in light
My child. My love, my love.

Lauren Thomas

Chapter 9
Grandparents

Matryoshka Dolls

We sit book ended
on the sofa
cooried close
my daughter and I

Feel Mum, swollen she turns
towards me, her belly
a ripening pod.

Inside my child, cells divide
and divide.
Curled crouched, coiled
my child fuses and swells.

I cradle her cocoon
and feel in my daughter,
her daughter dance beneath my hands
practising for later.

I cup once familiar flesh
hold another's foot curve, heart.
Practise.

Finola Scott

Mumma

Nothing sweeter than my own loving mother, the answer to every question, the soft, warm body in which to bury myself, when nothing else saves me.

She was there at the birth of my own daughter, washed me in the shower like I was a baby myself. I don't know if the water was made of my own tears.

Mumma, my bones, my heart, my blood, I see her in every good thing, rely on her judgement, hold her up to the light and praise her, carry her in the enamel of my teeth,

My teeth, my teeth, the web of bones in my aging feet, all of it a gift, a passing of the baton as we both walk the path of motherhood, her love doubling for my own child, my need for her only grows greater.

Rebecca Green

Acts of Care

Coming in from a night out
I would find
a hot water bottle left in my bed
for my cold feet

How joyful to feel that warmth

All the comfort
All the care
Right there

The vastness of your love
wrapped inside small gestures
Everyday
Immeasurable

Now you buy the shoes
that fit my daughter's tiny toes.
Making sure they fit,
shiny and new

All the comfort
All the care
Right here

How thankful we are for you.

Jen Copley

Salting the Blood

We come before the hordes
An early breakfast at Brancaster Beach
Blueberries packed in tiny plastic pots
Peanut butter sandwiches wrapped in paper
Blue swimsuit under my linen dress
Seagulls are our only companions
A waning tide ripples farewell
The sun winks at the clam shells
I want to soak your skin with sea
Teach you to jump waves
To run on an empty beach at dawn
My legs ache in the sand steps
As I carry you to the tide line
I place you on the wet shore
Hold your hand as you totter to the water
You wiggle your toes in the sinking sand
I hold you between my legs
My hands under your armpits
The wave comes and we jump
Your body is heavy
My arms are getting old
I lift you up up up
Nana Nana Nana
Again again again

The waves come in and in and in
Liam, Liam, Liam
They sing
Granny is salting your blood.

Briony Bax

Cheese and Pickle

I remember that day when I held onto your leg,
trying to give comfort as they looked inside your head.
I studied the patterns of your little blue veins.
I pictured them as paintings or as tracks for tiny trains.
CLICK CLICK BOOM CLICK on and on and on;
thunderous, oppressive – you were singing nonsense songs.

Some days now you stare for hours at a time at the
window, which explodes
with coloured patterns through the grime.
The flicker of the telly is reflected in the glass and
you cannot
understand, but it somehow makes you laugh.

My empty little mother; we are lost to one another.

You are still here but I don't recognise your face;
Your expressions don't make sense – your reactions out
of place.
Where are all the things that make up the you I know?
The cabbage soup diet, tap dancing, theatre show.

Where is the person who is meant to mother me?
Why don't you remember that's who you're supposed
to be?

You ask about your own mum, who died ten years ago.
Sometimes I don't tell you that to spare... you or me?
I don't quite
know.
My middle girl of four interjects, precise and slow
You're Nanny's mummy aren't you, Mummy? I nod,
I suppose so.
I am the cheese and pickle now, I'm spinning, out of sight.
But even under chains of grief there comes a speck of light.
My children hold the answers to the questions I hold back;
about what
your life is for, now that your mind's under attack.
Because my baby turns to you and smiles with delight;
she holds her
chubby arms up and you crumple at the sight.
There is no other choice but to recognise the love
That knits your bones together and holds you from above.
I do not have a mother but my children have a gran,
Or NANNY as they call to you as loudly as they can.

An old friend in the kitchen, I pause to pour the wine,
Hoping it might soften the news of your decline,
But then my boy of six decides to finish it instead:
Yes, he says, my nanny's ill, she's got a bad leg.

No judgement, no need for you to know the things
you've lost;
They utterly do not care, not counting any cost.
And I see your load lighten in their small giant wake.
You are kind to one another; always give more than
you take.

My perfect Buddhist mama, living ever in the now;
no words to craft new
thoughts, no memories to cow.
But love remains and love is all that matters in your end;
you're not my
mum, you are a new and gentle sort of friend.
And I can hold you in my head, etched like your
sweet blue veins.
I will keep you safe there; you won't be lost when
darkness reigns.

Georgina Wedderburn

The Year You Were Gone

I noticed you struggle to walk
I noticed how white and wiry your hair had become
I noticed the thin veiny patterns on the backs of
your hands
I noticed the rancid smell of faeces when you lost
control of your bowels
I noticed the way you'd look desperately into my eyes
willing me to make it better
I noticed the chaos of caring for the dying
I noticed the kindness in others eyes as they tried to
explain the unexplainable
I noticed the raised brown birthmark just below your
bottom for the millionth time in a different light, as I
bathed you and changed you, rubbed cream in and
helped get you comfy
I noticed the loud hiccups that escaped you as you slept
I noticed the rest of the world stand still and grieve too
I noticed nurses with covered faces and apologetic eyes
I noticed the exhaustion in my bones
I noticed the strain on my father's face as he kept on
keeping on
I noticed day slip into night into day into night into day
I noticed the way you squeezed my hand so tight and
didn't want to let go
I noticed you disappear before my eyes

I noticed you
I noticed you
I noticed you before you left
I notice that now you are gone you are everywhere

Sung Through Me

And now I see
the look my mother gave me
glowing candles on the tree
at Christmas
is the look I give to you
when you are deep in play
and singing in a chesty holler
about exactly what you're doing in that moment

And now I see
our chubby chuckles
double buggy rumbles over cobbles
our bumpy "aaaahs"
are yours
you are nearly three
my mother's whoops and calls are sung through me

And now I see
her tired eyes
are mine
as I clean around your highchair
trying hard to bring to life the home she made for me

I feel her fear now
when I grow angry with you

when you can't sleep at night
or won't sleep right now when I need you to

I feel her guilt for losing it at silly things
like sticking fingers in the margarine
or her regret at smacking me once
when I was nearly three

I feel her sadness on her deathbed
when she said sorry
for all the things she said and did
when I was your age now
Will you forgive me?

And now I feel
my mother's gentle hands
hardworking, calloused, rough
softened sweet with rose cream
are my hands
as I tuck your curls behind your ear
curtains opening
a winter's morning
my mother whispering
the duvet pulled under my chin

Jannah Warlow

Chapter 10

2020

"All of those who died today had underlying health conditions."

My boy is a wild potion of underlying conditions,
And is the most alive person I've ever met.
He's no less of a person –
Often I think he's more.

A fizzing, chattering, loving dreidel.
My frenetic firefly
Whose voice lights fireworks
His sparks reflecting in the eyes of everyone near him.

And yet,
If this virus took him,
You'd draw brackets round him.
Mark his name with an asterisk.
Write him off as an also-ran.
To protect the feelings of the people watching the news
that night,
while they finished their sudoku.

Sarah Parrott

Home School

A school at home, just you and us,
our makeshift, hopeful syllabus.
I'm not sure that we taught you much,
half-naked work call zooms and such.

At first we tried some maths, the phonics,
avoiding pre-lunch gin and tonics.
Crafts and paints, a primary hue,
how to turn the air a shade of blue.

And you became a fine big brother,
teaching us selfless love for another.
You told of atoms, skies and rockets,
drawings spilled from walls and pockets.

And I can see you taught us well,
as we laughed and cried and tried to spell.
I pack your lunch through misty glasses,
I'll be signing up for your evening classes.

Joanna Bennett

Leafy

Taking walks together quickly became our routine
the joy of your face as I put you in the sling
you didn't want to be confined to your pram
with so much to explore and take in

You squealed with delight
your little legs running through the air
at first you gripped my fingers tight
but once you had mastered it
you waved at everything in sight

In lockdown I looked forward to this highlight of our day
long days cooped up inside
looking for new ways to play
I wasn't sure how I would keep you entertained
tried to think of big ideas
buying new toys which were quickly cast aside

Little did I know that all it took
was plucking a leaf off a tree
you carried it clenched in your little fist for miles
and miles
as if you had caught the finest treasure
your excited chuckle as I would pick a leaf for you to hold,
a different colour and shape

puzzled at how to loosen your grip
sometimes letting the leaf sail away like a feather

During the summer I carried the picnic mat in the pram
and would lay it under a tree
we would lie on the blanket, staring up at the sky
and watch the movements of the leaves
casting shadows on our faces
as you began to crawl you would shuffle
towards the bushes inspecting these things
that waved at you in the wind,
exploring through nature these mystical places

It's autumn now and the leaves are falling
all around us like confetti
the ground is a colourful carpet
on which you will take your first few tentative steps
a whole year of walking with you through the seasons
is something I will never forget

Soon you will have your very own tree
we will decorate at home
but these leaves are a little prickly
like needles to touch
dressed with twinkling lights

I can't wait to see your big blue eyes light up

It looks like the second wave is coming
but I am not so worried this time
through your eyes I know there is much to explore
I will kit us out in our warmest coats, hats and gloves
ready to take on the enchanting outdoors.

Susie Butt

Awake

Awake
The day starts again
Snacks, crumbs, toys – piling up
I want to hold you tight
but I crave space for me.
I want to play with you all day
but I crave a minute's peace
The days are long
I count down the hours till you fall asleep
And then count some more till you wake up
The days remind me of the time after you were born
the isolation, the uncertainty, the jealousy of those that
'seem' to have it all together
We eat together, we get fresh air together
Then it's time for bed
You snuggle into my arms
You take longer to fall asleep than before
Once you are soundly asleep it is my time
but I am exhausted
I wonder what tomorrow will bring
I wonder if I'll manage to find the calm and space I so
desperately crave.

Emma Cottam

Skin

He is sitting in the back of the car
in his car-seat
staring out the window, swinging his feet
and he is thinking, I can see
turning over the news he's just received
that people can change their sex.
He says "I want to change too."
I raise an eyebrow "You do?"
"Yes, but not to be a girl.
I want to change the colour of my skin.
To look like you."

Now, a little piece of my heart breaks,
just like it has before each time he takes
this path in his mind.
I scrabble for something meaningful to say,
but I feel inadequate –
his dad is so far away;
stuck outside the country,
locked down
"You know you are beautiful: like sugar; golden brown."
"Mum, I know, but I don't want my skin to be different."
I take a deep breath and say:

"Baby, being different is hard.

That will always be true
especially when you're one of so few
children with brown skin at your school but
just think of this,
here's the unbelievable thing they don't teach
and that so many people miss:
that there isn't much
that's more amazing than skin
it keeps the bad germs out,
the blood and the water in;
it's made of layers and layers of see-through sheets;
covers every bit of us
from our head to our feet
and the top 1mm of it
contains the melanin."
He says he's heard the word before,
but needs it explaining.

I tell him it's an incredible chemical
held inside cells,
which evolution keeps choosing to help us excel
and thrive on this planet.
It produces so many hues:
shades of black, brown, yellow and red;
it colours our eyes

and the hairs on our head;
gives us freckles and moles.
He touches my hand,
his fingers following the constellation of brown spots
as he starts to understand.
I say, "It makes lions gold,
colours fish and birds,
gives ink to the octopus,
exists in the skin of whales,
and each and every one of us,
because nature loves variety
and even more impressively
it protects from the sun's harmful UV,
so that even when skin is bombarded with radiation,
it doesn't fall apart."

His eyes are wide.
I see the wheels turning inside,
the images taking shape in his mind
and he smiles.
"So, I'm a superhero then?"
He says. "My skin is my shield."
"Yes, that's right."
For now I breathe out,
one tiny battle against his fears is won.

But I know this conversation isn't done.
That it will always be my job to improve his world as many
times as it takes:
march into school again,
open uncomfortable conversations,
point out the mistakes in the system.

Because it may only be 1mm of skin to him and me,
but it's hundreds or more years
of racial oppression and history
that if we don't act against
will shape his future and his present.
So to be a mother
I must take all the things that my child has taught
me to see
and in each defiant and loving act
choose to be a revolutionary,
so he can change the world
he may have his children in,
whatever beautiful colour
they wear on their skin.

Lorna Burchell

Renewable Energy

They say to always let children know what's coming.
It may save you some trouble.
The play date will end in five minutes.
A simple warning even adults would appreciate,
like knowing about a Cat 5 hurricane
before it makes precise landfall.
For toddlers, we know the waters will rise,
tantrum waves we cannot hold back.

It's time to clean up now, so we can go to the library.
There, you will pick out books
to inform you of the things
I do not have the answers for.

The globe is getting much hotter, and by 2040
some cities will be underwater.
Who will you be in 20 years?
All degrees of information,
long legs, and beating heart.
Not calm, exactly, but warned and familiar
with your own rising adrenaline.
You were always the one who did not
yield to warnings, a species unto yourself.
I will not. I will not. I will not.

Katy Luxem

Chapter 11
For the Mothers

This is for the Mothers
on my street

The Mothers I pass
The Mothers I meet
The stories I gather
The stills I see
This is for the Mothers
From Me

This is for the Mother
With the maths degree
Cleaning the home
Of the Mother with three
Under fives
Who works at the hospital
Saving lives
This is for the Mother
With a streak on her nose
And across her cheeks
She's been wearing a mask
For that many weeks

This is for the Mother
With the skin like silk
That I pass on the pavement

With a six-pack of milk
Tomorrow's breakfast drink
She's on her own
With four I think

This is for the Mother
Who mothers her friends
Ears and hands she gladly lends
To their every trouble every fear

This is for the Mother
Who lives so near
But feels so far
So low so lost
Should mothering come at such a cost

This is for the Mother
Hoping to be
Grieving disbelieving
Empty
Broke

This is for the Mother

Who smokes by the slides
And my bias swiftly decides
Is somehow lacking
Not good enough

Oh judgement
How rough
And wrong you've been
Many times since I've seen
Her hold together
Sisters
Brothers
Mothering the children of other Mothers
Is it a bother
Not ever
Drop off
Pick up
Piece together

This is for the Mother
Reliable
Kind
Who for every child

Time and a biscuit
She'll find

This is for the Mother
With baby at her breast
This is for the Mother
For whom bottle was best

For richer for poorer
For better for worse
This is for the Mother
Who's a qualified nurse
But works in a salon
Painting toes
Why
Ask her husband
He knows

This is for the Mother
Striving
Thriving
Sliding backwards
Sinking
Gliding

This is for the Mother surviving
Just

This is for the Mother
Afraid to trust her instincts
Outside voices too loud

This is for the Mother
Who pushed beautiful life onto earth
And questions her worth every day

This is for the Mother
Folding tiny clothes in the laundrette
This is for the Mother
Who'll never regret
Who'll mother until
Those needing her love
Are old and grown

Because once you've known
Something which tastes as sweet
You want it forever

This is for the Mothers on my street

Laura Bradford

Torches

When the night mist shrouds the house
and silence is everywhere,
street lamps pierce the dark.

We write essays to each other on our phones
that lie waiting to be opened.
they are messages within a glass bottle;
moments in time ready to be revived uncorked,
offering comfort, hope, advice.

We trudge pushchairs through cool autumn air.
We get lost, we help each other wrestle
our wheels out of tight mud.
You never fail to ask how I am.
You tell me to pick up a pen. Write.

When it's too much, we send smoke signals
and await the rescue we know will come.
Your video call on screen cuts through
marble photographs masquerading the truth.
Though you are not here, you take my hand.

In the darkness, they wait for me,
holding out torches,
ready to guide me home.

Naomi Murcutt

To Another Mother,
at the end of the day

The brush is fat and soft and specially-bought
for golden wet curls tousled in lavender towels
that warm on the rail while we sing doe, a deer
and the water makes a whirlpool of bubbles
travelling down to Australia. She screams
as it snags and I remind
her that some things are worse than tangles.
That she could be
                    somewhere else.

                        I think of

        you. Smoothing and soothing as
        the ash-light fades,
        the rhythms of a thousand years. Making home
        without solid walls.
        You grabbed the brush in haste
        and you didn't have a list and you didn't have room
        but these small things make the difference,
        these talismans
        against the filth, the stench, the night terrors
        of camp. Half the bristles are gone,
        crimson roses faded from polished cedar

but it glides through your daughter's hair
like yours when your mother sung you to bed.
It survived.

I read her stories
of refugee cats, train journeys to dark places,
of the plucky trying to make friends
when their tongues won't cooperate.
I want her to learn
but I also want her to sleep.
They all have happy endings.

My soul pricks.
I mutter a godless prayer.

Karen Morash

For Margaret

I walk with the baby each morning.
He is angry and hungry
So new to the planet
His feet show a lectionary of scars.
Whilst we walk, you are close.
Shuffling in front of us
Smiling as I push past at the sleeping infant.

I walk with the baby post-feeds.
He is unsettled near-sated
To feed him a triptych
Of breast, and bottle, and pump.
Whilst we walk, you are close.
Tip-toeing around us
You look to your thumbs as I offer him mine to soothe.

I walk with the baby to clinic.
He is gaining too slowly
A votive candle on an altar
Of scales marked in the Red Book.
Whilst we walk, you are close.
Wednesday mornings you see us
Baby nestled in mother's coat safe from the rain.

I walk with the baby through boredom.

He will only take rest
In the nave of my rib cage
Always and ever his home.
Whilst we walk, you are close.
Holding me with a gaze
As you stop with tired lungs that work too hard.

I walk with the baby to the bus stop.
He likes to get out of the house
His babblesome Benedictus
Warming my mouth to a smile.
Whilst we walk, you are close.
Hearing his melody
Compelled to join into a polyphony all of our own.

I walk with the baby to buy bread.
His hands like soft bao buns
His voice a sweet Gloria
Singing 'Bread! Milk! Cake!'
Whilst we walk, you are close.
You tell me I'm patient
I know you're Margaret: it's a name that we share.

I walk with the baby beside me.
He likes to spot traffic

Passing the Peace to our neighbours
Yes – I know – growing so fast.

Whilst we walk, I remember –
The sleepless nights; the heel prick tests; the piles of
laundry; the swollen breasts; the help that could never
come and stay; the gungey eye that never went away; the
weekly anguish of baby-weighing; the small voice of calm
from Margaret saying
"You always seem like such a patient Mother."

Whilst we walk, I remember that I am patient.

Whilst we walk, I remember Margaret.

Helena Hoyle King

Mother (v)

Mother is a verb
I once heard someone say
It comes from what you do
Not from your DNA

It doesn't have to mean,
he blossomed in your womb
Or when she screamed her first,
that you were in the room

Mothers can be pairs,
love children and each other
The one who gave them life,
may not be someone's mother

So long as they feel loved
and safe within your care
You know that you are mother
They know that you are there.

Zoe Laura King

Kenning

A snotty-nose wiper, a cross word forgiver
A head-cook-and-bottle-washer, a bruised knee kisser
A lullaby singer, a warm milk-squirter
A shopper, a mopper, a feelings un-hurter
A spinner of tales, a souvenir-keeper
A leaver on of hallway lights, a rocker off to sleeper
A memory-maker, a lost tooth redeemer
A counsellor, a confidante, an always-on-your-teamer
A teacher, a healer, a soother, a hugger
A giver of wisdom, and chances, a MOTHER

Abigail Elizabeth Ottley

Overlooking the Motherlode

Although some of us built a human using our bodies,
we're not goddesses, (domestic or otherwise).
Our bodies house the aches and pains
from lifting whole humans; shushing and feeding.
We're body-builders, and endurance athletes.

Although our ears are attuned to our child's cry,
we don't have super powers.
The force that compels us out of bed
is a heady mix of love, duty and anxiety.
Always on call, we're emergency responders.

Although we can (usually) settle our children,
we're not psychic.
We learned their ways of communication
and their favourites through hours of observation.
We're translators, scientists and anthropologists.

Although our heads hold a library of information,
this didn't come as a download or as divine inspiration.
We read hundreds of articles and books,
asked lots of questions, and learned the hard way.
We're amateur psychologists, and resource acquistioners.

Although we can predict future tantrums,
we're not fortune tellers.
So much strategising now goes into leaving the house,
planning a day and packing a bag, including snacks.
We're project managers, forecasters, and chefs.

Although we can make 'magic' happen,
we're not magicians.
The surprises, the presents, the meet ups, excursions.
The decorations, the photos, the memories.
We're events coordinators, diary schedulers, and
entertainers.

Although we have been changed so much
we're not ever-patient angels
whose nature and knowledge was transformed
in the moment of becoming a mother.
We're conflict managers, hostage negotiators,
reconciliators.

We're not magic,
we're human.

Kirsty Harper

To The Mums

To the 'good' mums and the 'bad' mums
And the where the hell is dad? mums

To the not another game mums
And the never quite became mums

To the always missing their mums
And the lost and feeling scared mums

To the happy mums and sad mums
And the think they're going mad mums

To the maybe someday soon mums
And the laughing like a loon mums

To the going it alone mums
And the trying to make a home mums

To the think they've got it made mums
And the hoping memories fade mums

To the somewhere in between mums
And the never feeling seen mums

To the finding things so tough mums
And the hoping it's enough mums

It's enough, mums
It's enough, mums
It's enough, mums

Laura Pearson

Chapter 12
Love

Every-extra-ordinary Love

I find our love
In the drawer of doom
Right at the back
Covered in fluff
Stuck to a broken boiled sweet

I find our love
In the burrows of my brow
In the wrinkles
Round my eyes

I find our love
In the pile of odd socks
Mismatched rainbows
Tangled
Lost souls
Waiting to be match-made

I find our love
Down the back of the sofa
Sandwiched between hairclips
And sweetie wrappers
Beside the lost remote control

I find our love

In the morning juggle
With the cup of tea made
As we struggle
Out the door

I find our love
In the bedtime hustle
Floating on bathtime bubbles
Between stories read
And hands held
As they finally
Go to sleep

I stop and hold
My breath
As the daily dance
Of demands
Quietens
We find our feet
A relative peace
And sigh

Lucy Beckley

Ordinary Devotion

there is nothing ordinary
about this devotion
the five-times-a-night feeds
cups of tea undrunk, biscuits undunked
the rice cakes fed directly to the dog
the labia wiped and the assholes cleaned

there is nothing ordinary about the
stubbed toes or squashed fingers,
your head resting on my shoulder
just for a moment

nothing ordinary about the length
my nipple stretches as you stand up while feeding
turning 45 degrees as you do

nothing ordinary about the enormous
heartbreak of not giving you (just) cake for tea
your tiny fingers inordinately strong and
your tears outrageous
gone a beat later

nothing ordinary about the
six hundredth time we read

Picture This as you hold my thumb
and push your thumbnail under mine

nothing ordinary
about how gloriously
ordinary all this is

Johanna Darque

Overripe

Motherhood has made me overripe;
Softened and depleted
Tender
Bruised
And full of sweetness

I want to remember
You looking up at me,
Breastfeeding,
Beaming;
Eyes large and liquid with love.

I am knotted with contradictions;
Palm on your chest
Just to check
You're still breathing

Other times at peace;
Inhaling the grassy smell of milk
Lingering on your cheeks.

I want to remember
Little hands
Like antennae
Sleepily exploring

Our faces
Each morning

When thin light outside
Is politely imploring
But nestled together
Still snug in sleep's velvet
We choose to ignore it.

Your laughter is nectar;
The shrieks and snuffles
A sugar-rush
Propelling me like a bumblebee
Through endless days
And fleeting months.

Sometimes I struggle
With your immediacy,
Intensity
Nothing left to give
So I wring out droplets of guilt
Like an old flannel.

I wonder
How you will find this poem

Years later;
I hope it's not embarrassing.

Perhaps it is an intrusion
To capture these moments
Before you had language
To express yourself.

Forgive me –

Here is the message
I want you to know;

My love is a well-worn luck charm
It can fit in your pocket,
The palm of your hand
You can carry it with you

It can be wrapped
Around your shoulders
Like a duvet
On a day
When the world outside
Is too harsh.

It is the remembered warmth
Of sun on your face;
You can carry it with you
When I am gone.

Bethany-Rose Oakley

Heart Strings

These heart strings upon which you pull
Are not strings at all.
They are invisible bonds on this pulsating mass
We call a heart.
They are fast flowing rivers of senseless emotion,
Of love,
Of fear,
Of excitement,
Of future dreams,
They are arteries carrying pieces of you to me
And veins carrying pieces of me to you.
They swish and swirl and intertwine around each other
Freely, binding me to you.
One cannot live without the other,
Every beat of this heart beats for both of us.
And you wonder why, when I hear your cry,
My heart aches to help you and I rush to your side.
For it is as if I am crying myself.
But when it is you, my darling,
These heart strings tug my own heart away
And give pieces of it to you, to heal.

Nicola Gordon

Mirror

You are my mirror.
The reflection is new,
blurry
I do not recognise myself.
Beautiful though.
You look at me like you really see me.
And for the first time, every time, I love the reflection.
New, beautiful and strong
but also
Unsure, lost and vulnerable.
Forever now a part of something.
It is sometimes unnerving,
the intensity of it all.
It makes me look away.
Makes me question my worthiness at times,
when the reflection is the sun, the moon, the universe.
All things good and God.
The reflection of you, of me, in your eyes
As your mother

Helena Lyon-Shaw

What do you do?

I prise stubborn noodles off walls,
stare at cats, envy their unapologetic resolution
to do whatever the hell they want.

I linger in supermarket aisles, mull over
vegetables, find ways of sneaking them
into home-cooked meals.

I arbitrate, procrastinate, deliberate, educate,
precariously spin plates at unreasonable speed.
I fantasise about sleep, stand longingly

next to dozing infants, hoping that,
if I stand there long enough, I'll absorb
something. I air grab and body pop

around the kitchen to a young audience, either
unmoved, confused or preoccupied by crockery;
tough crowd. I sit sprawled in a bog-eyed stupor,

swamped by bedlam and lists.
Sometimes I hide behind cereal boxes
and take surreptitious bites of chocolate.

Some days I conquer rocky seas with my crew
on rafts made of cushions and graffitied throws.
Other days I gorge on ice cream

with dreadlocked mermaids, ride with ballerinas
on rainbow-coloured bicycles. Most mornings
I gobble up remnants of slumber

before my aching joints are tugged into action.
Sometimes I'd rather sit crumpled in a quiet corner
and be cradled in Spring's gentle breeze.

I am caught in a tug of war,
between the desire to curtail the chaos
and to keep hold of it tight, forever.

Chrissie Dreier

Age and Grace

My girl is fine,
tall and wiry as a springy stem
of wheat grass.
I watch her waft through her days
like a skein of silk unwinding.
Electric tresses ripple down her back;
the molten berry of her eye
captures fleet exposures as
her mind's quick shutter
never ceases clicking.

There is poetry in her
entrances and exits;
in the way her body smooths the
precious air around her.
Indeed, she is my poem.

This girl distils the light
of the stars that blinded me
at her creation.
She is the age I was when she nestled
inside me – small pea
in the pod of my sex;
sandy grain in the oyster
destined for pearl.

She is finding her way to those stars
through the thin air of parting;
she cleaves to her future,
its risks and adornments.
There will come a day when I'll
think she has left me forever.

Did I hold her enough?

Did I speak my love
speak it again
speak it yet again?

Christine O'Neill Sá.

Chapter 13
Join the Mum Poet Club

Affirmations

where is poetry?
in skinned knees &
soured milk crusted
under the car seat

when is poetry?
stolen naptime scribbles
carpool line, midnight oil

who is poetry?
mothers patting our
words on the back,
whispering their names
until they awake

Adrienne K. Burris

Wait with me

I'll rest here happy inside your book
Perhaps you're busy trying to cook
Or maybe you're stopping the kids from fighting
Whilst longing to do some creative writing
See, as mums we often have to wait,
At the Mum Poet Club we all relate.

Jemma Chawla

Seen

Each page, a stage,
for an unknown voice.
And each page gave
a mother a choice.
To be heard, to be seen
To unite, to dream.
To connect
when we're lonelier
than we've ever been.

Elizabeth Murphy

Permissions

All poems published with kind permission of the individual poets.

Acknowledgements

"First Born" by Ruth Aylett has been previously published in *Pretty in Pink*.

"When I Gave Birth" by Imogen Schäfer has been previously published in *Dispatches From New Motherhood*, published by Mothership Writers.

"I've Just Had a Baby" by Annie Ridout has been previously published in *Twenty-Nine: Poems on Motherhood*.

"That First Year" by Karen McMillan has been previously published in *Mother Truths*.

"A Rod For My Own Back" by Vanessa Napolitano has been previously published in *Isabella and Us*.

"Cuddle" by Ali Pember has been previously published in *Isabella and Us*.

"Plaiting Rapunzel's Hair" by Zoë Sîobhan Howarth-Lowe has been previously published on the 2019 Liz Ferrets Poetry prize shortlist and by Hedgehog Press.

"Son" by Angi Holden has been previously published in *Spools of Thread* by Angi Holden, published by Mother's Milk Books 2018.

"Matryoshka Dolls" by Finola Scott has been previously published in *Much Left Unsaid* pamphlet by Red Squirrel Press.

"The Year You Were Gone" by Alice Day has been previously published in *New Normal Zine*.

"Home School" by Joanna Bennett has been previously published in *Tiny Lungs*.

The Team

Edited by:	Katharine Perry
Associate Editor:	Julie Coates
Associate Editor:	Emily Way-Evans
Art Direction and Design:	Emma Dakeyne
Cover Design:	Emma Dakeyne
Illustration:	Julie Mackey
With thanks to:	Karan Chambers
	Neil Dakeyne
	Nicola Dellard-Lyle
	Jen Feroze
	Sarah Parrott
	Bella Zanetti

Profits from sales of this anthology will be donated to the PANDAS Foundation.

Other releases by the Mum Poem Press

The Mum Poet Club Guide to Self Care

The Mum Poet Club Guide to Self-Care is a poetry anthology that features over 40 beautiful, funny, comforting and inspiring poems on the theme of "self-care" written by members of the Mum Poet Club. It also includes a self-care activity book packed full of self-care lols and creative self-care activities to try such as journalling, poetry prompts, mindful colouring and a set of six self-care themed stickers.

Why Mums Are Amazing

Why Mums Are Amazing contains 14 beautiful poems celebrating mothers – all written by members of the Mum Poet Club and personally selected by award-winning poet Hollie McNish. Each poem has been specially illustrated by an artist and the collection is riso-printed on 170gsm paper made from recycled coffee cups. Profits are donated to the charity Pregnant Then Screwed and over £2,000 has been donated so far.

Both titles are available at themumpoempress.com

Join the Mum Poet Club

The Mum Poet Club is a writing group for mums who write poetry.

Joining the Mum Poet Club community will give you:

- monthly peer feedback on working drafts of your poems
- the opportunity to submit poems to be included in future issues of the Mum Poet Club zine
- exclusive access to Mum Poet Club events, such as poetry readings, workshops and our friendly and supportive open mic night
- an email newsletter once a month with poems to inspire, projects to get involved in, recommended reading and member news.

It's free to join, no writing experience is needed and everyone is welcome.

For more information, or to join the club, please visit:
themumpoempress.com

HOW TO

MAN

TO

CHERISH

YOU...

IF YOU'RE HIS WIFE

A NO-NONSENSE GUIDE FOR EVERY
WIFE OR BRIDE-TO-BE

STEPHAN LABOSSIERE

TABLE OF
CONTENTS

INTRODUCTION

Disclaimer: Before you proceed any further, I need you to do something very, very important. I want you to stop. Take a deep breath. Press your RESET button. What exactly do I mean by that? You may feel like you've done *everything* to improve your marriage and nothing has worked. You may be emotionally and mentally exhausted. You may not feel like you have the energy for much more. You may already have one foot out the door in your marriage. I want to help you change all that.

Pressing your RESET button gives you and your relationship a clean slate and allows you to start building with a positive foundation. Right now, you're consciously making the decision to move forward, so don't bring in any old baggage. This only makes the process more difficult.

First, I need you to let go of your negative mindset. Everything that has happened before today, all the failed efforts, every relationship problem, all hurts, disappointments, and all your previous relationship frustrations. You've got to let it go. I know that sounds easier said than done and it is. However, it's in your control to make it happen. You must believe you can flush that negative energy out of your system and heal. Your quality of life and the success of your marriage depends on it. I want you to visit www.healingformyheart.com to get the steps you need.

Again, I know it sounds easier said than done, but the fact that you're reading this book means you want your marriage to work so don't give up hope! You really have to *believe* things can be amazing going forward in your marriage.

In *this book* I will present simple, easy-to-implement strategies for how to get your husband to cherish you that yield results. I'm going to focus on the actions *you* can take right away to get things going in the right direction. Implement this new approach or maybe for you it's an improved approach, since I don't know what you've been doing up to this point. Apply it over time and you're going to see improvement in yourself, your husband, and your marriage. Reading and embracing the content in this book is going to get you on a much better path. I hope you're ready!

In case you're wondering, I'm not trying to put the bulk of the work on the wives. I've already spoken to your husbands in my first book, *How to Get a Woman to Have Sex with You … if She's Your Wife*. You're more than welcome to purchase that book and have your husband read it. That may require some blackmailing, begging, or a special torture technique, but if it will get him to do as you please, hey, it will be worth it.

With that said, I needed to make sure I spoke to women about this topic also because it takes two. Each individual must focus on what he/she can do to improve their marriage. This is the main reason why you're reading this book. You want a better marriage. Either it's not where it needs to be or even if it is good, you know it can be even better.

As you read this book I want you to be really, open-minded. If your marriage is going to work, if you're going to see things improve, it's important that you're willing to be open and receptive to what

I'm saying to you. Even if you take issue with some of the things I talk about, be willing to take some time and process them.

The reality is you're probably not going to agree with every point I make. I'm okay with that because what's important is that you hear the honest-to-God truth. I'm not just speaking truth from a male perspective either. I'm speaking truth from the perspective of a relationship coach who has sat down with hundreds, even thousands of people, including talking with thousands of married couples. I receive countless emails and direct messages every single day from women and men seeking insight on their relationships.

You may think men don't really care about relationships because men aren't as vocal on social media and in different social settings about their feelings. The truth is, men do in fact care. I hear firsthand about the things men struggle with and what they're unhappy about in their relationships. They talk to me about what they feel is lacking in their marriages. When I sit down one-on-one with these guys, they let me know what they feel, the roadblocks they face, and what they wish would change in their marriages.

I'm taking this opportunity to present these things to you from an unbiased position. I may be a man, but I am a coach first at least regarding speaking about relationships. I'm a third party and I'm here to help you. I'm not here to judge you. I'm not here to take advantage of you or make things easier for your husbands. I'm here to see marriages improve for both parties. In order for this to happen you must do your part.

In addition to having an open mind, you must be willing to implement what I share in this book, even if you don't agree with everything. Simply, try it! The information is of no use to you if you don't follow the instructions I lay out for you. I completely understand and agree with the notion that there is no one size fits all solution. Every man is different. However, men have a lot of similarities. I'm confident you'll be able to apply these simple techniques and see your marriage improve. Don't be reluctant and don't be unwilling to press forward with the information I'm giving you. Embrace it. Utilize it. Watch yourself transform into a *cherished* wife.

Chapter 1

UNDERSTANDING
HIS NEEDS

Do you agree with the statement, "All a man needs is good food, good sex, and peace?" Give him these things and you're good to go...or are you? Your man has certain things he's looking for out of life and things he's looking for out of you, specifically. Although you may feel like you know what they are, you might not fully understand them. To be perfectly honest, you probably don't know him as well as you think you do.

This next point is no secret. Some men struggle with having open and honest conversations about what they're looking for out of a woman, their desires, and their true needs. Not to mention the fact that a lot of men don't want to feel like they have to nag their wives for their needs to be met, even though that doesn't stop some from trying.

For example, if he's mentioned something a few times and nothing's changed, he's very likely to say to himself, "You know what, forget it. She's not going to change. She's not going to bother. It's not going to work with her." He's very likely to give up. Once this happens, the door opens to all kinds of other issues.

As I mentioned earlier, every man is different. However, men in general have a lot of similarities and share many things in common. With that said, there are seven basic needs men in general are looking for in a woman and from their wives in particular. As his wife, a man needs you to:

1   Respect him.

2   Support him.

3   Nurture him.

4   Value him.

5   Be transparent with him.

6   Please him sexually.

7   Stay physically attractive ... to HIM.

These seven basic needs are the foundation you want in place to truly speak to your husband's heart and to draw him closer to you. I want to take a quick moment to highlight the top three; respect, support, and nurture because they are often the least discussed in conversations about marriage.

Respect

Listen, if you don't respect your husband, the following problems are likely to arise as a result:

✗ You won't be able to love him the way he needs to be loved.

✗ You will speak to him in ways that push him away from you.

✗ He will become less desirable to you.

✗ You will struggle to be sexually intimate with him.

These are just a few examples of issues resulting from lack of respect. Clearly you can see that a lack of respect is very damaging to your marriage. You might say, "Well I don't respect him because he did so-and-so, or he hasn't done what I need him to do."

Listen, I get it. In no way do I want to ignore the part he plays in this dynamic. However, you're married to him. You're still there. So, you must be open to exploring ways that will help correct the issue, not contribute to it, or allow it to linger. The fact is, if you're going to stay in the marriage and you want to see things change for the better, respect must be in place. If there's a lack of respect for any reason, you have to address the issue by talking to him about it and getting to the root cause.

Focus on what can be improved. You can't dismiss this issue. You can't devalue it, you can't just say, "Oh well, he'll get my respect when he starts doing X, Y, and Z." No, you have to have a talk with your man about why there is a lack of respect and work together to correct it.

Support

Support is one of the least talked about items on a man's basic needs list. It tends to take a backseat to food and sex. However, support is one of the biggest pieces to the "happy marriage" puzzle. Understand that providing support to your husband is a necessity. It's something you must embrace and do often. I'll break down the importance of it and why you need to implement more of it in your marriage in the chapter on support.

Nurture

Being a nurturer is at the core of who you are as a woman. Nurturing is a part of your feminine essence. When you're not nurturing your partner, you're removing one of the fundamental principles of why a man is drawn to a woman in the first place. Plain and simple!

Let's look at momma's boys. You may be married to one and you may have already found yourself annoyed by his close attachment to his mother. You may not even like his mom and hate the fact that no matter what his mom does, she can do no wrong in his eyes. It may even be to a point where he's putting her over you and it's pissing you off.

Listen, I completely understand. It shouldn't be that way. I am a firm believer that once a man gets married his wife should come first. However, I want you to realize *WHY* he's so attached to his mother. The reason is simple, she nurtures him. She gives him one of the most important things he needs from a woman, other than sex of course, nurturing.

Now you may say, "Well he needs to go marry his mother." No, he doesn't need to go marry his mother. He needs to stay married to you. You're his wife. You need to embrace the things that draw him to his mother and become the source of these things. This doesn't mean you will replace her, but you have to tap into what makes that mother/son bond so strong. When you become his source of nurturing, it will shift the balance of power and make a huge difference in your marriage.

I'll go into much more detail as we continue. The remaining four basic needs, valuing him, being transparent, pleasing him sexually, and staying physically attractive will also be completely explored as well. Let's go deeper.

Chapter 2

SPEAK TO YOUR HUSBAND WITH LOVE & CARE

Kind words are like honey—
sweet to the soul and healthy for the body.
—Proverbs 16:24

It's Not Only What You Say, It's How You Say It

The way you speak to your husband is the first key to getting him to cherish you. You have to learn how to speak to him in a way that softens him up to you and that makes him *want* to give you what you need. You've heard the saying, "It's not what you say, but how you say it." This applies here. When you learn how to speak to him with love and respect, a whole new world will open for you in your marriage. Your life will change.

"How do I tap into this way of communicating consistently?" You ask. Let me paint a picture for you. Now, this might not be the most popular example for me to use, but I think it's a very good and accurate one. You may or may not have been to a female strip club before. If you happen to ever go to a female strip club, pay very, very close attention. What you'll notice a lot of the times is that the woman who makes the most money is not necessarily the woman who looks the best. It's not the woman who has the best body. It's not the woman who dances the best.

The woman who usually makes the most money is the woman who speaks to the customer the best. She can sit down next to a guy the entire night, not shake one booty cheek and get paid the whole time, as well as get drinks purchased for her. On top of that, she can have the same guy come back the next week and do it all over again. What does that show you? It shows you there's power in the way you talk to a man. This has nothing to do with sex. This is strictly about how you verbally communicate with your man.

To make this point even clearer for you, let me give you another example. Do you know a woman who always speaks to everyone with terms of endearment? Everyone is baby, sweetie, or honey? Have you ever seen that woman have a hard time getting a man to do her a favor? No, you don't. I don't care what you say, no you don't, alright! When a woman knows how to speak with all that sweetness, tenderness, and charm, men melt. Men are going to do what she asks of them.

Will this work on every man? No, but it is highly effective for the most part. Is it going to work with your husband? Yes! You know why it's going to work with your husband? It's going to work on your husband because he already married you. He already chose you as the person he wanted to share his life with. He's already deemed you worthy— he's already decided you're valuable to him. Use this to your advantage. You need to begin to come at him with charm, sweetness, and your natural feminine energy, like only you can. When you do, you're going to enjoy the response you get out of him. This will help you stay consistent and be able to enjoy the long-term benefits of properly communicating.

Compliment Him

How you speak to your husband is important, but let's take it one step further. Start complimenting him! Listen, I had one client who was a very good-looking guy, about 6'4, built. I mean this guy could have easily been a model. Women went crazy over this man. When he went out, women openly stared at him, flirted with him, and complimented him constantly. Of course, this fed his ego and he did enjoy it to a certain extent. One day he shared this with me, "Man, I get all these compliments from all these women, but I can't get a compliment from the one woman I want it from the most."

This can be devastating to a man. He wants the one woman he loves, the woman he chose to share his life with to be able to give him a simple compliment. She didn't tell him when he looked nice or how proud she was of him, she didn't admire his accomplishments. She had the type of attitude that she didn't need to compliment him because he was doing what he's supposed to do, nothing special.

Listen, I want you to destroy this way of thinking. It's the wrong type of attitude to have. Learn to appreciate everything your husband does.

Appreciation breeds production. That's worth repeating so let me say it again. Appreciation breeds production. When you show your husband, you appreciate all his efforts, even when it comes to simple things; such as, paying the bills and taking out the trash, you make him feel valued and loved. When he feels valued and loved, he automatically wants to do more for you. On the other hand, when you take him for granted, when you overlook and dismiss the small things, it makes him not want to do anything thing for you. Plain and simple.

You may say to yourself, "Well, it's his job." No, it's his choice. He can choose to do you right or do you wrong at any time. He can choose to mistreat you, or he can choose to treat you like his cherished wife. So, appreciate every time he treats you like a queen. Appreciate every time he shows you the love you desire. It doesn't mean you've got to throw him a party or bake him a batch of cookies every time. It just means you should show him love in return and acknowledge his efforts. It means you should give him positive energy, affection, and appreciation. All this can be done by using the right words. You can foolproof your marriage by becoming his biggest admirer and cheerleader and protecting it with love.

These are things you should want to do as his wife. Believe me when I tell you, if you're not letting your man know he looks good, trust me there's another woman who is, and this can create other, avoidable issues in your marriage.

Don't Talk, Just Listen

I also want to point out the other important part of proper communication, listening. Make sure you listen to your husband. Be present when he's communicating with you. What do I mean by be present? I mean you've got to give him your full attention. When your husband's talking to you, stop thinking about what you need to do next. Still your busy mind, stop your multi-tasking, and give him your full attention. Don't make what he's saying an afterthought.

You may be saying, "I do listen to him." Well, if you're doing multiple things while he's talking to you, you might be listening, but you're not paying attention. You're not tuned into him. He's just this extra thing on the side. Every time this happens it makes him feel less valued in your life. And guess what? He's not going to want to talk to you and he will eventually stop altogether.

Imagine, if he's telling you his dreams, his plans for something big and because you're doing multiple things and trying to listen to him at the same time, you miss it? He might not say it. He might not show it, but inside he feels crushed. Once this happens too many times, he's going to shut down. If you're not willing to give him an ear and your undivided attention, trust me, someone else is going to be willing to listen to his dreams, his aspirations, and his thoughts. Believe it or not, he wants to be heard and understood by you. However, for this to happen you must be present and attentive to him. Your being present shows him he matters to you. Let's take it a step further.

How do you show him you're happy to have him around? There are a lot of men who come home to nothing but nagging. All they come home to is negative energy. Think about it for a moment. What does your husband come home to from you? Are you kissing your husband when he comes through the door? Do you embrace him and rub his back? Are you showing him any kind of signs that illustrate to him, you're actually happy or pleased to see him and happy that he's home? Do you at least smile?

No man wants to be where he doesn't feel wanted. It's your choice to make sure he feels welcomed in your presence. Now you may be saying, "Well I don't want him home until a certain time or I don't like him too much right now." Okay, I get that. However, it's up to you to address the issue and make sure it doesn't cause you to make him feel like you don't want him there at all.

The fact of the matter is you need to show him that you want him home or else why would he want to be there? You can say that you want him to be home, but words don't mean anything if you're not backing them up with positive actions, and showing a true desire for his presence. So not only do you need to be present, you need to show him you value his presence. Both will make a huge difference in your marriage. We covered a lot, so let's quickly recap.

Points to remember:

- ✓ Speak to your husband with love and words of affirmation.

- ✓ Speak to your husband with positive, feminine energy.

✓ Compliment your man often and celebrate his accomplishments.

✓ Remember, it's not what you say, it's how you say it.

✓ Be present when he talks to you and show him you value his presence.

When you do these things, consistently, you will create an environment that draws your husband closer to you and reinforces the bond of your marriage. You will cause him to be more receptive to you. As a result, he will want to be around you more. Your marriage will be strengthened and elevated to a whole new level when you become his source of love and positive energy. You will experience something a lot of married people aren't experiencing right now, a true and loving connection.

Go ahead and try it. I dare you! Stop reading for a second and go kiss your husband. Whisper something sweet in his ear. Give him that feminine energy we just talked about. Start practicing these things right away. Start to implement them daily moving forward and you're going to see the huge difference it makes in your marriage.

Bonus Chapter

WHAT IS FEMININE
ENERGY?

I want to pause and stress the concept of *feminine energy* here. You might be thinking, "Why do I want to stress feminine energy? What's up with that?" Well here's what's up with that. Feminine energy is your *power*. It's the essence of who you are as a woman. Being masculine, being tough, and being overly independent, don't work to your true advantage within the dynamic of a marriage.

When you were single it was much more acceptable. However, once you're in a relationship, once you're married to a man who actually loves you, and who cares about you, you must embrace *interdependence*. This concept may seem a foreign one but it's one of the reasons you got married. To have a partner to depend on for support throughout the life you have together. Now that you have it, take it out of theory and practice it.

Interdependence within your relationship is important. However, it will be tough to embrace interdependence if you can't embrace your own feminine energy. If for some reason you're uncomfortable showing your feminine side, it's probably because there's a wall up. There's something holding you back and not allowing you to be vulnerable, not even with your husband.

In my example of the stripper speaking to her client or the woman always speaking to a man with terms of endearment, what's important to see is: they're not afraid of coming off as soft and vulnerable. They understand that their softness and vulnerability will get them what they want. It gives them power. This type of power will never work against them.

Eve didn't get Adam to eat the apple by barking at him and talking all kinds of noise in his ear. Delilah didn't get Sampson to cut his hair by being tough and independent. No, they both used their feminine energy. Using your natural, feminine energy gets you everywhere. So, ask yourself, why aren't you using your feminine energy more? Why aren't you tapping into it daily? Is it because there are things your husband has done that have made you guarded? Is it because you carried things into your marriage from previous relationships that cause you to hold back?

Break Down Your Walls

It's up to you to identify the wall(s) you have up. Walls restrict your ability to love and receive love in your marriage. Walls restrict your ability to give off the positive, loving, feminine energy that's so beneficial to you and your marriage. I want you to understand how necessary and important this is. Now you're probably thinking, "Well, how can I be softer? How can I turn on my feminine energy and give my man this sweetness you're talking about?

First and foremost, when communicating with your husband, if you communicate with the wrong tone, the wrong body language or the wrong attitude, you're setting yourself up for failure. Now you might be thinking, "I speak very calmly to my husband." Yes, but calm doesn't mean you're not being "stank."

Essentially, you can still be giving off a lot of negative energy, even when you're calm. I'm sure you've had an instance where someone spoke to you and even though they were very calm and very articulate their tone was still stank and negative. This experience probably resulted in you wanting to slap the hell out of them.

Now, imagine how your husband feels when you're speaking to him and you're coming off with this passive-aggressive energy. Do you think he's going to be receptive to it? He's not. Being calm, yet stank, is not going to allow the communication to go anywhere positive. It's not going to give you the outcome you're looking for.

You might be thinking, "Well why should I have to do that? If he's my husband, shouldn't he just respect what I'm saying?" Yes, he should respect what you're saying, and he should be attentive to your needs. However, no one can continuously get slapped in the face and still do what they're supposed to do. You can't keep being reckless with your communication and expect your husband to give you the love you're looking for. No one can continue to take negative energy and just be positive about it.

Chances are if you have a wall up of any kind toward your spouse it's a result of something they've done that wasn't resolved. You're probably still holding on to it, meaning it wasn't properly addressed.

Be willing to communicate how it made you feel. You're communicating it to get it off your chest, not necessarily to have it resolved. It may be later when he comes back to you to take responsibility and reconciles his wrongdoing. However, that's not the focus of your communicating. You can't control anything he does. So, your focus can't be on how he responds.

The most important thing to remember is that you can't change the past. You need to put it behind you. It's up to you to make a conscious effort to create the type of behavior you want to experience in your relationship now and going forward. No one is expecting you to be perfect at this new behavior immediately but be consistent in your effort.

If there needs to be more intimacy in the relationship, start practicing ways to create the intimacy. I've already used the example of kissing your man when he comes home. Regardless of what's happened, regardless of previous issues, you can still make a choice to kiss your husband when he comes home. The more you do it, even if the issues still exist, you'll become more comfortable. There is always going to be a need to work through issues in your marriage. Begin practicing whatever change you want to see. Over time you will resolve more issues sooner and they will have less of an opportunity to negatively impact your marriage.

Stop Transferring Negative Energy

Be aware of your negative energy. Sometimes you're carrying it and you don't know or aren't able to own it. Be mindful of it. Find a stress reliever. You can't help it if someone pisses you off at work, or someone rubs you the wrong way, or reality TV pushes you into a negative mindset. What you need to learn how to do is release that before you bring it home to your husband.

As a woman, you were built to nurture. You were built to love. You were uniquely built to give off positive energy. You are more than capable of overcoming negative energy. However, address any issues that exist hindering you from being your natural, sweet, and loving self. Identify, work-through, and remove all issues that keep you from speaking to your husband in a more positive way.

There's a huge difference between, "You need to go take the garbage out, alright? Don't forget. It's garbage day. I'm tired of always telling you the garbage needs to be taken out." vs. "Hey baby, please make sure you take out the garbage. We don't want to miss the day. Please make sure you take care of that for me honey, okay?"

Wow! There's a big difference in how those two statements come across. At the end of the day, it's the same message. You want the garbage taken out. That's it. That's all you really want. However, how you communicate what you want to him, makes a huge difference in how he receives it, and how he will respond.

The key here is to think before you speak. Put yourself in his shoes. Ask yourself, "If he came at me with the first statement, how would I take it? If his request was laced with negative energy, how would I respond to it?" If your hypothetical response isn't positive, why are you communicating to your husband this way? If there's anyone in the world you're *supposed* to talk sweet to, it's your husband! If there's anyone you're *supposed* to check your attitude at the door with, it's your husband. He is the last person you should be coming at with negative energy.

I get it. Marriage can be tough, and he might have done some things that you feel justify your negativity towards him. Let me say this, whatever he's done in the past is no excuse to give him attitude and negativity. You don't want to pour negativity into your relationship. The last thing you want to do is fight fire with fire. You'll burn the whole house down. I need you to stop holding on to things that anger you. Address any anger issues, so you can move on. You should always want to put your best foot forward when you're speaking to and communicating with your husband, both verbally and non-verbally.

Counteract any issues with love, positive energy, and with the sweetness that you were created with. You have it in you, despite what you want to believe or what you think.

Find an activity of release that allows you to destress and decompress those negative emotions so you're not bringing that to your partner. Get a massage every now and then, do gardening work, whatever, engage in activities that help take the edge off. Also, include the following techniques in your regimen to help you get better with how you communicate.

PRAY BEFORE YOU ENGAGE

Let's say you get home from work and you've had a stressful day. Before you get out of the car and walk into the house with a nasty, stank attitude, pray. Calm yourself and your spirit down. Anytime you find yourself being pushed to a negative place, stop and pray.

Praying before you react will help you put a stop to the negative energy build-up and help you catch yourself before it causes bigger problems within your relationship.

DECREASE NEGATIVE INFLUENCES

Also, be more mindful of the negative influences and triggers in your life. If talking to certain relatives' triggers negativity, limit them or address it. If you know watching certain shows (realty television), listening to certain music, being in certain environments puts you in negative place, be proactive about it. Make sure that you take inventory of what causes negativity in you and make the proper adjustments to eliminate it as much as possible.

Feminine Energy, It's Not a Weakness

You may have been raised in a household that made you a little hard. Maybe you were made to think being soft and feminine weren't positive attributes. You may perceive your feminine energy as a weakness. I'm here to tell you otherwise. It's not weakness. Understand that using your feminine energy on a man who loves you is never a weakness.

On the other hand, if you're being taking advantage of by your husband or mistreated when you're being sweet and loving, then the question becomes: are you married to the right man? Let me not get ahead of myself … we're going to talk about that later in the book!

Let me reassure you here, there's no way you can lose by being softer, more feminine, and sweeter to a man you love and who loves you.

Maybe things just got off track temporarily. Now that you're trying to get things back on track, he might be a little skeptical at first. He might look at you like, "Who is this woman? Where did she come from and can I get more of her?" That's it, if anything at all. He will love it. He will embrace it. He will hope the new woman you've become never goes away. You'll see how he responds to it and want him to respond that way more often.

Let me tell you something about men. Men are very logical. When we figure out that this new behavior will be more consistent when we react a certain way and it's what we want, we'll continue following suit. We will do whatever it takes to get the same good result. Plain and simple.

The same is true for your husband. All he really cares about is getting the same good results over and over. If you show him that yes, you're going to keep giving him that feminine energy, which is what he's longing for, he will keep giving you what you want in return. All this is possible by operating more from your feminine energy.

Chapter 3

THREE WAYS TO
NURTURE HIM

Feeding His Natural Appetite

"The way to a man's heart is through his stomach." While I don't agree with this saying 100%, I do acknowledge the importance of keeping a man well-fed. It's important for you to be mindful of what you pour into your husband's stomach, as well as what you're pouring into his heart.

You may be married to man who doesn't care about your cooking. You might not have to make sure he's well-fed because he might love to cook, if that's your husband, awesome! However, if you're married to a man who looks to you for his sustenance, for a nice plate of hot food when he comes home, well, embrace that fact. Ask yourself, "Am I keeping him well-fed?"

Let me be clear. I'm not trying to restrict you to only the kitchen and the bedroom. We're not living in the 1950s. I'm also not trying to tell you what your role is or should be in your marriage. However, if you're responsible for handling the meals, put some real effort into it.

Answer this question: Do you give him any variety? Men like variety when it comes to food. This doesn't mean you need to try a lot of different dishes he has no interest in eating. It means you should try a few different dishes and learn what he likes, and then stick to it.

A guy I know, his wife would try all kinds of different dishes and it got on his last nerves. She had the variety thing down, but she didn't consider what he enjoyed eating. She would always include things she knew he didn't care for. He's not big on eating a lot of vegetables, yet she always wanted to try dishes with lots of vegetables in them. He's like, "What are you trying to do to me? This is not what I like." This was annoying because his meals were important to him. She was throwing an important part of his life, eating, by including items he didn't care for.

Let this be a lesson to you as a wife. Stop trying to feed him what you want to feed him. Unless we're talking about a situation where your husband doesn't eat healthy and he needs a little extra push in the right direction. In this case, do what you have to do to try to help him along. However, under normal circumstances, find out what he enjoys and provide that for him. His meals are important to him.

You might even be thinking, "Did he really have to include this in the book?" Yes, I did. Why? Men complain about it, that's why! There are husband's that complain about their wives' cooking the same thing every night or that her cooking is simply not good. It's a problem for them.

Listen, I'm not telling you that you need to become a master chef. I'm simply saying, get your skills to a decent level, especially if you have children. If your husband doesn't like the food, I can almost guarantee the kids don't either. Trust me, this will put a smile on your husband's and children's faces.

Please don't take this as an insult. Don't internalize this point and take it personally. I'm providing you with different ways to improve your household and your marriage. Believe it or not, your ability to prepare great tasting food can make a difference to your man. It can also have a very powerful impact on the relationship. It gives him another reason to want to come home to you. It makes him happy that you're his wife. It helps him take pride in his household and marriage. Men take pride in having a woman who can throw down in the kitchen. Making sure he's well-fed and feeling good is another way to show him you care.

Remember that there is going to be a learning curve here for the both of you. Give yourself and him time to adjust. During the adjustment period learn to take constructive criticism from him. Ask him for feedback on what you cook and if there is any improvement needed in how or what you cook. Simply ask him what he wants you to cook. Now if he tells you, "Baby, I love everything you make. I'm good. You're awesome." Then mission accomplished, you don't have to worry about this.

However, if you worry about your cooking, ask your husband for his honest feedback. When he gives it to you, whatever you do, don't internalize it. Don't take his feedback negatively. Don't lash out at him or catch an attitude and be mad at him about his input. If you're going to say to him, "Why didn't you tell me this earlier? Why didn't you tell me you didn't really care for my cooking?" He's going to say, "I didn't want to hurt your feelings." He also didn't want you to overreact and get bent out of shape about it. Be open to what he says and make the necessary improvements. Once you get his feedback and adjust accordingly, talk to him on a regular basis going forward.

Feeding His Heart

Nurturing him is not just about what you're feeding his body. It's also about what you're feeding his heart. Are you pouring clarity into your husband? Are you honestly clear with your husband about your needs? Are you transparent with him?

One of the biggest complaints I hear husbands' make is, "I don't know what the hell she wants. She expects me to just know. I don't understand this woman." They're confused. You might be thinking, "Well he should know me better. We've been together X amount of years. How has he not figured this out yet? How has he not picked up on this? I've dropped hints. I've made comments."

Guess what? He still doesn't get it.

Men, your husband included, aren't as intuitive as women are. They aren't as detail-oriented and they aren't as observant. Nor do they pick up on things that you think should be obvious clues to how you're feeling. He wants your words. He wants direct communication as to what the problem is, what you need, and what you're looking for from him.

Have you ever gone to your husband and started venting? During your venting session, has he ever attempted to give you solutions and you've gotten frustrated? Your frustration comes from the fact that you didn't go to him for any solutions. All you wanted to do was vent. Now you're upset with him and he doesn't know why. He's feels like, "Listen, if you come to me with a problem, I'm going to offer solutions. If you don't want solutions, simply say, 'Hey baby, I just need to vent right now.'" Now he knows, okay, you're just venting. He can remove the problem-solving hat from his head and just open his ears and be comforting and loving.

Be honest and straightforward. Don't set yourself up for failure and don't set him up for frustration. Being transparent about your needs, in the moment, will get you what you want. However, if you're not telling him why you're upset, he won't get it, and he won't know how to help you in that moment. Tell him what you need and what you're looking for in that specific situation. Don't let it linger.

Learn to be transparent because the less transparent you are, the more confusion you create in your relationship. Where there's confusion, there's chaos. Plain and simple. There's no way around it. When you're clear, when you're concise, when you're transparent, you create peace in the household. A man loves it when he doesn't have to figure things out with you and when he doesn't have to overanalyze everything.

If he's a man who works hard to take care of things financially, if he makes sure the bills are paid and tries to meet your needs relationally, the last thing he wants to have to deal with is trying to solve the mystical puzzle of you. He doesn't want that. He wants you to make it easy for him by telling him what you want and what you need. He needs to know you're good so you all can move forward. That's it.

You may feel like it's not as fun if you have to give him the blueprint and tell him everything he needs to know. You may wonder, "Why can't he figure it out on his own?" You may feel more loved and more valued when he puts in the effort to try to understand and analyze things. I understand and get it. However, this is not going to work in your favor. That's the bottom line. That's the reality of it. Some things he may figure out. Some things he may take the time to really understand and dissect. However, for the most part, he won't.

When your husband is confused and doesn't understand you, it creates insecurities within the relationship. Other issues will begin to stem from these insecurities. He won't know how to handle them. If he doesn't know what's going on or how to handle it, he is now unsure of what's going to happen next. Now fear is present. Now he doesn't know how he can solve it and get things back on track. He can't solve for the problem if he isn't clear about what the problem is. The problem now grows into other problems and as a result things just tend to stay broken.

Please know that he wants to solve the problem. He doesn't want things to stay broken. He just needs to know what he has to do. Period, that's all he's looking for. Make it easy for him. The hardest part, which is his part is actually putting things into play, and moving forward with the information you give him, to work to make things better. So, don't withhold information from him and make the process more difficult. It's easier for the both of you if you just give him the clarity he needs from the beginning.

Being honest with him and straightforward makes everything easier. So, from now on, I want you to begin pouring transparency and clarity into your husband and into your marriage. Nurturing the relationship in this way creates the peace and comfort a man needs. Not just for your husband, but for both of you as a couple. Ultimately, confusion and chaos will damage your marriage and have a lasting negative impact.

Now if you give him all the answers and he still doesn't act on it, you've got a different issue. However, at least try to give him the information he needs to make the necessary corrections and let him take it from there.

Be Present

So far, I've talked about nurturing him by feeding his natural appetite and giving him good meals. I've talked about feeding his heart, by giving him the clarity he needs, so that he knows how to give you what you need in return. In addition to these two things there is something else that falls under nurturing that I've already touched on briefly earlier in the book. It's something that I think gets overlooked a lot by women. It is his need for you to listen to him.

Being present ties into listening, but I want you to understand the difference between listening and actually being present. Being present is more about being aware of him, valuing his presence, and paying attention to him. On the other hand, listening deals more with taking the time to process his words when he's speaking to you.

Listening is not hearing what you want to hear but hearing what he's saying to you. If he says, "Baby, all I want for Christmas is a bottle of liquor, some fried chicken, and you in the bedroom." Don't interpret it to mean, "Oh, he must really be saying that he wants me to take him out to a special place, somewhere he's never been before. I could do a whole bunch of extra stuff and he would be happy." No! You're not listening. He just told you exactly what he wanted. He was very specific.

Men are usually very clear about what they want. Men, for the most part, don't speak in code. They don't speak around things. They're going to say exactly what they want and get to the point quickly. It's up to you to decide to listen and do what he asks or to go completely left and come up with your own ideas.

What happens when you go left and divert from what he says? He usually doesn't like it and then you're mad at him. The funny part is he's thinking, "I never said I wanted this. I told you exactly what I wanted. You did the opposite and now you're mad at me for something that you chose to do?"

That's not fair to him. Be reasonable here. Listen to your husband when he's talking to you and being very specific about what he wants and needs. Take him at his word. Now granted, his words and actions should connect. They should go hand in hand. So, if he's saying one thing and he's doing something different, or he's doing one thing and saying something different, okay that's a problem. Now he's being the creator of the confusion. In this case you should ask him to pour clarity into you and be willing to listen to what he has to say and really process things before acting. Ask questions so you can gain a better understanding. He'll give it to you. Communication starts with listening.

Heed my warning here, when a man feels like he's not being heard and that you're not listening to him, he's going to feel dismissed and devalued. He's going to get frustrated by this. Listening to him is a part of nurturing him. You want to be heard, and so does your husband. You don't want him twisting your words. You don't want him doing the opposite of what you told him to do. You want him to respect you enough to listen to what you're saying. Especially when you know you're being clear and honest about what you want, what you need, and what's going on in your life at that time. He wants the same from you.

Listening, pouring love into him, feeding his heart, his spirit, and body properly, creates a loving and more peaceful marriage. Doing these things consistently will help your husband feel more connected to you. This strengthened connection is going to create better interaction between the two of you. You both will benefit from it because your bond will be healthier and you both will be happier within your relationship.

Chapter 4

PRAYER AND
SPIRITUALITY

. . . .

Faith Without Works is Dead

As a coach and as a man of God, I come across married women all the time who say they're praying that their husband's change. They're praying for things to be different in their marriage. They're praying that everything gets better. Pray, pray, pray, pray, pray. And you know what? I'm all for prayer, but prayer isn't enough.

Hear me out because you may be taking a step back like, "Whoa, what is he talking about? Prayer's not enough? Prayer heals things." I agree. Prayer does heal things. However, when it comes to your marriage, when it comes to praying for change in someone else, I need you to understand that you must focus on what you need to do in the situation.

Faith without works is dead. You have work to do while you're praying. Just praying for your husband, but not putting in the specific work needed on your part, is not going to be effective at creating any real change in your relationship. You're basically asking God to help you as you tie His hands behind His back.

God needs you to walk in faith. He needs you to follow His direction. He needs you to do your part if anything is going to change. The idea that God is going to automatically change your husband's heart is not accurate.

I'm sorry. It doesn't work like that.

Go to God for Instructions

Look at the story of Pharaoh and Moses as an example of God changing someone's heart. In book of Exodus, God told Moses to speak to Pharaoh and that He would harden Pharaoh's heart. People like to use this as an example of God instantly changing someone. I'm not a biblical scholar, but I believe many people misinterpret this scripture. What I believe happened is that God knew how to push Pharaoh's buttons. God knew that if Moses said "XYZ," Pharaoh would respond with "ABC."

It wasn't that God took over Pharaoh's spirit or body. It was more cause and effect than anything else. God simply knew how Pharaoh would react to certain things. Well guess what? That same principle applies to your husband. Just like Pharaoh, God knows how to push your husband's buttons too. He knows how your husband will react to certain things. However, Moses still had to go to Pharaoh and do his part. He had to say the things God told him to say. He had to follow the directions God gave him. You need to do the same.

If you're just praying, praying, praying, stop and ask yourself, "Okay, what actions should I be taking in addition to praying?" You may say, "Well, I am doing my part. I am doing what I'm supposed to do." No. My guess is you're doing what you think you're supposed to do. You're following your logic, or your friend's logic, or your pastor's logic or even my logic. I'm not telling you that any of these logics are flawed. However, go to God to get proper instructions on what you need to do in your specific situation and relationship.

God's guidance is the key to changing situations. Listen, there's nothing wrong with speaking to me, your pastor, your best friend, or anyone else, if you feel the person has the wisdom to help your situation. However, none of us should have the final say-so in guiding your decisions where your marriage or life is concerned. You must go to God. You have to speak to Him directly, on your time, and find out what He wants you to do. God will tell you exactly what you need to do in your marriage. Don't assume you know what's best. Your knowledge is limited, and you don't know better than God.

I've known women to stay in marriages that were completely toxic and damaging because someone told them simply that God doesn't like divorce. I too believe that God doesn't like divorce, but that doesn't mean you need to stay in a marriage that you never belonged in, in the first place. I'm going to get more into that later, in the final bonus chapter. What I need you to focus on right now is the need for you to go to God for action steps. Get His direction for your life and find out what you need to do, specifically, in addition to your prayers for your marriage.

Be Obedient to God's Directions

Ask God, "What do I need to do next? How do I approach this situation now and going forward?" Then listen for God to answer you in your spirit. There are certain steps you must take to get specific results. When you seek God's guidance, He will give you the specific instructions to get the results that line up with His will. After you seek God's guidance, you then have to actually implement it.

Make Sure You're Hearing God

You may say, "Well I pray, but God's not talking to me. I'm not hearing God." Well, it's not that God isn't speaking to you. You're probably just not listening to God's answers. Let me help you understand why this is the case. One issue you may face is that when you pray, you feel you're hearing yourself instead of hearing God. If you think you're hearing yourself, you're not going to trust what you hear, and you're likely to walk away from the whole process. You honestly don't know what to believe in that situation. When you can't hear God or when you're confused about what you're hearing, don't pull away. Find other ways to draw nearer to Him, so you can hear His voice clearly.

HOW TO DRAW NEARER TO GOD

✓ Fasting

✓ Pray in Peace

    ◇ In a peaceful moment

    ◇ In a peaceful area

    ◇ Focus in on the prayer and listening

    ◇ Don't pray where there are distractions

        • In a noisy place

        • When your emotions are running high in any direction

✓ Trust your Intuition

Women's intuition is always there. Most women hear it. You just don't trust it. You ignore it. You try to justify it or process through it logically or emotionally, instead of just trusting and following it. Your intuition is essentially God.

Imagine you're a child in your room doing a math problem. You're staring at this math problem trying hard to analyze it and figure it out. You begin to yell to your father in another room. You're asking him to solve the math problem for you. He's trying to answer you, but you can't hear him because you're in your room, still trying to figure it out on your own. Your father is saying? "That child better get up and come to me if she wants the answer." He's not going to keep screaming at you from the other room. The result: you're not going to hear him, even though he's tried talking to you.

Stop trying to figure it out for yourself. Get up, go to your Father's room in prayer (meaning go to God) and get into His presence. Remove the clutter of your mind. Stop trying to fit things into your logic. Get rid of the false assumptions and just really listen to the answer you get in your spirit.

The other reason why you might think you're not hearing from God is you don't like what you're hearing. That's the reality. If deep inside God's telling you to do something that you just don't want to do, well then, you'll say, "No, it can't be God." Or if He tells you to do something that makes no sense to you, you're likely to dismiss it and think, "Oh it can't be God."

Let me let you in on a secret. A lot of times, God tells us to do things that make no sense whatsoever. Sometimes the only way you can know for sure it's God speaking is because what He tells you to do is crazier than anything you could imagine. You'll think, "Why would the Lord have me do this?"

God uses certain situations to test your faith. When your faith is tested you experience God in a whole new way. He shows up and once it's over you'll say, "It had to be God." You won't be able to give credit to anyone else but Him. That's why it's going to sound crazy sometimes. No matter how crazy, hard, or confusing, trust God's plan.

Some people will say, "Well God's not the author of confusion." No, God isn't the author of confusion. God doesn't tell us different things for the same situation. That doesn't happen. It usually goes this way; "I feel like God's telling me this, but it doesn't make sense to me." Or "I don't get it," or "I don't want to do it". So, God's not confusing anyone. We confuse ourselves.

Shut off the background noise and tune into God. Learn to get out of your own way and listen. This is especially true where your marriage is concerned. Find out what God wants you to do and be obedient. It's really that simple. Whether you like it or not, you must follow God's directions and act. Do what He tells you amid other people possibly telling you the opposite. There's a good chance that no one else is going to agree with what God tells you to do. Your family and friends might not support your decision, but it's not for them, it's for you. Your obedience to God's direction is all that matters.

Even with everything I'm telling you in this book, guess what? I still want you to go to God, pray about it, and confirm that this information is for you. Am I confident this is for you? Absolutely. Am I confident this will work? Absolutely, but I'm not God. I don't have the final say so in this, God does. So, go to Him for the last word.

Be Patient

Understand that this a process and everything won't change overnight. With that said, I want to remind you that your husband and your marriage is a blessing from God. You have a responsibility to honor the blessing God has entrusted you with. What does that mean? It means that despite your husband's shortcomings and despite what has gone on up to this point, your job is to put your best foot forward as a wife. Not for your partner's sake, but for God's sake. This is what God called you to do. God called you to be an amazing, awesome wife. He didn't say be an amazing, awesome wife only on the days your husband is acting right.

When you took your vows, it wasn't contingent on your husband's behavior moment to moment. No, you vowed to love, to cherish, through ups-and-downs, sickness and health, you vowed to honor God through your union. Your husband is simply the beneficiary of your decision to honor the blessing God has given you. And yes, your husband is a blessing too. That's something you need to embrace even during the ugly phases.

Woman have been taught that they're the blessing in a marriage. Scripture backs up this notion as well. Proverbs 18:22 states, "He who finds a wife, finds a good thing." I absolutely agree. You are a good thing, but guess what? So is he and you're fortunate to have been blessed with a good husband. If you're not able to recognize what you have in front of you, how can you appreciate it? How will you honor it? How will you pour into it the way you need to, to see it grow and flourish? If you only think you're the blessing and he's just the guy lucky enough to have you, you have the wrong perspective. No, you're lucky to have him too. You're both lucky. You're both blessed. You both must honor what God has trusted you with, each other.

Let God Lead Your Marriage

Ultimately, God should be the leader in your marriage. God is not going to let you down. God's not going to forsake you, even when your husband does. He's not going to let your efforts all be in vain. Even when your efforts don't produce the results you're looking for right away. Everything will work in God's timing and for your good. This isn't just some cliché saying. It's for real. God must be first in your marriage. I can't say it enough, remember to put God first in everything you do concerning your marriage.

If you're saying, "Well I'm trying to put God first, but my husband doesn't, he doesn't believe in God" or "He's not on the same page as me spiritually." Listen, focus on yourself. Focus on what you need to do. You need to make sure that no matter what, you're putting God first. Whatever's meant to happen, you want to make sure that God leads you through it. Plain and simple. God will lead your marriage in the direction it's supposed to go. If you honor Him, He will honor you. God is faithful even when we're not. Let God have the final say and let Him guide you and the decisions in your marriage and you can't go wrong.

Chapter 5

SUBMISSION

The True Meaning of Submission

Shut your mouth. Sit down. Do what he says and everything's going to be alright. Wait before you throw the book away or curse my name. I was just joking! I'm not serious about what I just said, but I am serious about the act of submission in marriage. There are a lot of misinterpretations of what submission means, so let's clarify some things.

Submission is defined by Merriam Webster dictionary as, "the action or fact of accepting or yielding to a superior force or to the will or authority of another person." When I read that definition, I thought, "Oh Lord, they're not going to go for this." And you're probably thinking, "Superior force? Who is a superior force? Superior force, my behind."

Listen, I get it. I understand. What if I told you to look at it from another perspective? When you're accepting or yielding to a superior force, that superior force is not your husband. The superior force is God.

God has called you as a wife to be submissive to your husband, to submit to your man. Now, where the definition says, "or to the will or authority of another person," that part is talking about your husband. Biblically, God has given him the authority to lead you in your marriage. Now understand something, the authority to lead you doesn't mean he's supposed to be your ruler or a dictator. Being submissive doesn't mean he gets to run you or mistreat you. The call to be submissive is not to hurt or harm you in any way.

God calls men to love their wives as Jesus loved the church. So, trust and believe that submission in its truest form is a good thing. It's about a man loving, protecting, and providing. It consists of all these wonderful things that you have no reason to be against. Understanding the role submission is supposed to play in your life and in your marriage is important.

Now you're probably wondering "Why do I need to submit? Why can't we lead together? Why can't I be the leader of my relationship?" Well, technically you can. If it honestly works for you in your marriage and with your husband, go for it. Knock yourself out.

The reality is, ultimately it won't work. It's not going to work for your husband in the long run. It will eventually become a problem, if it hasn't already. Before we even get into why you leading the relationship is such a problem, you need to understand why proper submission is needed.

Why Submission is Important

In any entity consisting of two or more people, there must be a leader. There's always a leader. When two or more people come together and there's no defined leader, you have the potential for chaos to occur. Friction and conflict result in lack of leadership. Issues are going to go unresolved because everyone will want to be heard and there won't be any order to how things should be handled.

Listen, when everything's going all hunky-dory and everybody's happy, it won't be a problem. However, when something significant occurs and you're feeling strongly about your position, and he feels strongly about his position, there'll be a problem. You have no way of resolving the stalemate because there is no defined leader. This is when everything comes crashing down.

Now you may say, "Well that shouldn't be a big deal. We'll get past it, we'll figure it out." Not really, because the minute one of you compromises your true beliefs and feels devalued or dismissed, it's going to have lingering effects on your relationship. You may argue, "I'm the one feeling dismissed and devalued because I'm submitting to him and he's running things." Again, you submitting to him and letting him lead your relationship is not for him to dismiss or devalue you. He still needs to consider how you feel. He still needs to listen and communicate with you. You both need to discuss the issues and you both need to agree on how you'll move forward.

However, as the leader in the relationship, he does have the final say-so. As his wife, trust him to make the final decision in the best interest of your relationship. Understand this: I'm not telling you to submit just for the sake of submission. However, if you're married to a man and he's submitting to God, then there is a proper order to things and your relationship should be moving in the right direction. As a leader, he should lead by example. His submission to God has to happen first.

Again, submission is important. Everyone submits in life. Man submits to God, you submit to your husband, children submit to their parents and so on. Even if we're not talking about God and spirituality, we all submit to authority every day. We have to submit to our bosses, cops, teachers, and others who have authority in certain environments. There is no way we can get around it. Pretty much all day, every day, we're submitting to someone. There just seems to be a very negative perception when women hear talk about submission in a romantic relationship.

The Real Truth About Women and Submission

The reality is you don't have a problem with submission at all. You have a problem with trusting your husband to lead you. You have a problem trusting him to protect you, to give you what you need, and to do what's best for your family. Understand that these are the real issues, not submission. Now you can begin to address the real issues. Stop fighting submission as if submission or the idea of it is the problem. No. The problem, like I said, is your lack of trust and not believing in him enough for him to lead your relationship.

The lack of belief and the lack of trust may be a result of things he's done wrong in the past or they may be due to past issues you've brought into your relationship. Your lack of trust may have been ingrained in you before you ever got married. It might have been taught to you by your mother, your sisters, your aunts, or others close to you. Whatever is at the root of your issue, you now need to address the issue of lack of trust, so you can move past it. Submission is a positive, not a negative in marriage.

Submission is another way to use your feminine energy. By using it, you can make him feel more valued, more needed, more loved, and more respected. Submission doesn't mean you have to be his doormat. I do not want you to be your husband's doormat. I don't want you to accept any type of abuse, disrespect or mistreatment in the name of submission. This is oppressive behavior and is in direct conflict with what God has established as true submission.

Submission is important to the structure and dynamic of a healthy marriage. The proper order of submission will help your marriage operate at its highest level. I would hope you married your husband with the belief that he's worthy of your submission to begin with. Yes, two people can try to do the dual-leadership thing and have some level of success. It's possible. I'm not going to sit here and tell you it can't happen. However, it's not in line with the proper order of things, and your marriage isn't going to reach its full potential when each person doesn't operate in their true role.

Roles are important. I'm not speaking of gender roles specifically. I'm talking about roles in general. Everyone on a team has to play to their strengths. Your strength as a woman and wife is nurturing your family. It's showing love, it's caring, and it's taking care of the small details. Your role as a wife is also to be a helpmate to your husband.

Your husband's strength is leading and making sure that he's holding the family down. He's responsible for making the right decisions for his family and moving everyone in the right direction. Playing his role empowers him. It gives him added value in your marriage.

Whether or not you'll admit it, you want to submit. At the core of who you are as a woman, you want a man you can rely on. You want a man who can hold things down and make the right decisions. You want a man that you can trust to love and lead you. The issue is, as I stated before, you have a problem trusting your husband. Or you may have an issue trusting any man for that matter. Deal with this issue, so you can move forward. I offer coaching services that can help you overcome this issue and unlock the full potential you have as an individual and in your marriage. What you really crave in your marriage is submission.

Let me give you a real-life example. After a speaking engagement I had in Arkansas, an older woman in her 50s, named Mary came to me and asked, "How can I get my husband to take more initiative? How can I get my husband to do more and make some decisions?" My reply, " Mary, has your husband always been like this?" "Yeah." She said. "So why did you marry him if he never took any initiative?" She replied, "Well, I was okay with it at first."

Wrong, wrong, and wrong. She wasn't okay with it at first. She never truly liked it; she accepted it because it was more comfortable to deal with in the beginning. She accepted it because since she was in the leadership position to start she felt more in control of the relationship. She needed to be in control because she didn't want to be vulnerable. Her leading the relationship allowed her to avoid being vulnerable. She felt the need to lead and to have the control to feel safe. However, that wasn't necessary or healthy for the relationship.

At the core of who you are as a woman, being in control is not what you truly desire. Mary's now paying the price for her decision. You might be experiencing a similar situation. Galatians 6:7 says, "… For whatever a man sows he will also reap." If you lead at the start of your relationship, you allowed him to think it was okay for him not to have to take any initiative. Now 5, 10, 15, or 20 years later you want to tell him this isn't okay. Well guess what? You made it okay all those years ago. It's always been okay. How are you going to tell him that now it's a problem and expect that he's going to magically change?

Men become conditioned to what you deem acceptable at the beginning of the relationship. If you allow him to believe certain behavior is okay for too long, then that is what he's going to believe. To think he's going to make a switch halfway through is unrealistic and unfair to him. It's possible, but it's extremely difficult.

Let me explain in more detail what happens when things are out of alignment and proper submission is not established at the beginning of a relationship. Not only does it not work for you, it doesn't work for him either after a while. What happens in most cases, the man accepts the woman leading him and not being the man, she submits to. At some point, you stop respecting him, you start resenting him, and he picks up on it. He then starts to resent you. He begins to have an issue with you and you don't know why. He starts gravitating toward the woman who is respecting him, who views him as the leader and a man she can respect.

Even though he accepted your leadership role at first, he's not going to be happy with it in the long run. He will eventually rebel. You will eventually rebel. Either the whole marriage is going to fall apart or you two will stay together miserable. That's pretty much what happens every single time. It's extremely difficult to circle back and get it right.

It's Never Too Late to Change

Anything is possible. Miracles do happen. If you're currently in this situation and you've allowed the role reversal to go on for too long, guess what? There is still hope. It's not going to be easy. I'm not going to sugarcoat this for you. I'm not going to make you think this is going to be a simple process. It's not. You're going to have to start today to change the dynamic and set things in proper order.

Be honest with yourself. Recognize now that at your core, you no longer want to lead your husband. Admit you don't want him to take a backseat to you in making the decisions, in taking the initiative, and in carrying the burden of leadership in your marriage. Acknowledge your desire to be the one who is the nurturer, the lover, and that these are the things that truly speak to your strengths. Let him have the role of leading your marriage and give him room to adjust to the role change. If for some reason you feel like he can't handle it, address why you feel that way.

Now that you've been honest with yourself, it's time to communicate your feelings and position to your husband. Take responsibility for your mistakes early on that caused things to be off-balance. Explain to him any reserves you have about getting the roles right and him now having the responsibility of leading your marriage. Allow him to vent his feelings as well. If there have been trust issues, explain to him what he can do to regain your trust, so he'll be able to handle his leadership position properly.

Don't fight submission. Don't fight him leading your marriage. Finding out how to get him back on the path of being the leader in your marriage is best for the both of you. It's something you both will be happy with. Getting things in proper order will help get your marriage on the right track. So again, remove any negative perception you might have had about what submission is.

Remember that when God is involved in your relationship, you both are going to have to submit to God first and foremost. Realize there is an order of submission and it's a dynamic you must embrace. Submission is good for you and it's good for the health of your marriage for the long run.

Chapter 6

BE SUPPORTIVE

Be His Cheerleader

"Behind every great man is a great woman." Ask yourself, "Am I being that great woman to my husband?" Are you being the woman that holds your man down and supports him the way he needs? He chose you as the woman to spend his life with. He's looking for you to provide the positive energy, unconditional love, and support that inspire him to achieve his life's goals. Essentially, he's looking for you to be his cheerleader.

Hold on a minute before you run down to the store, buy pom-poms, a little pleated skirt, and create a dance routine, spelling out his name. That's not what I'm talking about here. What I'm saying is you need to be an energetic, loving, positive, genuine believer in your husband. You need to cheer, support, push, and encourage your man through life, in the things he needs to accomplish, help him to overcome the issues he's dealing with. You have to have his back. When he feels like you don't have his back that is the beginning of the end of your relationship.

It's important to find ways to pour encouragement into your husband. You may be thinking, "Well, he doesn't give me anything to support. He doesn't give me anything to cheer him on for, or when I try to be supportive, he doesn't seem to care or to value my support." Well, do you know how your man wants to receive your support? How does he like to receive your encouragement?

You may think your method of supporting him is enough and he should accept it and be happy with it, but is it really speaking to his heart and his needs? If it falls short, you start to feel like your efforts are being overlooked and he feels like you're not giving him what he's looking for. This creates a serious disconnect within your relationship. Take a moment to talk to him about it. Talk to him about your past efforts to show him support and what you can do better when it comes to supporting him.

A couple came to me to get some relationship coaching. We talked about a series of issues within their marriage ranging from household cleanliness to the way they interact with each other, intimacy, and other areas. After several sessions I was able to get them on track. They were both feeling better and they were happier.

I ran into the husband months later and asked, "How's everything going with your wife?" He replied, "You know everything's great for the most part, but I don't know." He stopped mid-sentence and I'm like, "What do you mean, you don't know? What's wrong? What's still missing?" He replied, "It feels like my wife just doesn't believe in me and doesn't support me. When I try to talk about my dreams and aspirations, she shoots me down. She tells me what I won't accomplish, not what I can accomplish and it's really affecting me."

Basically, she was putting a dagger in his heart. Despite everything else improving, despite him honestly saying, "Yes, things have been much better since they came to me for counseling," the lack support was still a missing piece. Unfortunately, this topic wasn't something that was brought up during our sessions. However, because this was missing, he still felt a void in the marriage and this void was causing a big problem for him.

As a wife, be mindful of the support piece. Men need a lot of support and encouragement. Many times men don't vocalize it. Mainly, because men tend to struggle with expressing this need. As the woman, and his wife, you must really tap into your intuition. Really tap into your ability to pick up on the little things and to recognize, okay, maybe there is a problem here. Maybe he feels like I don't give him what he needs in this area. And yes, ask him. Talk to him.

You are smart. When you speak to him, even if he's not being completely honest about what the problem is, you'll be able to see it in him when the subject comes up. You'll be able tell if something is off and if it is, then you'll be able to address it as best as you can. I'm not giving him a free pass to not be transparent with you because if I'm telling you to be transparent, I would want him to be transparent as well.

However, for the sake of making progress in the situation, I would want you to be able to recognize if there's a problem or an unspoken issue. Don't just go off your assumption, talk to him. Talk to him in a way that makes him feel comfortable. Help him open up to you and find out if this is a real issue for him or not.

Lack of Support Contributes to Men Cheating

I can't stress this point enough. Your husband needs you to be his main cheerleader. He needs you to really believe in him, to encourage him, and to push him to higher levels. This is so, so important. When you overlook his need for support, you open the door for him to go elsewhere for that void to be filled.

Now, let me clear up what I believe is a myth or a misunderstanding a lot of women have about why men cheat. Many women and you may be one of them, believe that men are cheating out of greed, a need for variety, or out of sexual desire. I'm not saying these aren't reasons why men cheat. However, whether you realize it or not, lack of support is one of the biggest reasons, or one of the biggest door openers to infidelity in marriage.

A professional colleague said to me once, "Make sure when you write this book, you mention that when she stops recognizing her man's efforts, or she stops encouraging, or she stops believing in him, that's what causes the problems." Even though I was aware of this issue, hearing him say it, made it even more real to me. As I spoke to more and more men, I started to see the pattern between lack of support and cheating. I started to see where it all began.

The husband stops getting encouragement and love at home. Women are so smart, which means another woman who's around picks up on the fact that he's not getting this at home. She picks up on the fact that his wife is not pouring into him and doesn't believe in him. He's lacking encouragement, support, and love.

Guess what she does? She starts building him up. She starts telling him how great of a man he is, how if he was her man, she would do everything his wife isn't doing. How his wife is lucky to have him. He starts buying into it. He starts eating it up because that's what he needs. That's what he's missing. He loves it and he wants more of it.

He didn't go to this woman with a desire to get caught up emotionally or to eventually step out on his wife. Please understand, I'm not telling you any of this to validate a man cheating. Nor am I telling you this to make any excuses for a man who cheats. I'm simply showing you an example of the result of lack of support in a marriage. This is a reality.

When you remove support and encouragement from your marriage and when you stop believing in your man, someone else is going to believe in him, build him up, and take him away. Or should I say lure him in because the reality is, they aren't taking him away. You pushed him away. You basically kicked him out the door. Even if he is still fighting not to walk out and trying to make it work. You've got one foot in his back and the other foot holding the door open. No matter what the situation is, it's going to lead to bad things.

Understand that I'm not trying to put it all on you. As a man he needs to be open and honest with you about his needs. He should be transparent. He should be the one to let you know that there's an issue with a lack of support. He needs to let you know how you can fix it. However, as a woman you're more in tune with him emotionally than he might be with himself, so be mindful of this going forward and be willing to step up if he's not communicating the way he should about this.

Give and Take

Ultimately, showing him support shouldn't be done simply because you don't want him to stray or because it's something he needs. Recognize that giving him support is also something you want to do. As a woman, you want your man to support you. You want your man to believe in you. You want your man to encourage your dreams and the things you want to accomplish. It's a give and take. If you can't give him the support he needs, how will you ever receive support from him in return?

Let me tell you, there are some men out there who feel like they give their wives all their support, and all their encouragement, but they don't get any in return. Eventually they stop giving it. I had one husband tell me, "Well she doesn't support me, so I'm not supporting anything that she does. I've given her everything. I've supported everything that she's done up to this point and I'm getting nothing in return." Is this the right approach? Is this okay for him to do? No, but this is what happens many times in relationships? Things tend to be one-sided.

You may be feeling the same way. You may feel like, "Listen, I've constantly poured into this marriage. I've tried to support him in the past and he hasn't supported me in return." Well, if you're going to remain married, you've got to strive to be the best wife that you are capable of being. If you don't want to encourage him anymore and you don't want to be the type of wife he cherishes, why stay married to him? What's the point of being there if you're not going to do it the right way? I'll answer the last question for you, it's pointless. You're defeating the whole purpose of being and staying married.

The purpose of staying married should be to make things right, to make things better, to put your best foot forward. Decide. If you're going to stay married to your husband, then continue to do what's needed to make it work. Focus on what you can control, you. So, if you want encouragement, love, and support, treat him accordingly. If you feel like it's not being reciprocated, talk about it with him, in a non-confrontational manner.

Let it be known, but don't stop being the woman that you need to be, the woman you were created to be, the wife that you are capable of being. Giving your man the support, he needs sets the right foundation for your marriage. It's an important piece to the puzzle that will allow you to see your marriage flourish and become all that you have hoped it could be. Showing him support might be the missing piece in getting your husband to respond to you in ways that maybe you didn't even think he could.

Again, sometimes it's not a matter of you not trying, but a question of whether you're doing it in the way he needs you to. That's why the two of you need to talk about things with each other. It's important that both of you really get on the same page. You both need to understand what you all need in your marriage specifically, to get it to a higher, happier level. What's important to him should be important to you also and vice versa. You want to make sure you're the one taking care of his needs, nobody else.

Bonus Chapter

PHYSICAL APPEARANCE & PHYSICAL ATTRACTION

Physical appearance and physical attraction often don't get talked about enough from the right perspective. Physical attraction is something a man needs and lack-of can have a huge negative impact on a marriage. Honestly, it's something you both need. You may act like it's not that important, but it really is whether you want to fully acknowledge that fact or not.

A lack of physical attraction may not cause you to leave your marriage, but it will cause you to approach your marriage differently. It will cause you to come at your partner with a different energy and with a different level of desire. Intimacy will more than likely see a decline, and this can create feelings of rejection and resentment.

Hopefully you're not already cringing at the discussion of this topic. If you're getting ready to fight me, I'm going to need you to put the gloves down and to keep an open mind. I know this can be a sensitive topic, but it is a reality we must discuss if you're serious about improving your marriage. The fact is: a lot of women struggle to keep themselves up after marriage. Men do as well but this book is for you, so that's where we're keeping the focus.

Listen, I know there are babies, there's work, there's real life. I'm not judging you or trying to be unsympathetic with the struggles that women face in keeping yourselves up. I know it isn't easy, and if your partner isn't doing his part, then it only makes things harder. However, the fact remains that when you don't keep yourself up because of life happenings it can cause real problems in you and your marriage.

It's important for you to understand why this needs to be a priority. The foundation of it is simple: what takes a relationship from platonic to romantic is physical attraction. Period. When you know someone, and they have a perfect relationship with their best friend of the opposite sex and you say, "Why aren't you with your best friend?" You know what they say? "I'm not physically attracted to them." It's plain and simple.

Anytime someone isn't romantically involved with someone they get along with amazingly well, it's because the physical attraction is not there. So, when you're in a relationship, especially a marriage and the attraction is gone, you essentially go from being romantic partners to being roommates, to being friends, to being play cousins. Whatever the hell you want to call it, you've removed the romantic aspect from the relationship.

A lot of people say, "The fire is gone. How do we get the fire back?" The fire isn't gone. The attraction is gone. Lack of physical attraction is what's causing the fire to go out. You bring the attraction back, you bring the fire back. Physical attraction changes everything. Ask yourself, "Have I really been putting time and effort toward my appearance? Is there something wrong with how I look now? Is he taking issue with that?" Now let me make something clear to you. This is not about me pushing you to look a certain way. It's about you not deviating too far from what he married. There's a very big difference.

I'm not insinuating that you need to be a size two or that you need to have a model's body, not at all. If your husband married you as a plus size woman, then being a plus size woman is not an issue. However, if you're appearance has changed drastically from when he married you, you now look like a different person to him. Someone he probably would've never approached to begin with. Hearing that said so bluntly might be harsh and it might be a hard pill for you to swallow, but it's real.

I had a hard time deciding on even including this topic in the book because this is such a sensitive topic for women. I was like, "they're really going to come after me for this one." But I felt like I had to tell you this. I had to put this in here because it's such an important topic. It's a reality that men and women aren't facing. We're running from it and it's having a detrimental impact on our relationships.

I sit down with husbands all the time, and guess what? The issue of their wives not, you know, not looking the way they used to look, comes up. It's not even just in the way your body looks, but even in the way you dress. Even in the smallest things you think he doesn't pay any attention to.

I once had a client who would come to me and complain, complain, complain. Every time he came home, his wife was in sweatpants, a do-rag, and a big, raggedy old shirt. That's not sexy! It's not, okay? Listen, it doesn't mean your husband thinks you should be in heels and a negligee every time he walks into the house or walks into the bedroom. However, make sure there's a good balance between the extremes.

You have to want to look good for your husband. It's not just about your appearance and your weight, but also how you dress and take care of yourself. If you used to wear nice little pretty lace underwear and thongs and now you're wearing Cotton grandma panties from Wal-Mart all the time, that's going to be a problem. The lack of consistency contributes to throwing things off.

You might say, "Well, if he loved me this shouldn't be a problem. If he loved me, then he shouldn't have an issue if I gain weight, especially if I've had his babies."

Listen, I hear you, but if you loved him, you would want to look good for him. You can't just put the responsibility solely on him and say it's just on him to accept your changes. No, you should want to maintain yourself for him, in the same way he should want to maintain himself for you.

Let me make that clear. I may be talking to you right now as a wife and telling you this is what you need to do, but this is not something I'm putting on just the women. I believe men must take care of themselves as well. Men need to be mindful of keeping themselves up too. This is a real and serious issue.

Here's where you want to start. Have an open, honest conversation with your husband about your physical appearance. Now I'm going to be real here, your husband is scared to death to tell you how he honestly feels about how you look right now because he doesn't want you being sensitive, catching an attitude, and hating him afterwards. Not to mention punishing him with the threat of no sex anymore because you're upset.

Honestly, this may be a very difficult conversation for you to have. You may not even need to have the conversation. You may already know where you need to make improvements. Be honest with yourself. You know where you've deviated and maybe he's already made some comments or shown a lack of interest in you sexually. In this case, you're fully aware of what needs to be done. So rather than overanalyzing things just start working on getting back to where you want to be.

Now listen, I get it. As we get older in life, it's impossible to look the same way we looked 10 or 15 years ago. I get that. So, believe it or not, men aren't as unreasonable as you may think they are. Most husbands that come to me, aren't saying, "I expect my wife to look exactly how she looked on our wedding day." They're not saying, "Listen, if she was 135 lbs then, she needs to be 135 lbs now." Nobody's saying that to me. Men generally don't mind 5 lbs here, 10 lbs there, depending on where those pounds go, just to be real with you. What they care about is when it becomes drastic, when it completely transforms your appearance and who you are visually to them.

It's about finding your happy zone. Your happy zone is the place where you're healthy, feel good, and look good to both him and you. For example; let's say you were already plus size when you got married because sometimes we're just assuming letting yourself go means going from being slim and in shape to being, larger and less in shape. Let's say that wasn't the case. Let's say he married you when you were thicker and then you lost a lot of weight and now he's asking you to gain the weight back. I don't want you under any circumstances to do anything that is going to be unhealthy for you.

While I want you to be attractive to your husband and be mindful of what is visually appealing to him, I don't want you to risk your health for it. I don't want you to compromise any deeper beliefs for it either. There's a line that must be drawn here. In drawing that line, I want you to find an area of compromise where you're happy with yourself and he's happy with you. Now if you can't find that happy place with each other, that's a deeper issue somewhere. However, I'm confident you and your husband can find that mutual place of agreement.

Again, if you're saying to yourself, "This shouldn't matter. If he loves me, then he should accept me for how I am." Well, sometimes the issue of gaining weight, changing your appearance, and not getting back in shape, goes deeper than just your physical appearance. It can turn into you not valuing his desires. It can lead your husband to believe that you don't care about how he feels and that you don't love him enough to want to do anything about it.

If he expresses his feelings about it and you know this is affecting the relationship because he's telling you it's affecting him, don't just dismiss it with, "If you love me, you would love me as I am". He could say the exact same thing to you. If you loved him, you wouldn't be so dismissive of his feelings about it. That doesn't mean you have to give an automatic, "Yes baby, you know what? I will work on it." But you should be willing to truly find harmony with the issue. Otherwise, he may start to develop a level of resentment towards you.

Let me better illustrate this point for you. I had a client whose wife had to undergo a medical procedure. For this medical procedure she wasn't going to be able to have sex for six months. So, even though his own sexual desires weren't going to be met, he was completely sympathetic and understanding to the situation. He was patient with her because he loved her. He did everything he needed to do for her. He worked with the situation because he understood that she was not physically capable of having sex during this span of time.

Sympathy is a powerful emotion that can help us accept a lot of things a lot easier. It may not make things perfect, but it makes it easier to roll with the situation.

The six months passed, and the doctor was like, "Okay, you're clear to have sex now." His wife decided not to resume having sex with him. He was pissed. She was now fully capable of having sex, but she was choosing not to.

How does this example tie into physical appearance and weight? Even though it wasn't about weight or appearance, the principle remains the same. Your husband is thinking, "This woman is fully capable of having sex. She's capable of losing weight and getting in better shape, of looking the way I want her to look. She's choosing not to." Since you're choosing not to, he's saying, "She doesn't care how I feel. She's not valuing my desires and she doesn't get that it's affecting the relationship."

Let me take you even further to help you understand this. I'm going to give you an analogy and this might sound farfetched, but I need you to work with me here. Let's say you married your husband and you valued the size of his package. He had a nice size package and you were happy with it. It was a great. Now that you're married, his package begins to shrink over time.

A poor diet, life, stress are all contributing factors. The shrinkage starts to impact you. The intimacy of the relationship, his overall health and well-being are all being negatively affected. His shrinkage problem doesn't just affect your bedroom experience. It affects his confidence, his demeanor, and how he views himself as a person.

Guess what? Whether you realize it or not, the changes in your physical appearance have affected your demeanor, your confidence, and your self-esteem. It's having a greater impact on your relationship and is bigger than just what he likes to look at.

Back to my shrinkage example, it's affecting the relationship. You find out that all he needs to do to fix the situation and to get his package back right is to eat better and exercise. You go to him and say, "Baby, you know what? I would really love for you to your package get back to where it was when we first got together. I don't want the shrinkage to be a problem that continues to negatively affect our relationship." He responds, "Well listen, this shouldn't be a problem for you. If you love me, then why are you worried about my package? Who cares if it's smaller? Don't you love me for me?"

Be honest here. You would be pissed. You'd feel like he's dismissing you and what you value. He's dismissing the fact it's affecting your relationship negatively. You'd be pissed because you know he's fully capable of doing something about the problem. It's not out of his control. However, he's making the choice not to. This is why the weight, body, appearance issue has such a damaging effect on relationships. It's not just about the visual. It goes from being visual to turning into an emotional issue.

He feels like you simply don't care. When you don't care, guess what? He stops caring. Now he starts having a certain attitude towards you. He stops coming after you to have sex. It has a domino effect on your relationship and everything goes downhill from there. Sometimes all the fights and arguments you're having stem from this one issue being unresolved. It then creates a whole bunch of other issues. Addressing this core issue as soon as possible, allows things to fall back in line quickly.

Again, I know this is a tough, tough pill to swallow. However, I'm hoping the light bulb is going off in your head. I'm hoping that you've really been open to what I've said. I want to stress to you, I'm only sharing this because it's the truth. It's what's happening in relationships. It's what many husbands are complaining about, but don't feel comfortable expressing to their wives because of the backlash they get for it. So, I'm going to take the backlash for them. I put it out there and I'm hoping that you're willing to receive it.

Knowing this information will help your marriage because you now know how your husband views this issue. When you begin to make changes for the better in this area, you're going to start to feel better about yourself and you're going to have more energy and a more positive attitude. You will see the positive effects on your entire life. Don't run from or ignore the changes you can make. Embrace them as well as the other things I've mentioned in this chapter and you will seal your cherished wife status.

Chapter 7

SEXUAL
SATISFACTION

It's All About Mutual Satisfaction

Sex is an important part of a healthy marriage. It's important for both of you to be satisfied and to get what you desire sexually. All sex is not created equal. This chapter is not about you just accepting the chore of sex. What I want you to understand is that your husband desires sexual pleasure from you and for you to satisfy him sexually. In order for that to happen, you need to know what he likes and how he likes it.

You may say, "I already know what he wants. I already know what he likes." Do you really? Are you sure? Have you talked to him about your sexual relationship? Have you really explored with him sexually? It's not just about what he likes, it's also about how he likes it. I can tell you right now, there's a good chance he has very specific ideas of what he would love to see you do in the bedroom.

Whether it's how you present yourself visually to him, how you sexually please him, or how he wants a sandwich once you're done. I'm sure there's something he's looking for specifically. You must ask him to find out. You also have to ask yourself, "Am I really tapping into his sexual desires or am I being dismissive about sex? Am I just giving into sex when it's convenient for me?"

I can tell you right now, if you answered yes to the last question that's not healthy for your relationship. Lack of sex and a lack of sexual pleasure create a lot of rifts and a lot of conflict in marriages. I can't tell you how many men I've heard complain about a lack of sex in their marriages. That's one of the biggest reasons why I wrote my very first book, *How to Get a Woman to Have Sex with You If You're Her Husband* because the issue is a real problem for men.

In that book I tell husbands what they can do on their end to make things better within the relationship, to improve their marriage and their sex lives with their wives. Now I want to share the things you can do on your end, to make things better sexually as well.

Sex Evolves

Sex is not supposed to stay the same for the course of your marriage. Just because you've been married a while doesn't mean things can't change. Men, like women, evolve. We start to develop different tastes. We start to develop different desires.

Sex in marriage should consistently be a learning process. You must continuously reintroduce yourself to your husband. There are always new things that he may be open to, or that he may be looking for. You want to be able to tap into that and explore those things. Be open and willing to talk to him about sex. Be willing to try different things out with him. In order to do this, you must be open-minded. You can't come into sexual relations with your husband with any preconceived notions of how it should be.

A couple came to me for marriage counseling. Sex was one of the subjects we discussed. At the time, the issue stemmed from what he was lacking in the bedroom. We discussed his concerns and we talked about what they could be doing better to improve their sexual relationship. They both agreed, and things started to move in a better direction. One day she comes home, and she says her pastor, who is a woman, told her that oral sex is unacceptable and should not be had in marriage.

Listen, I'm not here to tell you whether you should or should not have oral sex within your marriage. However, I am here to tell you that if your husband wants oral sex and you agreed to it when you married him, to just take it away, is asking for trouble. You can't make that kind of decision on your own, without talking to him first. I'm also saying that if you don't like certain things sexually, then make sure you and your husband reach an understanding of why these things are off limits. You both need to agree on the decision.

However, to simply stop doing things, to shut things down, and to take them off the table completely is selfish. He has his desires, just like you have yours.

The marriage bed is undefined. That's why I'm not here to define what's acceptable or not acceptable within your marriage. I'm simply here to stress to you the need to be on the same page with your husband. Just as your husband needs to be on the same page with you sexually. That requires a mutual effort. Discuss things and really try to understand each other's needs and tap into pleasing each other.

I mentioned your need to be open-minded earlier. Even if you have reservations about some things, again, be willing to communicate them to your husband. Help him understand why you may be hesitant to perform certain acts or why you're not into certain things. Then together you'll be able to get to the root of how to fix what is missing within your sexual dynamic. Then you'll be able to add whatever's missing and sex will be more pleasurable for you both. This will help you feel more confident in pleasing him and fuel your desire to have sex with him more often.

The Power of Experimenting

Another thing to consider when working to improve sexual relations with your husband is experimentation. I'm going to be honest with you. You might be married to a man you feel is conservative. One of those guys who's just not into all the extra stuff when it comes to sex. You might have interest in trying different things but are reserved about doing a lot of extra freaky stuff in the bedroom and experimenting because you don't want him to look at you a certain way. You don't want him to judge you and you don't want him to ask questions like, "Where'd you learn this? Where is this coming from? Who have you been sleeping with?"

I get it. It can be a bit discouraging for you to initiate kinky sex acts. I will say this, you know your husband better than I do. If you know there are certain things he's going to be against or that he's not open to, ask him why and approach him delicately. Go into the conversation with a mindset of understanding and don't attack him for it. It just may not work for him. However, if you're married to a man you know is a little more open, who would love for you to try different things, well now you have the green light to experiment and to test things out.

Again, don't do things that you know he'll be uncomfortable with. For example, some guys might break your arm if you get anywhere near their butt. It's a good idea to talk about what you want to try before introducing it in your routine. When you both agree, experimentation is something that will maximize pleasure for both of you and you can be free to enjoy it.

Try new things at least once to you see if he likes it. If so, keep doing it. Be consistent with it. That's the key. Don't just try it once and then make it something he can only get on his birthday, as a treat. Let the man enjoy you as much and as often as possible. Let him have at least four birthdays a year, maybe seven. I mean come on now. You can't just do it one time and shut it down for a while. That's just not fair. It's like you gave him all that good stuff and then you take it away. No, keep giving it to him once you know he likes something you've tried.

Also, make sure there's a balance. It doesn't need to be every day. It doesn't have to be every week. Mainly because you don't want it to get old. However, it should happen more often than not, to spice things up, and to keep the bedroom fun and enjoyable for the both of you.

Embracing Constructive Criticism

During my tour and speaking engagements, I talk to women about how to constructively criticize their men on bedroom performance. In this book, I want to focus on how you can best receive constructive criticism from your man for the benefit of improving your sex life. Be open to constructive criticism from your husband regarding his sexual pleasure. With that said, he's not allowed to insult you or degrade you in any way with his criticism. That's not acceptable.

However, it would be smart and best for you to create an environment where you both can talk to each other honestly. For example, "Honey you know what? I would love if you did this a little bit better." Or "I would love if you tried this" or "This could use some improvement." When and if he says it, don't take it personally.

Listen, everybody's not a sexual superstar, alright? You just might not have it all together. Just like with anything else, there are always things you can learn and improve on. However, you must be open to learning areas you can improve in. It takes the pressure off you when you can create an environment in the bedroom where you both talk openly and constructively criticize each other. Oh, my goodness, it opens the doors to greater, more amazing sex! It also makes both parties feel so much more comfortable and freer. Now you're not worrying about disappointing him. You can ask for feedback and have a chance to correct anything that's lacking. So, can he!

Be Consistent

One of the biggest issues facing married men, they're not getting sex consistently. Now what's consistent will depend on you and your husband's preferences. For some couples consistent is 2-3 times a day. That number might be too much for most people. For other's consistent is 2-3 times a week. I've heard some husbands say, "Listen, if I get it 1-2 times a week, I'm good." So, it really depends on you and your husband.

However, I'm confident that most husbands are not okay with once every two weeks or once a month. Yes, these timeframes do exist in some marriages. There are couples — hopefully you're not a part of one —that go without sex for extended time periods. In most cases the husband is not okay with it. He's not happy with having to wait so long to have sex with his wife.

You must be willing to make it a more consistent occurrence. Remember, this is not about sex being a chore for you. I want you to find ways to make sex more pleasurable and something that you want more of as well. Not as a chore, but as something you enjoy. We're going to talk more about what you can do to make that happen.

Sex is Not a Weapon

A couple came to me for counseling because of the husband's issues with lack of sex. He complained that he was only getting sex once every two, maybe three weeks. Her issue was he wasn't helping enough with the babies and he wasn't cleaning up around the house enough. She wasn't happy with that.

I understood both perspectives here. I suggested they compromise with each other. He agreed to help around the house more and to help more with the babies. She discussed the parameters in which she wanted him to help with other things. In return she agreed to give him more consistent sex. She agreed to have sex at least twice a week. The only week she got a pass from sex was the week she's on her menstrual cycle. She only got one week out of the month to use the menstrual cycle pass, she couldn't use it every single week.

Guess what? It worked. He was happier. She was happier. He was getting more sex. She was getting more help. It was a great exchange, but we don't want to stop there.

I don't want it to be just about you having more sex. I want it to be about more pleasurable sex for the both of you. That is the key. Before I tell you how to make it more pleasurable, I want you to notice something in the scenario with the couple I just mentioned. She was shutting down sex because he wasn't helping with the babies and he wasn't helping around the house the way she wanted him to. That is a big no-no.

Sex is not a weapon. It is not meant for you to use for revenge, to teach him a lesson, or to punish him in any way. If you do, you're setting a horrible standard in your relationship. If you start withdrawing the things your partner needs as some sort of punishment it will eventually backfire on you. That's not the way to go about it.

Listen, if there's a problem, talk about it. If there's an issue, there are other ways to solve it. I don't like the whole punishment idea. Especially, when it comes to sex. Sex never needs to be used as a weapon because that's going to make him resent you. If you use sex as a weapon too many times, guess what? He's going to start using it as a weapon against you too. Then he's going to stop desiring you sexually. Then you're going to start to feel some-kind-of-way and everything gets thrown off.

You don't want to push him into that kind of corner. You also don't want to make him feel like he has to walk on eggshells. He will think that at any moment if you all fight or if he's not doing something you want that you're going to take sex off the table. As a man, sex is part of intimacy for him. It may not be as important to you, but it's very important to him.

Studies have shown that men view sex as a way to communicate their intimacy to their partner. It's a way a man bonds with his wife. It isn't just a carnal desire. He doesn't just want to get off. No, he wants to share time with you. The pleasure that comes from sex is the bonus. When you remove that form of intimacy from him, it creates a lot of avoidable problems. So again, don't use sex as a weapon.

It's Your Turn to Initiate

I've stressed that sex shouldn't be used as a weapon for destructive behavior. However, sex can used as a positive weapon. I'll use the word weapon in a good way this time. Sex is your way of showing your husband desire. This is something he needs from you. One of the greatest misconceptions women have is thinking, "Since I'm having sex with him and giving it to him when he wants, I'm doing my part."

Okay great, but if you're never initiating sex, then there is still going to be a problem in your marriage. By not initiating sex, you're never showing him that you desire it or him. Now you may be saying, "Well I don't want it. I really don't care. I would rather watch TV, go shopping, or go do anything else, but have sex with him." I get it, but this is a very unhealthy mindset to have. It must change, or you will see your marriage suffer as a result.

TIPS TO IMPROVE UNHEALTHY MINDSETS ABOUT SEX

To help you change your negative mindset about having sex, you need to find the benefit for the act. Even if you say that sex is not satisfying for you right now, look at it as exercise. If you need to exercise anyway, burn off some calories having sex.

Change your perspective and the way you're looking at the situation. Find a plus side to it and remember that keeping him happy will positively contribute to the health of your relationship. Things will also improve in other areas as a result. Continue to focus on the benefits of engaging with him and being more willing sexually.

When he feels like you don't want it, he feels like you don't want him. As a result, when you do have sex with him, you're not going to be into it and now he's going to be less into it. Contrary to popular belief, he's not just happy having sex with you. He wants the passion, he wants the desire, and he wants to feel like you are enjoying him as well. At least that's what happens when a man loves you, alright? Now if he doesn't love you, it's a whole different ballgame. I'm hoping that your man loves you and he wants to see that you want him as much as he wants you.

Communication is a Part of Great Sex

Throughout this chapter, I've stressed the need to have more sex, but I'm a realist. I completely understand as a woman if you're not getting what you need out of the sexual exchange, you're not going to be able to keep up the sex consistently. You're also not going to be able to show him that you actually want him by initiating sex or any of the other things I mentioned above.

It's kind of like going to work and not getting paid. No one is going to keep going to work if they're not getting paid for the hours they've worked. You might be a woman who's been going to work and not getting a paycheck, or your paycheck is sporadic, or has been really low for a while. You might not have any benefit package, or the job isn't that great. I understand that.

What contributes to your shortage in pay is your lack of communication. Have you told your husband what you need in the relationship now? Does he know your expectations from the sexual interaction? Are you communicating it in a very clear, positive, and loving manner? This is the perfect place for you implement the things we've already discussed in the book. You're going to be transparent. You're going to use your feminine energy. You're going to be loving when you talk to him.

When you communicate about sex, you're showing him desire. You're showing him you want to pleasure him and that you want to connect with him intimately via sex. The more you start to enjoy the sex, the more you're going to be willing to have sex with him. This creates the environment for more pleasurable sex for the both of you, which is the point of it all.

It's a win/win. Make it easier for him to tap into your needs and to satisfy you as well. When you two are working together to create an amazing sexual relationship, you're going to strengthen your marriage. There'll be less to fight about. You're both going to be happier. There'll be more peace in the household and less animosity between the two of you. You're both going to be more unselfish when it comes to pouring into each other.

How to Have Happy Sex

Not only does he want you to initiate sex, he wants you to help him know when you're in the mood for sex. When he tries to get it and you shut him down, over time this can cause various problems. So, we're going to kill two birds with one stone here. You're going to do what I call, have happy sex.

What's happy sex? It's when you decide to initiate sex when you're in a good mood. He doesn't always know when you're in a good mood or when you're going to be willing and ready to have sex. If you give into him when you're not really in the mind set to do it, it's going to come off very blah, very uneventful, it's not going to be an enjoyable experience.

However, when you're in a good mood, you're already feeling good, your energy is high, and guess what? That's the perfect moment for you to go to him and initiate sex. Whether it is a quickie or another sexual act. Go ahead, make it happen! This way you've satisfied both of your desires while you're in a good mood, and when you're feeling more up to it. It also shows him the desire that he wants to see from you. Everybody's happy! Be willing to show him desire and be willing to initiate sex.

CONCLUSION

I've given you a lot of information to digest. Some of what I've shared may have been very hard pills for you to swallow. However, just like the bad tasting medicine your mom used to give you as a child, it's good for you. It's what you needed to hear right now. It's what's going to help you get the results you've been looking for in your marriage. It's going to take you into to cherished wife territory.

What it's not, is a quick fix. Everything I've mentioned takes time to implement. You will begin to see change over time. As you move forward and start implementing this information, I want you to be mindful of a few things.

First, I want you to understand that consistency is key. Listen, if you've been doing things in ineffective ways for years, it will take some time getting used to a new routine. You must reprogram your husband as well as yourself with these new approaches and new ways of doing things in your marriage. There's going to be a transition period and there may be a period of skepticism.

When your husband starts to see you being all sweet and nice, if he's not accustomed to that, he's going to think, "What is she up to? What does she really want? What is she trying to accomplish here?" Be open and transparent. There goes that word again. Be transparent with him about the fact that you're taking a new approach because you want to make the marriage better. Express your desire for things to improve, not just with you and what you're doing, but with what you receive from him in return as well. This is about how to get your man to cherish you as his wife.

You want to make things clear to him because in that moment of skepticism, he needs to understand what's going on. If you're not clear with him, he will jump to all kinds of conclusions and that can derail the entire process. Be honest with him and be consistent because now he might say, "Okay, let me see if she's for real. Is she really going to keep this up? Is this only going to last a couple days?"

It's very reasonable for him to have hesitations and questions about this new approach you're taking but stick with it. Don't be distracted by this. Stay consistent and keep it going. You might be thinking, "Well for how long? How long do I have to be consistent while waiting to see if he's willing to give me what I'm looking for in return?"

It usually takes 21 days to form new habits. Let's take it a step further and do 30. Again, consistency is key here. Not stop-n-go or a week and that's it. Shoot for at least 3–4 weeks, no matter what's going on. You're going to be the best wife you can be. If in 3–4 weeks your husband shows no progress whatsoever, now you need to go further to evaluate the situation.

Counseling may be in order. However, you must first take things to another level by implementing the action steps I've laid out in this book. Take your actions to the next level before jumping to any conclusions right off the bat. Don't say, "Oh well, he won't change. It's not going to work." No. Focus on being consistent with everything we discussed for 3–4 weeks.

It will take both consistency and patience. Remember, you're not sprinting, you're running a marathon. This is a process. I'm not saying after 3-4 weeks, he has to be perfect because that's not realistic. I don't expect you to be perfect either. I'm not saying that you're going to get everything right every day during this process. I am saying that you must put forth the effort. Make a conscious decision to be the best wife you can be and be patient with yourself and your husband.

Be patient with him. It might take him some time to become receptive to your efforts, as well as with working with you to get things right. Don't beat yourself up if you have days where you feel off or like you slipped or fell off the new routine. No, just get back on track and stick with it. Continue to make the necessary improvements and push through it.

Ultimately, you've got to be willing to persevere through this. You've got to really believe in the process. It's so important to talk to God during this process. I mentioned it earlier because you're going to need God's strength to fight through any moments of resistance, whether it's resistance within yourself or from your husband. You're going to need the strength, the focus, and the willingness to overcome the past and continue to move forward. Allow God to guide you through the process and listen to Him for specific direction because when you do, you're going to get the payoff.

Look at it like you're going on a new diet. We'd all love to lose 10 to 20 pounds in three days with little or no effort. Unfortunately, that's not how it works. You have to stick with the diet over a period of time in order to see any results. Many times, we give up because after a week, we didn't lose the weight we wanted to lose. Had we stuck with it for a week or two longer, the weight would have begun to fall off.

I can't stress this point enough. Consistency is key. Be patient, stick with it, and understand it's a process. At the end of this process, if you stick with it, you'll end up with a husband who is cherishing you because you're worthy of it. Since you've shown up and been consistent, he will as well. I'm confident your husband is going to want to cherish, love, and respect you when you can give him all the things we've talked about.

Remember this is a lifestyle change. You're changing your mindset, your approach, your whole perception of your marriage and the wife you need to be in your marriage. Now that you know better, do better. You have no excuses. You can't say, "Well no one ever taught me. No one ever told me." Well I just told you, alright? Now you know what it takes. This is for the long haul. Everything discussed in this book is always going to be needed in a relationship for it to be healthy and happy.

Bonus Chapter

YOU'VE MARRIED THE
WRONG MAN

Throughout the book I've made the comments, "If your man really loves you, this is going to work." There's a reality that you may be facing whether you want to acknowledge it or not. That reality is: you may have married the wrong man.

I'm all for keeping marriages together. I'm all for seeing people succeed in love and be happy. I fully recognize the fact that God does not like divorce. However, I don't believe God wants you to be miserable and, in a situation, you never belonged in. That's the thing, you never belonged with your husband, but for various reasons you chose to marry him.

Individual reasons vary of why women marry the wrong man. You might have gotten pregnant unexpectedly, so you got married. Your family pressured you to marry him, or you felt it was time for you to have a man and some kids, so you married him. He treated you better than anyone else ever treated you, so you married him, but you were never in love with him. You wondered, "When will I ever find a man this good again?" So, you married him.

The reasons are endless. You may have married for money. You may have married for some level of security. You may have married him because you wanted to keep up with your sisters, your cousins, your friends. Whatever the reason is, you didn't marry the man you were ultimately supposed to be with. Now you may be asking me, "Well how do I know? How do I know if I'm supposed to be with this man or not?" Well, let me ask you something. Did you ever ask God if you should marry him?

What I've found is that for 99% (I'm being nice by saying 99%) of women that I've coached and talked to even casually, the answer is NO. For 1% of women who say, "yes," they did ask, you know what they tell me? "Oh, I asked God. God said no, and I still married him anyway."

My question to them becomes; "How can you expect good things to come from your marriage when you didn't let God lead you to the man you belonged with?" Most of these women's marriages have ended in divorce or they've found themselves in miserable marriages because they didn't consult God first.

Let me give you a specific example. I recently had a female client who came to me because she was feeling unsure about her relationship. She was in a long-distance relationship. She talked to me about how he wanted to get married, but she was hesitant. We discussed her hesitations further. He wanted to move closer to her, everything seemed to be about what she would be doing for him. It seemed like he had nothing going on for himself. He was going to latch-on to her and the legacy she was setting up for herself.

After our discussion, I concluded and the realization that she didn't belong with this man. It was very clear to me, but I don't expect anyone to just take my advice. I insisted she pray about it. I told her to ask God if she should marry this man. A couple days later she emailed me and told me she prayed about it and immediately she felt God was telling her this was not the man for her. So, you would think, okay, problem solved. Disaster averted.

Let's move forward. Of course not! It never happens that easily.

A couple months later I get an email from her saying: "I should have listened to you. Why did I marry this man? Oh, my goodness, it's been three days since my marriage and I completely regret my decision. I don't know what to do."

As much as I know God doesn't like divorce, as much as I desire to keep people together, if possible, I can't just sit there and look at a situation like that and say, "Oh, stay married anyway." How could I say, "Oh, that's where you're supposed to be," or "God brought it together." God didn't bring it together. She already acknowledged that God told her no when she asked Him in prayer. She had reservations before she walked down the aisle. Her regret kicked in no more than three days after saying, "I do."

She married the wrong man.

Just because you've stayed married to him for 5, 10, 15 years, it doesn't change that fact this might be your reality as well. The truth remains the same. When you look at this book and you say, "This won't work," or "I tried this, and nothing happened," well it's not because the tools are incorrect or that what

I'm telling you is not as accurate as I proclaim it to be. It's because you're dealing with the wrong man.

Now, I'm not saying all this because I want you to rush out and go file for divorce today. Before you make any decision at all, please take a deep breath. Let's process what's really going on. Once you've discovered you've married the wrong man, the next step is not filing for divorce. You still need to follow the directions I've given in this book.

Despite making the decision to marry your husband, it doesn't mean that your marriage can't be turned around and made into something amazing. I've seen crazier things happen. It's possible. On the flip side, I'm also aware that there is also a possibility that nothing will ever work to save your marriage. It's possible that nothing can change the fact that you don't belong with your husband and the marriage needs to end.

The only way to figure it out is to follow the action plan I've outlined in this book. When you're being the woman you're supposed to be, an amazing, wonderful wife, one of two things are going to happen. Either your husband will rise to the top with you or he will fall further behind, period.

It's going to be very clear once you're being your best self. It will be clear where he stands in your life and if anything can truly change. Don't just assume things can't change. Put the information you have learned in this book into practice and see for yourself.

In addition to an improved effort on your end, you also have to pray about it. Now, I'm not going to lie to you. If you pray about it and God tells you to go, hey, go. You don't have to do anything in the book, just follow God's instructions. However, what I normally find is when I tell women to pray about it, God doesn't want them to walk away on the wrong foot. He doesn't want them acting a fool and then getting a divorce. That doesn't serve any purpose. Let me give you an example.

I have a friend who was married to a man who I believed was the man for her. They fell on hard times. He lost his job and he wasn't doing what he was supposed to do as a husband. She got frustrated and reached a point where she felt God telling her it was time to go. She did everything she could do. There was nothing left for her to try that would fix her marriage. She got a divorce. She moves on and she meets another man and gets into a relationship.

The relationship gets close to marriage but falls apart. She meets a new guy, but she doesn't tell me about this guy.

You know why she doesn't tell me about him? She didn't tell me because from jump she knew this was not the right guy for her. That's the thing with women, you all know this intuitively for yourself almost from the beginning. A woman's intuition is amazing. You don't need weeks, you don't need months, and you don't need years. You can feel it right away. The question then becomes will you trust your intuition, or will you rationalize past it? Will you give yourself the reasons to embrace this man or will you just trust that your spirit is saying he's not it?

Well, she gave herself reasons to continue seeing him and she ends up marrying this man. After marrying him, guess what? A year into the marriage, a secret comes out that he has a child she knew nothing about. Of course, she's pissed. It was a very tough pill to swallow, but trying to be a good wife, she wanted to make things work. She swallowed that pill and moved forward. They stayed married.

She came to me after a while explaining to me that things were getting kind of rough. They were having some issues and they weren't happy. I told her flat out, "I never believed this was the man you should have married." I didn't believe he was the man for her, but again, she needed to pray about it. She agreed she would pray about it. When I checked in with her a week later, she said she prayed and God told her to work on her marriage. I said, "So be it. If God said to work on your marriage, you need to work on your marriage and go with that."

She updated me again a few weeks later and said everything was getting better and that she was good. I think to myself, "Great!"

Some time passes, and her ex-husband decides to reach out to her. She happened to text me as well around the same time. Now mind you, we're just friends and there's nothing more to it than that. Her husband sees the text messages and gets upset. He demands both my and her ex-husband's number because he wants to call us. She refuses. She says, "Listen, I already told my ex-husband not to call me anymore," but she didn't want to give him his number because she didn't want any kind of larger drama to develop.

She also didn't feel like she needed to give him my number either. When she told me this, I said to her, "Give him my number. He's your husband. He has a right to know who I am. Let me explain to him that I'm just your friend and that no disrespect was intended."

My text simply said, "Hey, how you doing? Everything okay?" Nothing suspect there, but I think it's fair for him to be able to speak to me and know what's going on. However, I told her, I didn't think she should give him her ex-husband's number because if she's already put her ex-husband in check, there's no need to go there. I also told her to pray about whether she should give him both numbers.

When she goes back to him, to give him the numbers, he says, "Oh, you're too late. You don't respect me, I don't trust you. I don't want the numbers anymore." She insisted on giving him the numbers at this point, but he wouldn't take them. The next day she comes home from work and finds a note on the table from him saying, "I'm leaving you and I want a divorce. I'm going to my baby mother's house to live with her."

Let me explain something to you right now. Nobody just ups and leaves and goes to their baby mother's house and moves in with them. It just doesn't happen like that. Clearly this was brewing way before the text messages even came about. Chances are the text message fiasco was him looking for a reason to validate his exit plan. Why did I use this story? I used it because God told her, "work on your marriage." She did, and it didn't end up working out.

She did her part in trying to be a better wife and she was still released from the situation. She didn't have to get a divorce, he did. Again, when you're doing what you're supposed to do, things are going to happen in your favor. Either he's going to step up or he's going to step out. Plain and simple. That's exactly what happened. If he's not the guy, if you truly are with the wrong man, it will show itself. It will be revealed and the ish will hit the fan one way or another. When it does, your hands will be clean and you 'll be able to say, "I did my part."

When you're acting a fool, when you're not being the wife you're supposed to be, you're giving him a free pass essentially to act a fool in return. You're validating his negative behavior. He'll just say, "Look at her. Look at what she's doing." The blame will be put on you, whether it's deserved or not. This tactic will be used against you and nothing will be accomplished. He will have no guilt or accountability for his actions.

Again, if you have married the wrong man, essentially put your best foot forward and do not get a divorce. The marriage will run its course if it's not meant to be. When you don't give them anything to work with, it turns everything around. It's hard for someone to constantly be so shady to someone who's being so good to them. Trust me, shady people can only validate their shady behavior with negativity. They will look for any small thing to say, "Well she deserved it. Look at what she's doing," to try to deflect the blame and responsibility.

With that said, I would love it if this chapter doesn't apply to you. However, I had to put it out there because this is real. No one is talking about it. Everyone's being fearful of pushing anyone out the door. I'm not trying to push you out the door. I'm trying to help you realize your truth. I don't want you to be in denial about your situation, go to God. Talk to Him about what needs to happen next.

Ultimately, it's not about what I say, what your pastor says, or what your friends say. Do what God wants you to do. If it's to stay married, make it work. If it's to leave, do what needs to be done on the way out. One way or another, you need to be the woman God created you to be. Be the wife you were called to be and let the chips fall where they may.

FINAL THOUGHT

There's a chance you need to experience a more in-depth healing process in addition to hitting your reset button. If this is the case, head over to, www.findingloveafterheartbreak.com and receive updates on my upcoming release, *Finding Love After Heartbreak.*

In this upcoming two book set, I will dive deep into the steps you need to take to heal from past hurts and relationship disappointments, so you can experience the love that's waiting for you on the other side of pain.

Also, feel free to visit me at, www.stephanspeaks.com for more relationship resources and information on upcoming speaking events.

ABOUT THE
AUTHOR

Stephan Labossiere is a man on a mission, and that mission is to make relationships happier and more fulfilling.

As a certified relationship coach, a speaker and author, Stephan seizes every opportunity to help both men and women overcome the challenges that hinder their relationships. From understanding the opposite sex, to navigating the paths and avoiding the pitfalls of relationships and self growth. Stephan's relationship advice and insight helps countless individuals achieve an authentically amazing life. Stephan empowers millions to take charge of the difficult situations standing in the way of the life and love they seek and to make impactful changes on a daily basis.

Dedicated to helping, and devoted to *keeping it real*. Stephan's straightforward, yet compassionate delivery style, attracts a versatile clientele including; notable celebrities, civic and social organizations, academic institutions, singles, and couples alike, who can and are ready to handle the truth!

Seen, heard and chronicled in national and international media outlets including; the *Tom Joyner Morning Show*, *The Examiner*, *ABC*, *Huffington Post Live*, and *GQ* to name a few. Stephan is highly sought-after because he is able to dispel the myths of relationship breakdowns and obstacles—platonic, romantic, and otherwise with fervor and finesse.

To coin a phrase by an individual who attended one of his speaking engagements, "he's definitely the relationship guy, all relationships all the time."

With an international following of singles and couples alike, the name Stephan Labossiere is synonymous with breaking down relationship barriers, pushing past common facades, and exposing the truth. It is this understanding of REAL relationships that he brings to everyone he encounters.

OTHER BOOKS
BY STEPHAN

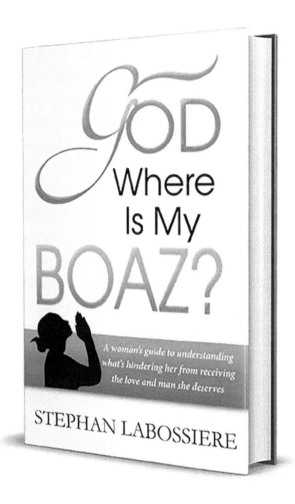

www.GodWhereIsMyBoaz.com

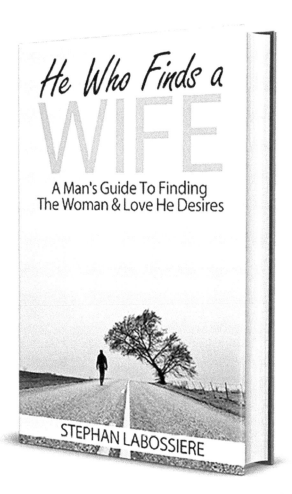

www.HeWhoFinds.com

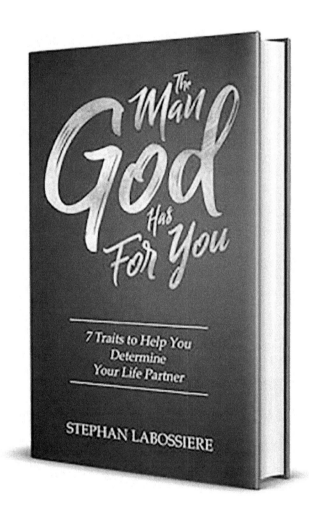

www.TheManGodHasForMe.com

Resources and more can be found at
www.StephanSpeaks.com/shop/

You can also follow me on
Twitter & Instagram: **@StephanSpeaks**
or find me on Facebook under
"Stephan Speaks Relationships"

Lightning Source UK Ltd.
Milton Keynes UK
UKHW011827140219
337358UK00019B/377/P

MATILDA
AT THE SPEED
OF LIGHT

A New Anthology
of Australian Science Fiction

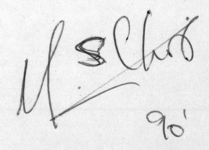

To
Leigh Edmonds
and Valma Brown
for
The Notional

ACKNOWLEDGEMENTS

Terry Dowling, "A Dragon Between His Fingers", published in *Omega Science Digest*, May 1986; Greg Egan, "Mind Vampires", published in *Interzone No. 18*; Freda McLennan, "It's Not What You Say", published in *Omega Science Digest*, November 1983; Ania Walwicz, "fairytale", published in *Difference: Writing by Women*, Waterloo Press, 1985; Cherry Wilder, "Odd Man Search", published in *Alien Worlds*, Void Publications, 1979; Yvonne Rousseau, "The Truth About Oscar", published in the *Bulletin*, December 1981; David Lake, "Creator", published in *Envisaged Worlds*, Void Publications, 1978; Humphrey McQueen, "Stiletto Inheritance", published in *Island Magazine*, March 1982; Francis Payne, "Albert's Bellyful", published in *Transmutations*, Norstrilia Press, 1979; George Turner, "Not in Front of the Children", published in *Aphelion No. 5*, 1987; Damien Broderick, "Thy Sting", published in *Omni*, June 1987; and Leanne Frahm, "On The Turn", published in *Shadows 9*, 1986.

Contents

Introduction

The strangest thing has happened recently to science — but then, of course, the strangest thing is quite often the one thing you can be sure *will* happen. That makes no sense, I grant you, for what we expect to happen is surely pretty much a repeat of what always *has* happened ... isn't it? One generation cometh and another passeth away but the land abideth forever. Yea, and the sun also rises. Regular as, well, as clockwork, or a sunrise.

That's changed. Clockwork changed it, if you're prepared to accept clockwork as a suitable metaphor for technology, with science as the pendulum (or spring, or battery) that powers the remorselessly turning hands (or flickering light-emitting diodes), moving us ceaselessly into a future which is no longer just one generation replacing another on the face of the abiding earth.

Our clockwork is interfering with the earth. Even the sun comes to us through a haze, and the haze traps the sun's bright yellow heat and melts down the polar icecaps, trickle by trickle, and the waters rise and the winds shift, and the land, the land dries or is inundated, and all the creatures that creep or scuttle or flap across its face will be changed, sure as the sun will rise tomorrow.

But that's not the surprising thing. We're accustomed already to future shock, we've been taking merry little jolts from that current for at least a decade, tickling our nerve ends with the prospect of cataclysm. If doom is closer upon us today

ix

than yesterday, well, what is an inch compared with the down-pressing over our necks of infinity?

So change per se is not the surprising thing, I insist. We can hardly any longer be taken aback to hear that the whole unthinkable vastness of the world is being reshaped and put at terminal risk by our clever feral brains and hands.

The new thing is this: because it is science which has done this thing, we had supposed that science was something special, a new way of thinking, quite as startling as upright locomotion in an ape. Now we begin to learn, to our uttermost astonishment, that science is not the unprecedented phenomenon we had taken it to be.

About ten years ago, anthropologists left the colourfully daubed and tinted tribesfolk whom it had been their lofty pleasure to observe and record, and started to infiltrate the places of high power in our own civilisation. With a cultivatedly innocent eye and ear, they loitered in laboratories, peering at men and women in grubby white smocks who sliced up rats and metered gravity waves. And they found that science was not a special way of thinking. It was not the superior form of cognition happily discovered four centuries ago by Sir Francis Bacon and now built into the sinew of our culture.

The surprising thing, you see, was that science (according to these slightly dumbfounded anthropologists) is just a sort of story-telling. A kind of narrative. The myths of technocracy.

Probably you think I'm exaggerating. Listen to the sociologist Bruno Latour, from a report published in 1983:

"Now that field studies of laboratory practices are starting to pour in, we are beginning to have a better picture of what scientists do inside the walls of these strange places called 'laboratories' ... The result, to summarise it in one sentence, was that nothing extraordinary and nothing 'scientific' was happening inside the sacred walls of these temples."

Ah, but sociologists! What can you expect from a bunch of envious pseudo-scientists, eager to prove that their own ragbag of speculations, ideology and wishful thinking is just as good as nuclear physics and recombinant genetics?

It's not that easy. Sifting through these reports, you get an overwhelming sense of the socially-constructed nature of scientific claims, the central importance of interpretation, and what is called the *underdetermination* of scientific theories by the facts which we naively imagine support them. Despite the myth of the crucial experiment which will separate the wheat of truth from the chaff of error, nobody really tosses out a favourite theory purely on the basis of experimental disagreements. Any plausible theory is apparently supported by a host of facts, and apparently undermined by a competing host.

What's more, "facts" are not that pure and simple either. University departments of science do not assiduously scrutinise the "facts" of astrology and parapsychology and mystical cures for cancer, and then find them wanting; these "facts" are simply ignored, because scientists know full well that facts are always constructs, put together by human minds — and these particular "facts", because they have been constructed in the context of ridiculous theories, are too offensive even to trouble debunking.

What is only just coming to be widely recognised is that this critical razor cuts both ways. Because the "facts" of science are equally constructed, they are equally partial, fallible, doubtful. Theories precede each one of them — we cannot even interpret a photograph without a theory of what to see — and theories follow them, dropping like leaves before the gales of social interests or revolutionary disdain, as the storm of feminism has blasted away the once rock-hard "facts" which "proved" male superiority.

So science is the kind of story we twentieth-century sophisticates tell ourselves about the universe and the creatures which inhabit it, including us. Its laws are not the laws of "scientific method", sought for so long by anxious philosophers, but the laws of narrative and myth.

Can you believe that?

Bruno Latour, who does, admits the "naive but nagging question: if nothing scientific is happening in laboratories, why are there laboratories to begin with and why, strangely enough, is the society surrounding them paying for these places where nothing special is produced?"

It's not a knockdown argument, however. If nothing metaphysical was happening in medieval monasteries, as plenty of atheists would surmise, why did society pay for *them*? If nothing of security is being fostered by the overwhelming multiplication of nuclear weapons and "conventional" arms, why are we all paying so much for them? The answer, as always, lies at the intersection of power and knowledge. Religion and the profession of arms and the exercise of theoretical and laboratory skills are all arenas for the deployment of authority, the insertion of levers, the exertion of force.

But surely more can be said? Isn't there a difference between science and magic, between crude political bullying and cool technical persuasion? As Latour notes, "The relativistic position ... looks ludicrous because of the enormous consequences of science. One cannot equate ... the careful procedure of corpse interrogation in the Ivory Coast and the careful planning of DNA probes in a California laboratory; the story-telling of origin myths somewhere in the South African bush and the Big Bang theory."

Or, to come at it from the rawest, bloodiest bottom line: isn't the special thing about science that, from an equation, it can build a bomb capable of exterminating a city? Can a mantra or a dogma do as much?

Yet Latour finds one invariant factor which characterises the activity of modern science: its practice of *inscription*. A lab was a place of diverse instruments, some of which "filled large rooms, employed many technicians and took many weeks to run. But their end result, no matter the field, was always a small window through which one could read a very few signs from a rather poor repertoire (diagrams, blots, bands, columns) ... When these resources were lacking, the selfsame scientists stuttered, hesitated, and talked nonsense ...". Leave them their "rational" minds, their access to scientific "paradigms" and "methods" — without those specified ways of writing and diagramming, without the story-telling tools of science, scientists fall away into a curious tongue-tied loss of power.

If science is a sort of fiction, a brand of story-telling, what of the story-telling which has come to be named "science fiction"?

Science fiction, speculative fiction, is the explicitly *literary* landscape where these issues are given imaginative form: dressed gaudily in metaphor, mounted on tin starships, sent out to joust against buggy aliens and mind-reading foes which are, finally, the limits of our own constructed knowledge, the fringes of our as-yet-unsayable fears and hopes.

Too often it is an evasion, a retreat to cosy positivism, to the authority of a theology which now worships at the lab bench instead of the altar. Just as often it's a game for children, a different sort of backsliding into an adventure playground.

Sometimes, though, it lives up to its name. Sometimes science fiction is the literary fiction we write about that other fiction which has the power to blow the abiding earth in columns of filthy ash into the haze of the always-rising sun.

This book comes just twenty years after John Baxter's first A & R collection of Australian sf, a decade after my own *The Zeitgeist Machine*. Baxter voiced many hopes at that time (when he, like many of his contributors, was still in his twenties). "Local writers of sf need no longer apologise for their profession ..." he wrote, as one might utter a wishful enchantment, "Australians are beginning to understand that science fiction can be as viable a means of commenting on life in Australia as poetry or painting."

His senior contributor, Captain A. Bertram Chandler, still the best-known Australian sf writer, is sadly gone from our number. Others, such as Lee Harding and Baxter himself, virtually abandoned sf in favour of other modes (children's literature in Harding's case; media interests and non-sf novels in Baxter's, though of late he has returned with the experimental radio drama *Little Wing* and the screenplay for *Time Guardians*). Other innovative and accomplished practitioners have arrived, most notably the established novelist and critic George Turner, who is perhaps today the nation's premier sf ambassador. David Lake and Victor Kelleher, both — like Chandler — adult immigrants to Australia, have published more sf and fantasy than most of their native-born rivals, and seen it awarded prizes and reputation.

Other names have emerged into sunlight only recently. Few have attained strong presence abroad, and it is hard not to diagnose a distasteful taint of provincialism in the American or British editors who fail to seize upon this excellent work with cries of glee. The inevitable snare awaits the local writer's feet: to be published in the lucrative overseas markets, you must already have an attractive reputation, a "track record"; to earn this reputation, you must first be published there. Some of us (Turner, myself, Lake) have in some measure broken through this ludicrous obstacle, yet our arms remain pinned behind us in the exact degree that we keep our Australian accents, locales, point of view. One can only hope that developed and growing talents such as the writers celebrated in this collection will not always remain our secret.

And what of the stories, the writers? Terry Dowling's engaging tale about Tom Rynosseros is one segment of an evolving sequence set in a future Australia at once familiar and eerie, told in a voice which blends his own with *hommages* to J. G. Ballard, Cordwainer Smith, and Jack Vance. Greg Egan's story, as befits an experimental film-maker, is horrific, surreal, and bleakly funny. The sepia-toned humour of Yvonne Rousseau's time-travel fable fetched applause from Barry Humphries when it first appeared in the *Bulletin*. Humphries, who spends much of his time strutting the stage in the glitzy gowns of Dame Edna Everage, would have equal reason to enjoy Humphrey McQueen's outrageous political speculations. Not that Australians have abandoned the traditional sf story: David Lake and Freda McLennan ring adroit changes on tales which would not have gone astray in anthologies selected by American Golden Age editors such as John W. Campbell or Don Wollheim (as Lake's was, in fact, chosen for Wollheim's

Annual World's Best SF). Cherry Wilder, a New Zealander who spent important years in Australia, lives now in Germany, but her story here was written before she departed; it is suffused, as she has observed, "with nostalgia for the twentieth century". Leanne Frahm excels in quiet tales of horror, usually with a marked Antipodean tang. George Turner is in unusually light-hearted if venomous voice. Perhaps the same might be said of my own piece, were I not notorious for being invariably light-hearted and venomous. Absolutely lethal in her scrumptious fairytale is Ania Walwicz, painter and performance poet. Scottish-born psychiatrist Frank Payne tells an exvberant Aussie bush yarn of life after the gene wars. Finally, the two stories original to this volume are sf at the cutting edge: Lucy Sussex' delightful feminist romp which boldly goes where no man would dare to tread; and the luminous fusing, in Philippa Maddern's gemmed story, of scientific philosophy and iconographic mythology — an enactment, perhaps, of that very fusion of science and imaginative narrative which we have been discussing.

It is 200 years since whites brought the seeds of an English-speaking culture to Australia; it is a suitable time for us to burst free, at last, from the twin tyrannies of distance and difference. If the past is another country, where they do things differently, so is the future — and we shall *all* be living there. It is suitable, as we hump our blueys to the strains of "Waltzing Matilda", that the songs we sing by the hot blue light of the late twentieth century furnace should be songs in that boundary-less tongue, that voice of fecund fiction, which is framed by science: songs of the fiction of science, the science of fiction.

Matilda is waltzing no longer. Matilda is rushing into tomorrow, and we with her, at the speed of light.

A Dragon Between His Fingers

TERRY DOWLING

When he was ten, Shannon inherited a flawed Toby dough-beast from his uncle and raised a quarter-jack upon it.

The Toby was an old animal, its sides stained yellow from the baths, and feeble with age, but Shannon had tried and succeeded. For almost a minute, peering between the third and smallest fingers of his right hand, he had seen a quarter-jack, a dragon called a sirrush.

"It was the Dragon of Babylon," he told his father afterwards, who told Scarbo, who years later told me because of the cargo we were carrying, and led me to raise the matter with Shannon that day.

"I never did it again," Shannon said.

"But once is enough, eh?"

"I'll never forget it, Tom. You never can. I saw my dragon. It made me seek out Dan."

Shannon told me how he and Dan had spent the following summer with the Toby, trying to raise dragons upon it, quarter-jacks and half-jacks, without success — two young boys working their hardest to develop the gift of dragon-sight. The dough-beast had died soon afterwards, its DNA coded short-term. Later, as a young man, Shannon had captained a sand-ship named *Sirrush* in memory of his dragon, a light, very fast 60-footer courier vessel which he lost to Timmsmen pirates on the desert outside Wani, two years before he joined the crew of *Rynosseros*.

1

I knew of that *Sirrush*, and how the relentless Timmsmen had driven her into the sand and taken her, but Scarbo's news of him raising aspect on the Toby as a boy came as a surprise. However random and undeveloped it might be, Shannon had the gift. He was sighted.

It was just as well that I knew, all things considered.

We were ferrying three dough-beasts from the Massi-Kallinga vats to You-Guess-What. They stood in long wooden pens on the deck, their four-legged, grey potato bodies motionless, little more than passive, omnivorous life support mechanisms for their marvellous, overdeveloped hind-brains, with sufficient autonomic functions to ensure life but not even let them feed themselves properly. Without tribal jackmen aboard, young Hammon had the job of shovelling gruel into those slack maws twice a day. In return, the creatures gave some of us dragons — or, rather, could do so now that we were lucky enough to be this close to them.

Shannon had seen a sirrush, and in the two years we had sailed together we had never come close enough to a Toby for Shannon to betray his secret. Most sighted people discussed the gift if they had it, just as I acknowledged my own sensitivity to the haldanes. But Shannon had lost a ship; a young man's first freehold vessel, a small charvi, but his alone. The past intruded too much.

But now I knew about that past and I was glad. And envious too.

Shannon had seen his sirrush. Scarbo had once seen a manticore, a billong, and two of the higher bunyips. Stare as I might, through one bifurcation of fingers after another, hand by hand, I saw only the blunt hippopotamus lumps of grey flesh, mindlessly staring out at the desert as we ran along the Great Arunta Road. I accepted that I didn't have the gift, but I knew as well that I would always need to prove that I didn't, that I would keep trying.

The cargo troubled Shannon. He kept to the poop, alert for raiders even when it wasn't his watch. Timms and his band of highwaymen would do anything to secure newly made dough-beasts to sell back to the Ab'Os for their corroborees. They would even take on an armed and escorted ship like *Rynosseros* and a fighting crew to get such a prize. Full-jack dough-beasts took years to produce, and these three were primes, just the thing to touch our reptilian memories and bring forth the Plumed Serpent of the Aztecs, Quetzalcoatl, or Kukulcan of the Mayans, or Tiamat, the Chiaos and Lungs, or the great Rainbow Serpent itself.

We all knew Timms would try, or one of his highwayman colleagues, The Eagle Cleland Buchanan, or the notorious Captain Ha-Ha. That was why we ran in a W battle formation with escorts — two 80-foot tribal sand-ships ahead, *Dancing Man* and *Jimbo*, and two 90-foot National vessels behind, the *Bellona* under Gray Ridley, and Radkin's *Ozymandias*. The hot late-morning sky was bright with our kites straining out ahead on taut cables, with a dry blistering tailwind keeping up our hopes for a three-hour journey.

I finished helping Scarbo and young Hammon trim a lazy parafoil, then went to the poop to check the instruments.

"You could have laid over, Rob," I said, mentioning it again.

Shannon kept his eyes between the desert and the helm display. I saw anger in them all the same, but relief as well.

"It's okay, Tom. Really. It gives me a chance to practise. Three primes; I'm bound to see something."

"Good. Teach me how," I said.

"In a way, you're lucky you don't see them. Once you do, you've always got a hand stuck in front of your face when a Toby's around. You keep hoping. I don't know how long I could've kept it from the rest of you."

"I envy you all the same."

"Tom, seeing the dragons is a mixed blessing. I can love them because I know them somehow. They are atavisms. What I saw as a boy was that beautiful, that familiar. Dan agreed with me. We sought them together. But it's still like a drug. It's real but not real. We've left that behind."

"Well, for me it's like wetting your finger and trying to

make a wine glass sing. You keep needing to do it until you succeed. I'd like to see a sirrush.''

"Do what I used to do. Go down to the pens and stand up close. That's how Dan saw his first quarter-jack, and his full-jack basilisk.''

"The basilisk that almost killed him. Scarbo mentioned that too.''

"It was after our Toby died. My uncle took us to the vats, and Dan tried to raise aspect while our backs were turned. He said he saw a basilisk. He cried it out to us before his mind said to die. My uncle told me that was how the basilisk-template worked. The death-look. Dan was lucky. But it changed him. He was hospitalised for months.''

"I'll go find a sirrush," I said.

Shannon looked up and smiled. "Call me if you do.''

I saw nothing, of course. Just the blunt heads, the low thick bodies. And crouching there on the deck before the pens, I had the usual mix of doubts and acceptance.

The rationale wasn't hard to accept at all. It was easy to concede that our evolution from reptiles into mammals had left us with powerful reptilian memories, that as a race humanity had always had a predilection for dragons. They were a fundmental part of its race consciousness.

It was nothing as simple as remembering Tyrannosaurus Rex. That deep psychic stratum was filtered through the subconscious, through symbols and imagination, through analogs, cultural correlatives, mammalian taint and projection. It was diluted, distorted, but it was there — amplified and focused out of the mammalian body-field by the dough-beasts, given as a coherent signal back from their hypertrophied hind-brains, perceived by the mind through the ridiculously simple, Kirlian-intensifying hand-lattice.

At last, the human race could see its dragons, its reptile beginnings, its unhuman forebears. The deepest, most primordial archetypes had forms at last, recognisable familiar forms. When the tampering from other conditioning strata and mind-sets was complete, there was a bestiary to encompass our wildest dreams, to explain our deepest fears, or so the sighted ones assured the rest of us. A heraldry for the Ab'O Princes and the world at large, though all the exported Tobys had short-term genetic codings. The Ab'Os thus kept the monopoly; sold dragons to the world.

But like the wine glass singing, like believing in the haldanes, what I knew and what I felt were at odds. I kept seeing the Tobys as dream-amplifiers, as overrated man-made image transmitters and nothing more, as something of a hoax. Though it didn't look like it, there was probably reptile DNA in their genetic make-up; hence the bias towards dragon imagery. A lot of National scientists believed that, though they had never had Shannon's luck — a geneticist uncle, accepted by the Ab'Os, who had once brought home a flawed dough-beast instead of destroying it outright.

"No luck, Tom?"

I looked up to see Shannon standing over me. He had been relieved at the helm by Strengi.

"Not a scale, Rob. You?"

"Not a scale."

We walked together back to the elevator deck and shared the watch with Strengi, making ship-talk and watching the desert and the escort fleet spread out across the Road around us.

It was double-hard for Shannon. Not only were the dough-beasts there, in plain sight or back under the tarpaulins draped over the cages to keep off the sun, but we were watching for Timms, the one who had taken *Sirrush*. Shannon had once told me something of his fateful meeting with the brigand, of how Timms, in his air-cooled, augmented, bronze and leather talos suit, eyes burning through the eye-slit of his great helmet, had boarded *Sirrush* and announced that he would spare the crew, even though they had defied him and tried to flee.

I would have defied him too.

I imagined losing my own ship to him, of having her taken from me to be used as a privateer vessel or a blockade runner, or in the wars between the Princes. My thoughts went back to the ship lotteries at Cyrimiri, to the day I had won *Rynosseros* and first saw the hull being lifted out of the storage cradle by the moving gantry and carried to the chandler's yard where I had an old battered travel platform rented from Captain Albert, and a dozen cast-off kites borrowed from Red Lucas. Recalling her being lowered to the housing and locked to the table, getting wheels again, legs for the desert Roads, led me back to Shannon's loss in a way that kept me silent, that made me watch for Timms and hope — for reasons other than the safety of our cargo — that he wouldn't come. But that he would as well.

It was an added difficulty having the Emmened mission commander aboard *Rynosseros* for this first part of the journey, here to ensure that the beasts reached his people safely. Sos Wain Chrisos stood at the bow, a short self-confident Ab'O in dark fighting leathers who seemed completely unaware that his strength of will translated as arrogance.

I had avoided him since a disagreement over the loading of the Tobys at Massi-Kallinga, but now I went forward to make my peace with the man.

"Ah, Captain Tom! Please!" he said, and seemed conciliatory enough. "We are making good time."

"We are indeed, Chrisos," I said, climbing up to him.

"You still fear this highwayman?"

"Timms is clever," I replied. "These Tobys are worth the Emmened fleet at least."

"You know my views, Captain. We must not honour these brigands too much."

I went to answer him but decided to change the subject instead.

"Has Timms been much of a burden to your people?"

Chrisos shook his head. "Not since The Eagle Buchanan was taken by Kurdaitcha in the Ambrilles."

The news surprised me.

"The Emmened took Buchanan?" I thought of the ancient Dreamtime stories, of Ab'O assassins moving silently in their Kurdaitcha shoes of emu feathers. The world has not changed that much.

"We got them all," Chrisos said. "Their jackmen came to us, but no Tobys. All the brigands have jackmen these days."

I watched the desert, my eyes half-shut against the glare.

"I saw you by the cages," Chrisos said after a while, still trying to ease things between us. "Do you see the dragons?"

"No," I said. "Shannon and Scarbo do. Not me."

"I am sorry. I knew you were a sensitive in other ways. They are beautiful beyond words. Our scientists have discovered the secret mainsprings of our past."

There was no arguing with that, but I still felt something worrying, something unwholesome in how the Ab'Os, and the sighted Nationals too, made use of that knowledge, always took the chances they did.

"You cannot go backwards, Chrisos," I said, and hated how envious and petty I sounded, as non-sighted people always did.

The Ab'O smiled.

"But it is not backwards. The dragons are still with us; for whatever reasons, they are there to be brought out and used."

I could think of nothing more to say. Chrisos was right. Despite the risks, despite the danger posed by some of the manifestations, the dragons brought harmony, healed the mind. Too many people said that they did.

The Ab'O scientists had given new meaning to all our pieces of dragon-lore; to St George fighting his own powerfully-projected dragon dream in the North African desert; to Sigurd, Beowulf and Herakles defeating theirs; others ranged against the nagas and wyverns of the mind, the ladons, salamanders, chimeras and amphisbaenas.

A dough-beast could accommodate many different dragon-vectors at the same time, quarter-jacks and half-jacks, depending on how many individuals were seeking. But with full-jack resolution, the manifestation was so strong, so concentrated, that all who sought aspect saw the same dragon, and risked the same consequences of that powerful summoning. A skilled jackman, working with a prime, could even determine which dragon he sought, imposing a template on the Toby that other sighted ones shared and few could override.

Such a delightful irony — the dragon fighters themselves causing the dragons, often the innate amplifiers, triggering dragon memory, sharing it at a mass level, subduing it again with mass hallucination. Or being the foil for some local shaman who could control his people by calling up a genetic echo of Allosaurus, an imperfectly-conceived Ankylosaur, or a blundering harmless Steg. The effect was the same; the legends grew. Set into its rituals, the wild talent meant a viable and potent powerbase. So what if the creatures were distorted beyond all sense of herpetological truth, the gryphons and tengus and manticores; imagination and inventive nightmare intruding on the memory to sway the form?

The power was always there. Dragons meant power. The display of them healed, lulled, resolved something in the mammal breast which evolution had not quite taken from it.

Yes, it was strange what the mammal mind did to that race memory, what it had added to the original. I had less cause to fear some dim, impossibly remote, infinitesimally tenuous connection with Tyrannosaurus Rex than the twisted mind-enhanced residues being raised through the nearly mindless Tobys. Shannon's sirrush might kill a sighted person with dragon-shock, while its ancient dinosaur ancestors might have been scavengers and egg-stealers, coelurosaurs like Struthiomimus and Compsognathus, possibly more afraid of someone like Chrisos than he would ever need be of them.

I pretended to watch for Timms, then remembered from stories I'd heard that he too was powerfully dragon-sighted. I made an excuse to Chrisos and returned to the helm.

Like the other Armoured pirates who survived the continual Ab'O hunts, Timms knew how to use tribal law against the likes of Chrisos — knew exactly when to strike.

We lost the National vessels at the border of You-Guess-What because of the ruling that only a handful of approved State of Nation vessels could cross tribal ground. The moment we went to turn off the Great Arunta Road on to Lateral 83, *Bellona* and *Ozymandias* veered off and began to alter course for the coast.

As a tactical manoeuvre, now that we were three instead of five, we stopped long enough to move the Tobys into the storage bay of *Dancing Man*, and left the empty pens, swathed under their tarpaulins, on the deck of *Rynosseros*. It took us fifteen minutes, longer than we had rehearsed, but the Ab'O tacticians felt it added to our chances.

I went on board *Dancing Man* with Shannon, who insisted on staying with the Tobys too, to practise dragons, he said. The three ships broke formation then, *Jimbo* heading off to the southwest on a little-used tribal Road, *Rynosseros* continuing on the Lateral to the tribal capital, and *Dancing Man* steering a course into the northwestern desert.

I felt the whole manoeuvre was obvious, preferring the battle formation to decoys. But Sos Wain Chrisos was tactical adviser to the Emmended on this mission, and tribal law had limited his options too. I was glad not to have the responsibility.

He ran *Dancing Man* at top speed, fully kited and powered as well, while Shannon and I hid below with the Ab'O fighting crew and the Tobys.

It was there in the rocking, musty gloom of the storage bay that Shannon saw his next dragon.

There was very little to do waiting there, so he was making the lattice as a way of passing time, going from one beast to the next, working down his hands as he crouched on the deck. The Ab'O warriors didn't like it. Tribal law meant that they could not seek aspect or share it unless they had permission.

But Shannon was a privileged guest. The tribesmen averted their gaze, muttering now and then and keeping watch through the four dirty sand-scoured ports.

"Tom!" Shannon said, and I knew at once what was happening. He was peering through the middle finger and ring finger of his right hand at the dough-beast on the end, a Toby with a dark blemish on one shoulder. The creature stood very still, its dim eyes glazed, its wide toothless mouth fixed in a stupid cartoon grin.

Shannon continued staring, so I knew there was no dragon-shock involved, no basilisk-stare, sandrake-sting or fire-vector to fear.

Before I knew what I was doing, I found that I was working through my hands too, first the left, then the right, with no luck. I saw one Ab'O moving his fingers at his side, fighting the impulse to try as well.

"What is it?" I asked.

"I think ... it's manticore! Or billong! No! It's tiamat! A tiamat!"

The Ab'Os muttered enviously. Most of them could access the dragons, wanted more than anything to do so whenever aspect was raised. But they dared not. Sos Wain Chrisos had a Clever Man on his ship, constantly alert for such things as haldanes and mind-fields. Transgressors would be caught and punished.

"Oh ...!" Shannon cried, awed by the beauty of what he was seeing. But his rapture was short-lived. Shouts were heard from above; the ship's bell rang out repeatedly over the roar of the wheels.

"Timmsmen! Timmsmen!" came the cry.

I steadied Shannon as he came out of his trance, and helped him stand, then followed the tribesmen up on deck.

At the rail, I used my pocket glass to scan the raiders.

Four ships were coming at us, low fast ships, lighter than *Dancing Man*, running under drab battle-kites. The one in the lead was Timms' flagship, *Sorcerer*, with Timms himself standing in the bows, a powerful bronze figure with his helmet tipped back and a fierce gravure fear-face underneath hiding his real features. That was the sight which had made so many captains surrender their ships.

But Shannon was more concerned with the vessel second

in formation, the one flying the Armoured Head pennon that was Timms' sign.

"It's *Sirrush*!" he cried. "Tom, they've got *Sirrush* there! The one flying the Iron Ned! I knew they'd keep her. She's fast; mostly wood and fibreglass and ceramic."

"Easy, Rob," I said.

"But she's intact, Tom! They didn't destroy her!"

Two warriors looked round to see what the outcry was, then turned their attention back to the approaching raiders. Chrisos already had two death-lamps aloft, trying to catch the sun, and his kitesmen were bringing hotpots, fighting-kites and harpoons to the deck.

We ran to help, though I knew this had to be a nightmare for Shannon — preparing to make war on his own vessel.

As it turned out he need not have worried. Timms had prepared this too well.

Before we could use our weapons, three harpoons struck the hull, their cables fastened to land-anchors thrown from the decks of the Timmsmen ships.

When the first anchor grabbed, the momentum of *Dancing Man* tore the harpoon's barbed head out of the charvi's stern assembly, though the vessel slowed noticeably. It began to gather speed again, then the other hooks took hold. With a mighty wrench which threw us all to the deck, *Dancing Man* was jerked about savagely on its pedestal. Drive lines snapped; emergency overrides in the central pin slowly locked the wheels. The vessel careened wildly, nearly toppled, righting itself by the barest good fortune. At the same time, a spring-shot boomerang spun into the kite-lines, severing some, fouling the rest and dragging the canopy to the desert.

And that was it. The raider ships rolled up to us and stopped. Sos Wain Chrisos and his men were obliged to fight and did so, bravely and uselessly, falling man by man to snaphaunce fire, deck-lenses and spears.

Shannon and I had no such obligation. We kept our hands away from our weapons and handed over our blades willingly when the raiders swarmed aboard. We were led back to *Sorcerer*, where Shannon had his second meeting with Timms and I had my first.

The desert highwaymen were consciously romantic figures. They often worked carefully at their images, using media consultants, psychologists, getting advice from the network people in the coastal cities. Timms was very successful at this. I had heard of the captains who wound down their kites at the first glimpse of his Iron Ned, preferring to lose cargos and possibly their ships rather than oppose him.

I understood why this was, having seen him standing in the bow of *Sorcerer*, looking across at us. The man on the quarterdeck was of medium build, though the talos battle-suit made him look taller and more massive — the gleaming bronze plates sewn to leather, the joints, clasps and armatures concealed under smooth couters, pauldrons and poleyns. So cunningly was the armour made that he did indeed resemble a man of bronze, an idealised Ned figure, though now both parts of his double mask were tipped back. The fearsome bronze morion with the Ned eye-slit was open as before, but now the heavily-circuited gravure fear-face underneath was split as well, revealing suntanned cheeks and forehead, a strong jaw and craggy brows over deep-set blue eyes.

Shannon cried out when he saw that rugged face.

"Dan! You! My God! *You* took my ship! Damn you!"

The highwaymen around us raised their weapons. Timms' heavy brows sank into a frown, but one of humorous concern, not anger.

"Your ship, Rob?"

"Yes, mine, damn you! Mine!"

"I repaired her, Rob. She's a fine vessel. I'm glad to have her."

"For God's sake, Dan ..."

"Rasselou! Take Captain Shannon down to the commons and confine him. He has had a nasty shock."

"Why, Dan? Why? You knew it was me that day! You knew!"

"Which is why you are alive now, Rob. Take him!"

The guards dragged him away, down to the commons.

"Tom Rynosseros!" he said then, turning to me. "I am honoured to meet you, sir! Rob doesn't understand destiny. He was meant to bring *Sirrush* to me."

"You live dangerously, Timms."

"I bow to expedience, as we all do. I earn a living. I like being a dealer in dragons."

"It looks good for your legend, I suppose?"

"Careful, Captain!" Some of the humour left his face. "My own men already call me the Basilisk." And he laughed.

I suddenly understood what the fear-face was meant to represent.

"You murdered those men ..."

"No!" The humour vanished altogether. "They know my code. Chrisos chose to fight. He had that choice."

"You knew the Emmended plan."

"I did. Of course I did. I have agents." The tanned face softened again.

"Then ...?"

"Yes, Tom Tyson. Your *Rynosseros* is safe. She got through. We knew Chrisos had the Tobys."

I felt a deep relief, then thought again of how it must be for Shannon.

"What happens to us?" I asked.

"I have no quarrel with you. That is why I spared *Rynosseros*. I create no vendettas with Nation. Cooperate and you go free, of course."

"When?"

"We go to rendezvous with Bunna, spokesman and head Clever Man for the Emmened. We transact business. When that is done, you go with Bunna and the Tobys back to *Rynosseros*, then return to the coast."

"What about *Sirrush*?"

"What about *Sirrush*, Captain Tyson? Talk sense! You expect me to give her up? Shannon would not like the changes I have made to her."

"I want ..."

"I don't care what you want!" Timms cried. "Enough! We go! Rasselou, confine Captain Tyson on the deck with his friend."

And with that he sealed the fearsome gravure face, brought down the great Ned helmet of the talos and became the gleaming legend of himself.

I was taken down to the commons and locked into leg-stocks next to Shannon. He had recovered from his initial surprise but still watched the figure on the quarterdeck in bewilderment.

"Tom, I've always believed we have to value our continuities; the things we carry with us. Friends, family, confidences, things like that. Dan was my best friend. I loved him, probably more in my recollections of him down the years than I ever did at the time. We were close, both sighted. We shared a great adventure. We had the old Toby to work with. How many people get a chance like that?"

"Very few, Rob?"

"I'm too naive, aren't I? Too trusting?"

"I'm the last one to ask."

"But he took *my* ship! And innocent men's lives. We were only boys then, but he was never like that."

"Perhaps the basilisk-shock changed him. Too much dragonism might ..."

"But *my* ship, Tom! Don't you see? It's like me taking *Rynosseros* from you. I couldn't do it. He *knew* it was me then. He kept his helmet closed."

The Timmsmen fleet sailed north until we reached the border of You-Guess-What and were no longer on tribal land.

We approached a vast dry lake, an empty glaring strand that stretched almost to the horizon and shimmered in the afternoon sun. Timms sent up a lookout on a Cody man-lifter, who signalled back that a solitary Emmened charvi was waiting at the lake's centre.

Satisfied, Timms left his lookout in the sky and took his four raider-ships down on to the lake, having them stop 500

14

metres from the Emmened vessel, close to a low rise of sand with a crown of broken stones at the crest. It seemed to be the only natural feature marking this desolation.

The Tobys were led out onto the rise so that Ab'Os could see them, and tethered under makeshift awnings, then fed and watered by a junior jackman, a young Niuginian from Timms' crew. The beasts blinked stupidly in the heat, and looked none the worse for all that had happened.

A wooden Toby pen was brought from the hold of *Sorcerer*, carried to the rise and placed near the dough-beasts. Shannon and I were locked in it. We stood in the shade of the tarpaulin and watched the transactions.

The silence on the lake was nearly absolute, broken only by the snuffling of a Toby, or a quiet word from one jackman to another.

Ten minutes went by, then shimmering indistinct shapes moved out from the Emmened ship. Some came ahead of the rest, heat-distorted figures, spectral and bonelike, with two others like columns of light moving behind them across the intervening ground. They resolved into four djellaba-shrouded Ab'Os, tribal jackmen, and two Clever Men in their ceremonial suits of mirrored leather. A second group were warriors carrying spears, boomerangs and nulla-nullas, a ritual guard which stopped midway and squatted on the sand.

The Clever Men came to within several metres of Timms and stopped, two pillars of dazzling light.

It was almost like a carefully rehearsed ritual dance, a pavan. The four Ab'O jackmen came forward, their faces visible now, painted for corroboree with the lines that represented stylised hand-lattice. Timms stood his ground at the foot of the rise, a shining golden figure carrying a heavy Bok laser. His helmet was closed; we could hear the suit's cooling unit working away. Highwaymen were drawn up about him, while his own jackmen, all Niuginians, were close by the tethered Tobys already carefully controlling which dragons could be coded from their dull minds, thereby preventing Bunna's jackmen from raising aspect first.

When the Ab'O jackmen were close enough and did lock in, their fingers splayed out stiffly in front of their eyes, they saw full-jack basilisk, sandrake and a fiery billong. They screamed and broke trance, one near death from basilisk-glance, two others in fire-shock from the billong's breath. Only one survived mentally unharmed, and he was badly shaken.

The Clever Men knew then that they were helpless. Timms had skilled jackmen, and their own mental powers were effective only against the other Ab'O mystics who could access the haldanes. These renegade jackmen were not susceptible to mind-fighting, and the ritual guard was outnumbered and less well-armed.

The bargaining would go ahead as arranged.

Timms approached the Ab'O party, a forbidding sight in his bronze talos armour.

"You want the Tobys?" he said. "You want these primes?"

One Clever Man stepped forward, a tall old Ab'O named Bunna, his calm dark face framed with tufts of grey hair above the dazzle. He didn't answer the highwayman, but he glanced over at the Tobys tethered on the rise, the beasts he was buying twice over.

"Well, Bunna?" Timms said, the hot sun gleaming off his bright talos shoulders.

"Kurdaitcha will come for you, Timms," the Ab'O said. "No chance now."

"Forget your Kurdaitcha, Bunna. We've got dragons and weapons. We've got hi-tech and good fast ships."

"You go too far. The tribes will work together to get you."

Timms laughed. "I doubt it. We're part of a system, you and I. When you lose, someone else gains. It won't happen."

"The time is coming. Our Kurdaitcha assassins don their feathered shoes. You will not hear; you will not know."

"Do you want the Tobys or not?"

Bunna nodded once. He knew when to count his losses. He knew, too, that Timms would work the northern and western deserts after this — that he had fast, non-metal, insulated ships, hard to read from tribal satellites. Though that was nothing to guide Timms' actions. He was on a hundred death-lists already.

"Good," Timms said. "You can give oaths for your Prince and tribe?"

Again Bunna nodded.

"Then we can begin. We shall do it beast by beast, for oaths, money, and other special considerations. *Sirrush* will then ferry them out to your ship."

So the bargaining began, first — pledges against vendetta in exchange for one dough-beast. The voices carried across the white sand to where Shannon and I sat at the cage-front observing it all.

It was a strange scene in the glare and terrible heat, quite dreamlike. A man of gleaming bronze spoke with two creatures of dazzling quicksilver, while other white-shrouded figures lay about them in dragon-shock, with a clot of darker shapes out on the lake — the Ab'O guard — and beyond them the solitary Emmened ship, barely visible, shimmering in the heat like spun glass.

In the foreground, adjacent to our cage, the softly snuffling Tobys stood under their awnings, quietly stirring now and then, with Timms' jackmen close by. These men had relaxed aspect now that Bunna's jackmen were wounded, and had moved down the rise a short way to be nearer their chief. To the side, the four raider ships waited, their parafoils idle in the overheated air, a single spider-line leading to the Cody man-lifter stirring in the thermals high overhead, its tiny rider alert for Emmened vendetta ships.

Shannon and I sat at the front of our cage, grateful for the tarpaulin, trying to hear every word.

With each beast bought, Timms signalled a jackman who ran back up the slope, freed a Toby from tether, and led it across to the open storage bay of *Sirrush*. It was a slow curious process, one of Timms' own rituals.

Finally, only one beast stood under the awning, the one with the dark shoulder mark. The business was almost over.

Then I noticed that Shannon was making the lattice, lifting a hand slowly in front of his eyes. The remaining Toby felt the mind-field and looked at us, entranced. It snuffled, then stood very still.

"I'm getting it!" Shannon said, very quietly.

I said nothing, torn between urging him on and telling him it would do no good.

The Toby stood motionless, its blank expression even more comical now that a human mind was directing thoughts at it.

Timms' jackmen were good. Whether augmented with implants or just highly attuned to any signs of dragonism, they sensed the Toby being used. The two still on the rise with us turned about, dropped into the crouch, their hands making the lattice. The others came running back from *Sirrush* to join their comrades.

I saw their eyes widen. Next to me, beads of perspiration glistened on Shannon's brow. He sat huddled, staring at the Toby between the first and second fingers of his left hand.

"Quarter-jack!" he hissed between his teeth.

"Which one?" I asked, daring to interrupt, my hands spread uselessly in front of my face, fearing dragon-shock and what it might do to him.

Shannon didn't answer. He concentrated on the Toby, working at aspect.

The jackmen down the slope didn't know whether to keep their ground or flee. One looked quickly about him, at the Tobys being loaded on to *Sirrush*, but it was already too late for any coherent result.

"Half-jack!" Shannon cried. "God! It's half-jack! It is!"

He had more than a flawed, worn-out animal to use now. The Toby with the blemish was a prime, the best the vats could produce. Even I could feel the coiling darkness of a mind-field, a chilling, terrifying wash of occlusion and dragonsense, but without the images, without the deadly stigmata. What *were* they seeing?

"Which?" I cried. "*Sirrush*?"

"My God!" Shannon cried in turn. "My God! Full-jack!"

The jackmen fell dead where they stood. The rest of the Timmsmen heard their death-cries and went for their weapons. Timms left the Ab'Os and began to raise a hand-lattice, driven as all poor-sighted human mammals were to see our dragon forebears, despite the cost.

But the highwayman stopped himself. He knew it would be beautiful beyond description and that it would probably kill him. A few of the others tried though; one Timmsman screamed and fell, another collapsed without a sound, a third curled up into a foetal position at his leader's feet.

"Kurdaitcha!" he managed to say, then began groaning softly.

Held by their disciplines, the Clever Men kept themselves steady. Their fingers did not even twitch.

Timms showed indecision now. He was no doubt recalling Bunna's words earlier. The compulsion to look had to be greater than ever, pouring over him from the Toby, urging him to share the vision it carried.

"Which one?" he cried, raising his Bok laser. "Tell and I'll spare you!"

But Shannon did not tell him, though our lives were in the balance.

"I'll destroy your ship! I'll burn *Sirrush*!"

Shannon stared at the Toby, not turning away for an instant. Perhaps he could not; perhaps he chose between dragons; perhaps he knew exactly what he was doing.

"Tell me!" Timms screamed, and fired his Bok laser at *Sirrush*. The hull flared, burst open, burned on its travel platform. The crew and one of the Tobys died in a gout of flame.

"Tell me!"

"Full-jack!" I cried, blind to dragons, trusting what it

meant to the sighted ones. "You got that, Timms? How many full-jacks have you seen?"

Timms could not hold back any longer. He had to look, had to know. He brought a hand up in front of his eye-slit.

And he screamed as the others had, and he died, his eyes hidden from me by the great helmet, but no doubt as full of terror and wonderment as those of his jackmen. For a moment, his armoured suit held him erect, then he collapsed heavily onto the sand, the cooling-unit still working away.

Shannon fell to the sand as well, sobbing, trembling with exhaustion. Then he looked up, and saw the smouldering ruin of his old ship. Tears ran down his cheeks.

"He killed *Sirrush*. He took her from me again."

"We can't go backwards, Rob. You have *Rynosseros* now. Good mammal name that. Better."

Shannon looked at me blankly for a second, then laughed through his tears.

The warriors were running in from the lake. Beyond them, out of the haze, came the hidden Emmended fleet, summoned from the lake's far side by radio or satellite transmission. Bunna came up the slope to us.

"Which one, jackman?" he asked. "Which one?"

"Quetzalcoatl," Shannon told him. "The Plumed Serpent."

"The Rainbow Serpent!" Bunna said.

"No," Shannon replied. "Quetzalcoatl. Aztec."

"Same thing. It's what we told him."

"It is?" I said, as he opened the cage for us.

"Yes," Bunna replied. "Feathered assassin. Kurdaitcha!"

Mind Vampires

GREG EGAN

There are moments when my mind misses a beat. I find myself, in mid-step or mid-breath, feeling as if delivered abruptly into my body after a long absence (spent where, I could not say), or a long, dreamless sleep. I lose not my memory, merely my thread. My attention has inexplicably wandered, but a little calm introspection restores my context and brings me peace. Almost peace.

I suppose I am a detective, a private investigator, for why else would I be prowling the corridors of a posh girls' boarding school, softly past the doors of the dark-breathing dormitories?

I suppose the headmistress rang me, hysterical. I'm sure that's right. She was sixty-two and had begun to menstruate again. What a surprise for her, what a strange shock. No wonder she went straight to the telephone and dialled my number.

She was calm in her office when I arrived in person, if a little embarrassed. Women have problems, she said. These things *do* happen, she explained. Rarely, but one cannot attach any significance. I find it very irritating to be told one minute to hurry and the next to get lost; I could have shrugged and walked out, abandoned her right then, but I have my code of ethics. My reputation. My pride. For her sake, for the sake of those in her charge, I frightened her into hiring me.

I described the next few stages to her. Prepubescent girls, even infants and newborn babes, would also start to menstruate. Sweat, tears, saliva, urine, mother's milk and semen would all turn to blood. Dead rats and birds would be found every-where. Water pipes would issue blood, and every container of any kind of fluid, from disinfectant to dye, from vinegar to varnish, from wine to window-cleaner, would be brimming with blood.

There is definitely no semen on school premises, she said. I think she was trying to make a joke. I showed her a colour photograph from a previous case, the kind the police don't like me carrying about. She turned pale and then wiped the per-spiration from her face with (oh yes) a white lace handker-chief, which she carefully examined for any trace of red. Then she signed.

New England. Connecticut? How?

Young soldiers come home with bad dreams.

Atrocities in a muddy trench, a bloody trench.

Young soldiers who would rather be dead than return to their friends and families bearing this European curse. A horrible embrace, a horrible feast. Much better to feed the rats and the worms.

The smell of the trenches drawing them for hundreds of miles. They devour the gangrenous parts. Later the healed will attribute this to the rats. Struggles in the mud, the blood rains down. Screams are natural enough. Nobody will ever guess, they'll be lost amongst the shell-shocked.

"I'm responsible for the girls. You must be discreet."

"Discreet? There'll be no discretion when the snow turns red."

I may be wrong. Sometimes there is no carnival of horrors; fear of detection dampens their natural flamboyance, their love of dark theatre. But it's a new moon tonight, the nadir of their strength, and already they have announced their presence! Whatever shows so little caution is afraid of no one.

"You mustn't cause a panic." Her chin trembled, she pleaded with her eyes. "You know what I'm concerned about."

I knew, all right.

"If there were nothing to fear but fear itself," I said, "wouldn't life be sweet?"

So I prowl the corridors, watching for signs, preparing for the fight. My reputation is the highest, I have never lost. My clients shake my hand, hug and kiss me, shower me with gifts and favours. No wonder.

A thin young girl, a somnambulist, wanders past me and my heart aches at her vulnerability. In my mind her swan neck becomes a giraffe neck, a single throbbing artery tight with blood ready to gush and sate the hugest appetite. How sickening, when the skin of her neck is so pale and delicate and, I am certain, cool as the night.

In the prisons, where they mutilate their limbs with razor blades, there is feeding every month. The gatherings in the alleys of abortionists are indescribable. The torture cells: well who do you think run them? I stay away from all of these. I am no fool. Large old families in large old houses, the better schools, the quieter, cleaner asylums call for me. My reputation is the highest.

The gardener's apprentice, a quiet young lad named Jack Rice, disappeared two days ago. The headmistress thinks it's just a coincidence (such a helpful boy). Nobody knows his family's address, but his father is said to be a veteran and to shun the light of day.

A legless spider moves its mandibles in distress.

A girl cries out: "Whoa, nightmare!"

Strange, dark flowers appear in the fields. They open at midnight to send a sickly sweet narcotic scent to corrupt the most innocent of dreams.

Fear comes to me, but only as an idea. I think about terror, but I do not feel it. Fear has saved my life many times, so I do love and respect it, when it knows its place.

I enter the dormitory itself, I walk quiet as a nightgown between the tossing beds. Over one bed, two heavy men in dark coats shoulder a fluttering kinematograph machine with the lens removed, while a third man holds open a girl's right eye. The pictures flash into the empty spaces of her brain. Fear will not save *her* life; it has seduced her, possessed her, paralysed her, as it has done to thousands, sweeping the countryside like fire or flood wherever that one dread word is whispered. Even far from the sites of true danger, men and women hear that word, form that image, and choke on the terror that rushes up from their bowels. It is a plague in itself, a separate evil with a life of its own now. I nod at the men, they nod (so very slightly) back at me, then I walk on.

I find Jack Rice easily enough, his hobnailed boots protruding from the end of the bed. I call to the men in dark coats to come and hold him still, for that is what they do best of all. His girl's disguise fades as he struggles. I wonder what revealed the boots. Perhaps his guard was down as he slept. Perhaps he dreamt he was discovered, and so blurred the borders of the dream by bringing on its fulfilment. I smile at this idea as I drive in the stake.

The tales they later tell me are familiar: the girl he killed, the girl whose form he took, had mocked him cruelly. We find her body, the lips and tender parts consumed, in one of the many damp basements, crawling about gnashing its fangs, but very weak. A matchstick would do for a stake. I hope her parents will not be awkward.

The headmistress tries to thank and dismiss me with her chequebook, but the ink of her fountain pen has changed colour, and she cannot sign the cheque with her trembling bony hand. Oh dear. Jack's father will be angry. Jack's mother will be grieved. I hope he was an only child, but the odds are against it.

The dark-coated men, unperturbed, move from bed to bed with their sawn-off projector. Their enemies are different, but sometimes they will pause to come to my aid. They're fighting mind vampires.

Breakfast is dismal the next morning, for all the milk had to be thrown out. The heated swimming baths are closed, but a cloying odour escapes from the steam-dampened, padlocked wooden doors.

I ask around the village (of course a village) for word of Jack and his family. Oh, the young vampire lad, they say merrily. He never gave an addresss, of course. Hardly the thing to do. I mean, would you?

I hunt the old dark-hidden, overgrown houses as the fortnight slips away from me. Jack's walking in sunlight and feeding so far from the full moon are disturbing. What will his father be like when he decides to strike? Every cellar I breach nearly stops my heart, but they are all empty and peaceful; cool air and silence protest their pure innocence to me as I scour cobwebbed corners with lamplight. I smile at the unfairness: I *cannot* rejoice that a place is clean, that I smell no evil, that I will face no risks for a few kind minutes, for every safe house is a failure, every moment without threat only postpones the danger I must face in the end. I'd rather not be who I am, but my reputation is the highest.

Bloody pigeons, headless in the snow, unsettle the girls. There are more nightmares, more nightwalks; a warm, damp, unnatural wind blows an hour before dawn. I fortify the windows with steel bars, garlic and crucifixes, but there is always a way in left unprotected, it is inevitable.

Perhaps it is my weariness, but the shadows I cast seem to follow me with increasing reluctance. Indeed they conform to my movements, but I swear that they do so an eyeblink too late. My reflections do not move at all: they stare, transfixed, over my shoulder, fascinated by that empty space, hypnotised by its potential occupants.

The headmistress complains, she expected so much more of me. The strain is becoming too much, she sobs. Her weeping blinds her, and when she smells why she falls screaming to the floor.

I continue to search, but I fail for the first time ever to locate their hiding place. They will only face me when they choose to do so, at the very height of their powers.

I leave my room at the inn and sleep in the attic of the

dormitory building. From my bed I hear the girls swapping secrets, and through my window drifts the stench of the dark buds which break through the snow.

I dream that I lie naked in the middle of the moonlit fields. My eyes are closed. I feel sharp snow against my back. Footsteps, girls whispering. I recall walking past two students, overhearing: "Oh, much handsomer than Jack!" When they saw me they blushed and turned away. A warm, wet tongue slides across my eyelids, my lips, down my chin and throat, awakening each tiny point of stubble it brushes. Between my ribs, across my stomach, it leaves a snail track of sticky, moistened hair. Soft lips enclose my penis, the warm tongue wraps and caresses it. A young voice: "You didn't! You *can't* have! With him? Oh, tell us!"

As I shudder and struggle to prolong the pleasure, a phrase enters my mind and jolts me into awareness: "The erect penis is engorged with blood." Engorged. Engorged with blood.

Suddenly I have vision: I see the scene from above. My hands are behind my back, my legs splayed, my back arched. I am utterly naked and defenceless. A glistening streak of red bisects me, and a giant she-vampire clad in black iron armour sucks at me noisily, an animal sound.

My view expands, and despair takes hold of me: ringing us is a circle of her kin, some fifty feet across. Each one bears a poison-tipped sword and a grievance against me for their friends that I've dispatched.

The tongue works frantically, and I understand that she has been forbidden to strike with her fangs until the instant of ejaculation. My concentration falters, and I feel the lips draw back.

Awake, shaving, I cut myself in three places. In the shaving water I find a swollen leech; I slice it open and the water turns black and foul.

A serving girl discovers the headmistress; she has hanged herself in her Sunday best (now who will sign my cheques?) after writing the word with lipstick and rouge upon every surface of her room. The servants leave to cross the ocean, and the teachers run away to marry their sweethearts.

I must defend the girls alone.

As if in an instant, the moon is full.

The lights of the village go out.

The snow turns to putrid flesh, blood creeps across all floors and up all walls. The girls huddle stickily in clots of terror, but I scream at them to master fear, to use fear, to never let it cripple them and conquer them. And they are strong, they do not succumb.

Jack's family come up from the basements, where they have been, no doubt, for months. Four tall brothers, three hissing sisters first. The iron cross, the mallet, the stake: all grow slippery in palms sweating blood. Yet I will defeat them, I will not lose my nerve.

I gather the uneasy students into a single room and ring them with a fence of crucifixes. The Rices are cunning, they taunt me from a distance, speak of the siege they will subject us to which will turn us into cannibals. The school girls plait each other's hair for comfort; the brothers, more handsome than Jack, flirt brazenly with them, drooling out romantic nonsense. One girl's yellow eyes unfocus, and her hand flies to her neck. I am already behind her as her skin blooms with grey. She takes two steps towards her lover, then vomits insect-riddled blood as my stake crashes through her heart from behind. Her friends desert her, and she told them such pretty tales.

I venture out with my own protection and corner them one by one. They are far too proud and foolish to keep together for safety. Two of the brothers grow bored and visit the village tavern. One sister wanders alone through the empty dormitories in search of a new pair of shoes. It doesn't take me long. I feel some hope.

Jack's parents come next, dressed plainly, their fangs concealed. They talk of the terrible loss they have suffered.

ander me in front of the girls, telling them that I killed
ack and the girl he loved (how can I refute that?) and
will kill them all. They urge the girls to expel me from
the room for their safety's sake: they need not leave the room
themselves, but they must not let me stay or they will all die
in agony to satisfy my craving for blood.

In their fervent, pleading seduction they come a few feet
closer than wisdom would have decreed, and I spring my trap:
a wire net in which two dozen crucifixes are embedded. They
crawl and writhe as I smash in the stakes. Their hearts are like
granite but I am strong and purposeful and I do not flinch.

I catch my breath. Hunched over the pair of corpses
crumbling into dust, I feel a slight vibration through the floor.
Before my reason has grasped its meaning I find myself,
incredibly, weeping with terror.

I turn to a roar louder than thunder. Jack's father, it
seems, smuggled home a friend, ancient and powerful. For a
moment I cannot move: enough, surely I've faced enough!
Splintering the old stone floor, red chips flying. So fast, and
I have hesitated, there is nothing now that I can do. All the
girls are gone, down into the very oldest basement, when I
skid into what remains of the room. I grab a cross and try to
leap into the hole in the floor, but blood spurts from it with
such pressure that I cannot even approach it. I roar useless
curses at the thing which has defeated me, as the red tide
sweeps me from the building and dumps me, a helpless insect,
upon the rotting snow.

The dark-coated men, unperturbed as always, press their
projector to my tired right eye, and their soothing pictures flash
into the empty spaces of my mind.

My reputation is the highest, but they're fighting mind
vampires.

It's Not What You Say—

F R E D A   M c L E N N A N

"And so," Far Ch Char Nce said, "as the Liskan Nation no longer has any interest in joining the Association, we have decided to open our space corridors to the Krian Confederacy. Do you understand?"

Yes, I understood. I thought of Krian warships coming down the Liskan corridors into the heart of this sector where the non-military traffic is thickest.

I thought of how much less damage they would have been able to do ten years ago, before the Association of Democratic Planets had sent me to encourage general development in Dead Sector, with a vague general offer of Sector Protection to gain me acceptance. I thought of how the Liskans alone in the Sector had requested membership of the ADP, and how the Association Government had overruled my objections.

"I feel that you understand," said Far Ch Char Nce, his little violet-fringed Liskan face flickering with noble and restrained emotion. He looked like a well-fed and safely seated Public Representative at a performance of *Oedipus Rex*.

"God damn it to hell," said Esborne, the solar flare regeneree they had given me as information agent and assistant political officer. "What are you going to do, sugar?" he asked me intelligently. (They should have kept him at Headquarters for the prayer meetings.)

"Nothing," I said. "Not a thing. The Liskan application

for Membership has not yet been approved, and both sides retain the right to withdraw at any stage of negotiations.

"We'll close this office, inform all the Powers and Planets in Dead Sector that a state of extreme danger now exists, and withdraw."

And that was precisely what I intended to do. But as I rose to compact my desk and its attachments I saw Far Ch Char Nce watching me with an air of disappointment. And I thought of how he and his nation were prepared to allow the slaughter of millions of Intelligences and the enslavement of billions more, for the sake of entertainment.

And I killed him. I picked up a chair, swung it up over my head and smashed it across the back of his pale, thin, violet neck where the ichor was pulsing under the skin in his excitement. He fell forward, dead.

"What did you do that for?" screamed Esborne, whom I'd always thought too big to scream. "And after you decided . . . women!"

He stopped talking and grabbed the communicator which, of course, we had never used before. Far Ch Char Nce had always telepathed out any messages we wanted to send among the Liskans, as well as all the messages we didn't want to send, but had to. We couldn't stop thinking just because we had to represent the ADP among the most efficient telepaths in the galaxy.

"Revivification unit, revivification unit!" he howled into the communicator. But a Liskan mobile medical unit burst through the door before he'd finished saying it. Every one of them was a dirty ink blue, every one of them wore a completely uniform expression of astonishment, and every one of them kept well away from me, even when it meant that one of them had to step on the corpse.

I picked up the chair and sat on it. And stayed there thinking nothing in particular while they applied revivification and cranial regeneration processes to Far Ch Char Nce in my presence, before my eyes, and mostly on the conference room coffee table.

It was unbelievably horrible. Someone would have to order a new table.

"They don't understand you," said Esborne, hovering in an agitated way. "And I can't say that I do, either."

In all the history of the Association of Democratic Planets, no representative had ever committed a murder. At least, not in person. There wasn't even a precedent for punishment.

The corpse of Far Ch Char Nce was imitating life. In fact his skin was a much healthier colour than that of any member of the medical team, who still looked stunned. But he showed no sign of intelligence.

"Quite dead," muttered Esborne. I knew that. And almost immediately the indicator began to show the flowing wave pattern of mental activity from the patient.

"I don't believe it," I said flatly.

"That puts you on the side of the entire Liskan Nation," said Esborne. "Why the hell did you kill him?"

"Apparently he wasn't dead," I said. That was better. At least, there were precedents. In the history of the Association of Democratic Planets some dozens of representatives have made assaults of various kinds on representatives of Negotiating Powers.

"Oh, he was dead," said Esborne. "That's why they came at a run. When a Liskan Intelligence of two Ch degrees of nobility suddenly cuts off in the middle of an interplanetary negotiation, the entire nation knows that he's dead."

He was even beginning to telepath again, if you could judge by the way the medical team were responding to him.

"That's ridiculous," I said. "They might be able to regenerate him after injury, but they couldn't possibly bring back life and intelligence after death."

"Yes they can," said Esborne, more cocky, bluff and hearty by the minute as it seemed that we might survive. "The Liskans are the best medical practitioners in the galaxy. Solar flare victims have good reason to know it."

The Liskans continued to look sick, which was not what you'd expect. A compliment as comprehensive as that should have turned every Liskan within telepath range rich mauve with pleasure. Instead they stayed ink blue, and if anything looked even worse as they telepathed with Far Ch Char Nce.

Liskans are seldom distressed by each other's sufferings. They actively enjoy them as an inexpensive source of acute sensation. But the ones on view all looked as sick as if they were Far Ch Char Nce's mother or current marriage partner, and as they were all about ten degrees short of his nobility they could have had no close relationship with him at all.

At last his reactions stabilised and they rolled him into a life-protection unit and hastily moulded the walls into position about him. We sagged with relief, and waited for them to wheel him out of the room.

Instead they picked him up, life protection unit and all, and laid him face down on the floor, unmoving, at my feet.

"Don't!" I said in horror. "Pick him up!"

The leader of the medical team lay on the floor beside him and inched forward on his stomach. Candidates for Democracy, my foot! He touched my foot, as I pulled it back under the chair as far away from them both as I could.

"Behold," he said, "I enunciate for the noble Far Ch Char Nce, who conveys that the Liskan Nation withdraws its manifesto and begs to renew its application for Membership of the Association of Democratic Planets."

"Eh?" I said.

Esborne stepped up, frantic. "But what the hell for?" he bellowed.

"Be pleased not to yell," said the medical team leader. "The Liskan Nation have no wish to be disassociated from planets that send forth a representative such as Her Inexplicable Terror. That is all. And now be pleased to allow us to withdraw with the patient."

They withdrew on their stomachs and backwards, right out the door.

"What happened to the last Other Worlder who attacked an official Liskan negotiator?" I asked Esborne.

"Burnt him to a crisp," he said chattily. More chattily than he intended. He was thinking about something else.

But if they hadn't changed their minds about one of the most damaging decisions that had ever occurred to them because I attacked their chief negotiator, then why?

"Liskans are certainly not Democratic," I pointed out, "but they don't usually crawl around on their stomachs, not even before Members of the Grand Council."

Esborne sniffed. "I think they were avoiding looking at you," he said. "Your Inexplicable Terror. When did a Liskan ever call anything or anyone Inexplicable?"

For the Liskans are the only known universal telepaths, students of ways of thought and infallible detectors of lies of any kind by Intelligence of any kind. For more than 100 years no negotiation of any importance has been concluded except in the presence of a Liskan observer.

"Somehow," said Esborne. "Somehow you've beaten the telepathy factor."

And, of course, the Boredom Factor, which meant less to the worlds at large, but a great deal for my immediate career as Political Officer Dead Sector, and Resident Negotiator among the Liskans.

The Liskans are also the emotional gluttons of the Universe and they tend to find most human beings on the dull side. But of all human beings I, not merely Democratic but also Egalitarian and Tolerant, was possibly the one most likely to drive them mad with boredom.

The very first Liskan I'd ever met sidled up to me when I was having my first pair of boots measured on Splinto, to give me the innermost thoughts on myself of the clapped-out old bureaucratic desk jockey whom I was replacing.

"He thinks that you are a spoilt Centrist brat and bitch," he said with enjoyment. I thought it over. "He's probably right," I admitted.

He sucked a few of his fringes, which I've since discovered is a Liskan habit when baffled. "His Entire Cluster," he said, meaning the political officer's 2,000 statisticians, secretaries and assistants — not one of whom spoke one local language — "say that you are nothing more or less than a True Born Isolate to come here without a Cluster of your own. Not even a skeleton working party. Not a single one of them will stay with you, you know."

"What a pity," I said, but of course he went off to tell them what I had actually thought — that nothing about any of them would suit me half as well as their absence.

It is recorded that I protested my own qualifications to conduct any negotiations with the Liskans before any of this business started. But it did no good.

When I sent that message to the ADP there wasn't an unplanned, unexplained contingency in all the forty-eight planets where I have Special Visiting Rights, including Splinto, where I still have my boots made.

The sector is called Dead Sector because it is totally without military action between planets, and therefore no source of fun for Spaceforce. (Life is more fun in Dead Sector, and you're more likely to get yourself killed in Live Sector.) Trade and tourism traffic is so thick that no ship, private, civil or military, can proceed at even the first factor of Star Travel Speed. Interplanetary speed lanes have been suggested, but rejected. Who wants people shooting off to spend their money, energy and life credits elsewhere when you can keep them wallowing around among your own civilisations in a state of bemused interest?

When the Liskans had their Grand Idea I was just a happy, independent political/cultural officer (990001), booting round Dead Sector with a nice little blue Pegasus badge in foldform in my pocket along with my library and wardrobe.

There were reasons to be happy.

I had never shown the badge to a single Intelligence, so I could work in perfect discretion. My work was allowed to speak for itself. For the first time in my life I was really free, in places

34

crowded and in places solitary. The Service lived up to its motto, "It's lonely out here."

And my personal problems of psychology and status were strictly my own affair, though Mother mentioned them a few times when she was running for office, to show that while she was and is a pre-eminent Candidate she also suffers the disadvantages and disappointments that may afflict any Being. Very Democratic of her. But then even Mother does not campaign in Dead Sector.

Then the Liskans fell in love with Democracy. (Who doesn't sometime or other?)

And they alone, of all Dead Sector, decided to join the ADP, heart and soul, nobility and commonality, Hereditary Arbitrator and all, to the total joy of all citizens of the Free Planets except me.

They tell me some of my fellow citizens even wept with joy and pride to hear about it, including a number of people who had never met a Liskan.

"But what are you worried about?" demanded the Meiorian ADP Bureau Chief who tracked me down to tell me the good news. (Appropriate if you've ever met a Meiorian. They're three metres tall or more, winged, beautiful, and radiate good will, enthusiasm, and a lot of heat. To complete the angelic image they don't even copulate. Baby Meiorians are born by a kind of spontaneous combustion if two adult Meiorians think particularly intensely about each other, in flight, and at a measured distance 101.345 kilometres. I lost a friend that way, once, and have often wondered since whether he's really dead, or absorbed into the radiant substance of the Meiorian born right where he was practising in his Cluster's wind-skiff on Nelia. Other species try to ensure that where there are resident Meiorians of different sexes on their planets they never fly at the same time.)

"Everything!" I said, and set out the list. "They're telepaths. They're excitable. They're gluttons for sensation. And there's almost no Being in the Universe that willingly tolerates them."

He beamed in his kindly headquarters way. Actually radiating, of course. Most uncomfortable.

"They are an historic Nation — the honest brokers of the Galaxy," he enthused. "As for the rest, this is the first application for Membership that the ADP has received for twenty years. Every representative of the Free Planets will bend over backwards to help them. And we are all very proud of you!"

He unfurled his wings and glowed in farewell, and flew up to a Nelian Spacetrans which had quarters specially insulated to carry a Meiorian of an enthusiastic frame of mind.

The Nelian crew televised themselves onto my personal communicator to say farewell properly, and we surveyed each other with gloom. (Everyone who hangs around with Meiorians feels exhausted most of the time.)

"Thanks for calling, and farewell," I said. "Remember, you can't work up to first factor travel until you're out of Dead Sector."

"We saw that for ourselves getting in," said the Captain. "Zich."

Zich means approximately what it sounds like, and is an expression of emotion used a lot where I come from. I used it more than usual for the next few days when I found that no transporters of sound mind wanted to go near the Liskans since they had fallen in love with Democracy.

In the end I found a droog transporter with a highly unstable crew and worse than the average problems in recruiting assistance. I agreed to repair their centrifuge and run it for them in return for a journey to the Liskans. (Mother insisted that all her family should master basic technology, and I've worked centrifuges for half the beaten-up old tubs in my sector to overcome transport problems. It saves a lot of life credits, too.)

The work is dull and unpleasant, and Beings naturally tend to leave you alone, which gives a political/cultural officer excellent opportunities for planning programs, filing reports and checking data with Nellie the Headquarters Computer.

Luckily Nellie Da Puter was navigating me on that trip,

so I was informed when the droog carters changed their minds half way. They were all set to get in a couple of long voyages while they had a full working crew, but after I told them I had a tenuous relationship with a Spaceforce Captain who would be waiting to meet me they decided to keep their word.

"Well, he's there, I suppose," said the Top Droog as we put down at Liskan Port, and I whacked in a few attachments that should keep the centrifuge working for a few more years. (After all they had carried me to the Liskans when no one else would, scatty as they were.) "Which one's his?"

"Which what's whose?"

"Which ship gets around by order of the Spaceforce Captain who's waiting to meet you?"

The droog transporter was settling through a positive galaxy of Spaceforce, ship after magnificent ship. And it suddenly occurred to me that the advanced-design craft settling majestically with us was probably the barge of the Spaceforce Admiral who had been sent to formally accept the Application for Membership. There was confusion all round when I emerged at a run from the Transporter to welcome His Excellency and explain Protocol, except among the Liskan officials who naturally waited for me to get there and perform the introductions.

Unfortunately, the Admiral and most of his staff were human, the first Intelligences I had met for over a year to react to me as a female conspecific. We were all taken aback. Their surprise seemed to be fairly distributed over me, my clothes and my chosen mode of transport — and probably the fact that they felt they had seen me before, somewhere. Naturally they looked past me for the rest of my Cluster, and naturally there wasn't one, so the exercise confused them and annoyed me.

"The way I see it," said the Admiral, resplendent in his golden shoulder tassels, "this is no place for a woman."

That was a choice and helpful thought to be transmitting to the attentive Liskan Nation. I stripped off the overalls (greasy, I admit), decided that the Liskans wouldn't know whether I had a clean face or not, or wouldn't care, so it didn't matter, and felt through the pockets of my sober shirt and trousers outfit for a small blue bead.

It was the first time I'd ever used it, but I was too intent on dealing with the Admiral to enjoy it. That's the way things usually happen.

I whipped my hand through the unfold twist and Pegasus opened out, blue and glowing, leaping up and outward. I set him with his wings brushing my collar bone.

"Well," said the Admiral in annoyance, and shut up.

There's a Spaceforce saying, "I'm not arguing with your Badge, but that doesn't change my opinion of you." And that's what the Admiral thought he thought, but he didn't. He lives in a hierarchy, and the Badge is the only thing that could change his opinion of me.

At that moment, with exquisite telepathic tact the Liskan's great crystal Dome of Reception moved up and around us, the Grand Council of the Liskans and the rest of the 600 Ch Nobility already standing within it in traditional postures of attention, ready to telepath everything that was said and thought to all their Sympathisers, covering the entire Nation.

It was an impressively symbolic moment, rather beautiful. The Admiral drew himself up and advanced to welcome the Nation Applying for Membership. I was very proud of him myself.

However the Liskan Nation, at home and en masse, is an extraordinary experience, very different from the discreet company of the one or two Professional Witnesses whom we have all met sitting in modest prominence at various transactional conferences.

The Headquarters Cluster who briefed the Admiral's party must have failed to pass on my warnings. Or perhaps he simply wasn't capable of anticipating a silent, ecstatic nation of rich violet, fringe-eared bipeds quivering with mass emotion at every word he said. He very nearly did bend over backwards.

And there was no comfort in the one thing that everyone knows about the Liskans. If he fell back on bluff military subterfuge and uttered a single lie the entire Nation would turn from rich violet to a sort of dirty blue-white right before his eyes.

This unfailing visible reaction to a lie, or to whatever happens in an Intelligence that tells a lie, is the reason why no one of any sense will conclude an agreement that has not been negotiated in the presence of a Liskan. Of course it's also the reason for a lot of stupid official negotiators, who faithfully believe everything their Governments tell them.

"I have come to accept your Application on behalf of the Free Planets," said the Admiral gamely.

The Liskan Ch Nobility swayed with emotion and the Admiral's staff cringed. Che Nce Ch, the Hereditary Arbitrator and a particularly sensitive telepath, regarded the strangulated Admiral with close attention. Of course the Ch nobility seldom have any experience of Professional Witness work or other comparatively menial purposes that might take them abroad, so the Admiral and his Cluster were a new experience to them.

His attitudes were too rich and strange for them to interpret, although they were strongly aware of them. A telepath in that position is rather like an ordinary Intelligence listening to a conversation in a foreign language.

The Admiral turned pale and looked worriedly at the prepared statement in his hand. It hadn't seemed too intense or emotional before, but when he rehearsed it there hadn't been anyone dancing to it.

For some incredible reason, right then when I was still trying to put off taking any action and anxiously aware that the Liskans knew me well enough to interpret anything that came into my head, I had a vision of the range of almost human, almost female Beings to whom the Admiral was alleged to have said, "Let me call you sweetheart."

The eyes of the Liskan Nation switched to me with eager, emotional curiosity. A couple of sophisticates tried experimental giggles.

The Admiral lost his head. "My friends!" he bellowed, as he had bellowed in 10,000 situations where sweethearting was not appropriate even by a stretch of his imagination.

"My friends," croaked the Admiral again, snorting with revulsion — and nearly swallowed his tongue as Che Nce Ch, First Among Many, began to develop the famous lie-detector pallor.

Friends, indeed! When there was not a social gathering from There to Earth that would not melt away at the first sight of a quivering violet-fringed face.

"Most favoured among Liskans," I said to Che Nce Ch directly, not in a spirit of flattery but as a bald statement of fact. He is, for instance, ceremonially massaged with ichor of a quality that every other Liskan saves to drink on particularly important occasions, such as a quarrel resulting in murder.

Che Nce Ch's colour came flooding back, and the other Liskans that I could see had barely slowed down in mid-wriggle.

"And your Nation at large, most powerful of the telepaths," I continued, stepping smoothly to a respectful distance to one side of the Admiral. "You who have been called the Honest Brokers of the Universe." (True statement. They'd been called that, among many other things.)

"The Admiral expresses to you the hope of all our peoples that we may become true friends, for all time." (True again. That's our habitual attitude at the beginning of any association.)

Che Nce Ch made a sweeping gesture of Polite Negation with his forty fringed hands.

"Pray believe that beyond mere satisfaction we feel a most sublime ecstasy in contemplating democracy," he said. And not a Liskan changed colour. That'll tell you.

As a matter of fact the Admiral and his staff and I believed it too. The Staff looked as if they were ready to believe everything about anything, clustered in a tight little agonised bunch like sobriety advocates at a Nelian breathing orgy.

Compared to them, the Admiral looked good, and he was eating spacesickness pills. The only anti-nausea measure he had to hand, I suppose.

However we were now in the correct Liskan High Etiquette situation of exchanging truths on an ecstatic basis. To bring it to a satisfactory conclusion the guest-victors (us) should make a joke at our own expense.

"And yet this idea was first a product of Human Intelligence," I murmured, making a sweeping gesture of Polite Negation with my ten-fingered hands. The Liskans howled with joy, and the Admiral, who obviously can't get used to the way the rest of the galaxy regards humanity, swallowed a fresh handful of his pills. (What was a Spaceforce Admiral doing with that stuff, anyway?)

"Perceiving merit in an idea may be an even greater achievement than originating it," said Che Nce Ch in grave reply, celebrating as host co-victor.

That's what the First Galactic Forger is supposed to have said to the First Galactic Treasurer, so the Admiral recognised that it was time to grin.

"Welcome," he said. "Welcome to our company, our representatives, and — let us hope — to the company of all the Free Planets." And even I believed it.

It was worth thousands of hours of negotiation in itself. But eventually we had to get back to reality.

Barely one sleep period later the Admiral had to be brought to admit that there was something he couldn't do, and that no one in his large and multi-talented fleet could do either. They still can't. They can't tell the truth in a constructive way, because frankly they're not used to it.

There are all sorts of little fibs and false attitudes as well as Grand Interplanetary Lies used regularly to keep everyone busy, interested, and moderately peaceful in all major organisations, but unless there's a Liskan around most Intelligences are not really aware of them, even while they're using them.

The idea that there's something he can't do comes hard

to a high-ranking old tough who's wheeled his squadrons through the galaxy without let or hindrance, who's lied with panache to indulgent kings and seduced grateful queens, and has been rewarded with the highest military honours the ADP can bestow.

But the fact had to be faced when he said at a private meeting with only Far Ch Char Nce in attendance (that is, the whole Liskan Nation) that if it had only been a matter of wiping out the Liskans he could have handled it without problem.

The vast public of the ADP would not approve his solution, or his idea of humour.

"Stupid goddamn civilians," said the Admiral. "What can they do about the Liskans?"

One of his Staff Captains who was slightly less subservient than the rest said, "Well, sir, they can grant them preliminary rights of citizenship. And after two years of negotiation according to the forms, they can conclude an agreement giving the Liskans full rights of membership in the ADP."

"Or not," said the Admiral.

"Behold," said Far Ch Char Nce, stepping forward with a multiple flourish. "A vast number of our Nation wish to enlist in Spaceforce to serve the glorious Association both near and far."

The Admiral was already discoloured by emotion, but at that he looked as if we would have a dead member of the High Command on our hands. He probably suspected that the Liskans wanted to infiltrate Spaceforce to counter his twitchy yearning to wipe them out — or wipe something out.

But the Liskans knew enough about the Free Planets to understand that the Admiral didn't really expect to get away with murder.

The awful fact was that they had fallen in love again, this time with the rigidly structured, highly tense military situation that he represents, and which is really the complete opposite of Egalitarian Democracy. They saw his staff, from Space Captains down, snap to it when the Admiral gave an order, or merely expressed a wish. And the Liskan soul craved to join in.

"Like hell!" said the Admiral baldly. "They're not quivering like jelly all over my ships."

Of course they would. Historically we have always had this problem of military acceptance when a new species joins the ADP. Sometimes there has been a sound technical reason for the military reluctance — Spaceforce was still using a lot of electricity when the Meiorians joined, and their cadets short-circuited and fused things from Here to There until technology caught up again.

However. Rejection is not an acceptable solution for egalitarian democracies — not over an issue like "your citizens make our Admiral sick". To be fair the only Liskan visible, Far Ch Char Nce, merely looked excited by the Admiral's reaction, but I could see no further use for him — or his Spaceforce.

"Thank you for your invaluable assistance, Admiral," I said. "You and your staff will be required to leave this Sector now, today."

It was as polite as I could make it, and I even bowed a bit, though a little late, but after all he could accept it as a news report.

It was obviously the best news he and his staff had received since they landed. I was accepting responsibility and they were free of it. Besides, cold flat direction was probably what they expected from the representative of the Political Planning Council.

They positively relaxed. They had been living at the boil for hours. Far Ch Char Nce looked puzzled. As far as the Liskans are concerned, no emotion is ever too intense.

"I won't pretend that I'm sorry," said the Admiral frostily. "I take it that you're staying for a while?"

Well really, there was only one answer to that question.

"And don't exceed first factor speed in our Spaceways, if you please."

The Admiral glowered. He had every reason (from his point of view) to expect me to be respectful if not positively servile. And while it would have been a nuisance if I had tried to delay the Spaceforce departure, it would have been much more flattering than speeding them on their way with a traffic warning.

"You're not, for instance, partially Liskan, are you?" enquired the least subservient of his Staff Captains.

Far Ch Char Nce answered for me, with that lively pleasure in giving information which is one of the reasons why almost no Being can tolerate his Nation. "Liskans don't interbreed with Human Beings. Notice, if you please, how few Intelligent species do," he said. In view of the Admiral's domestic background it was not a very tactful statement.

"The Captain, like the rest of us, is just wondering why you're not — uh, excited, about being left behind by yourself." The Admiral closed ranks with his officer, with military precision.

Being "left behind by myself" in my own sector!

"Because I'm a True Born Isolate," I said curtly.

The Military reaction was so acute that a number of Liskans fluttered into the room with tendrils quivering for maximum exposure.

"True Born Isolates are not eligible to join Spaceforce," said the Admiral in crisp disgust.

"True Born Isolates don't want to join Spaceforce," I said sunnily, turning military disgust into military wrath.

The Liskans loved me — the only time they ever have. Something about single-handedly upsetting the dearest pride of a Spaceforce Admiral and his 400 staff went straight to their seat of approval, wherever that is.

It's just a normal situation for me, and once the Liskans picked that up they jumped for joy.

The only member of the ADP group who laughed with them was a big Solar Flare Regeneree whom I'd vaguely associated with the Admiral's Chief of Staff. He stepped forward.

"I have the honour to inform you, Madam, that His Excellency Far Ch Char Nce and I have been selected to assist you," he told me. "My name's Esborne."

There's no such name, of course. Most Solar Flare Regenerees decide to drop their old names along with the rest of their old selves when they recover. Then it hit me.

"Madam?" I demanded in a modified howl that alerted the interest of the assemblage.

"Oh yes. You've been appointed 99900123 Dead Sector," said he, regenerate teeth gleaming brightly in his large rubbery mouth.

"Congratulations. If you can handle the authority. And the status," said the Admiral. That's the way it would look to a man who's spent his life working his way up a hierarchy.

"We don't have authority or status," I snarled. "Well, it depends on what we're doing." Because we all have days when we represent the full power and interests of the Free Planets, though most of the time there's no reason for us — or anyone else — to think about it.

The Admiral looked as though I were obviously not able to handle the authority or the status.

"The only privileges we have are the right to commit suicide, and the right to accept bribes" — they sucked in their pure military breath in horror — "because we never have any opportunity to spend them anyway."

The Liskans cooed and quivered. "How delightful," said Far Ch Char Nce. "How much you have annoyed them all! It is the most splendid thing you have achieved. Can you not keep them to play with while we conduct this negotiation?"

"No!" said the rest of us, as one.

"I fear it will be dull after all this," said Far Ch Char Nce.

And that was the truth, the whole truth, and nothing but the truth.

I realised it before the Admiral's squadron was out of communication range, and pursued them with pleas for some interplanetary entertainment sections, debating societies, a Meiorian wedding party. Anything.

"We don't do things like that out here," said the Admiral coldly, closely surrounded by his working Cluster. It looked to me as if they were playing chess, but it may have been an exercise in strategy. "You just use whatever means are available to you. After all, you and your assistants have the authority and the status."

The authority and the status. As if they mattered.

Negotiations with the Liskans on their admission to the Association of Democratic Planets went badly from the start. The trouble was, that there really wasn't much to negotiate. It's just a long, drawn-out process of making sure that the Nation Applying for Admission knows what it's getting into. The rules have been so thoroughly tested by multitudes of Intelligences that it's bound to be dull.

In other circumstances we would have brought in some talented liars to create problems of a temporary but interesting nature. But you can't do that with Liskans. I applied to remove the negotiations to this year's Capital of the Association, but the Law forbids it — negotiations must be conducted entirely among the Nation Applying for Admission, even when it's the Liskans, and we're boring them.

In all honesty I must confess that my behaviour and that of the Committee supporting me was not entirely ... suitable.

I require more space and more isolation than most human beings, and I found both Esborne and Far Ch Char Nce inclined to cluster round me, causing me acute psychological irritation.

Esborne — ESBORNE! — of all Beings, was conducting Tenuous Relationships with a number of Liskans. I discovered this when he was nearly killed in an emotional exchange with a member of the Liskan nobility, and I persuaded them to stop, although it was the only excitement to date connected with the negotiations.

Well really, I thought he'd know better. He must be a Member of the Service, after all. Anyone spending any time among the Liskans must remember that they require an extraordinary degree of emotional stimulation as part of their breeding pattern. It is only to be expected when you realise the degree of emotional intensity involved in their everyday lives.

Any breeding-partner Liskan is just as likely to be severely maimed or even killed as to become a parent, and this is probably the basic reason for the outstandingly high standard of Liskan medicine. However, even a Liskan medical team finds it harder to regenerate an injured human being than most other species, and Solar Flare Regenerees are notoriously living on borrowed time anyway.

So I introduced the Cult of the Small Dog, deciding after careful consideration that though hypermanic the Liskan Nation would always enjoy too much pleasure from the sentiments of a suitable dog to revert to the pleasures of sadism — well, in connection with dogs, anyway. At least in this respect they are far more reliable, predictable, and even worthy than many other Nations.

Liskans everywhere took up dogs. Small, cosseted, sentimental dogs of revoltingly low intellect, even for dogs. We had transporters bringing them in from all over the Free Planets, so from a dog-free society we changed to a dog-ridden society in one beautiful Liskan season. A Cultural Survey group of Meiorians arrived to investigate our souls and left in haste as a protest against the presence of such numbers of living beings of limited intelligence.

(As a matter of fact there are no "lower animals" anywhere on their planet. This is one of the reasons I sometimes think that human beings are not so bad after all.)

The Liskans were delighted. They don't like Meiorians even when they're not investigating their souls. Apparently telepathing with them is intensely painful.

From being fashionable, dogs became absolutely essential. Far Ch Char Nce, who always tells me everything twice anyway, because he knows it annoys me, explained it all several times for his own enjoyment.

"The Cult of the Small Dog has been accepted as a factor in the Liskan Culture of the Moment," he said. "No Liskan of any degree of nobility would now feel at home without a dog, any more than most human beings would feel at home without their Cluster, or a Meiorian would be comfortable without being slightly radiant."

"Have a heart," I said.

Not he. He immediately annoyed every Liskan of less than noble standing by calling his favourite dog "Cheery Chap". That double "ch" to a Liskan is something like another Being saying "Majesty" and meaning it.

"As I am noble, my favourite dog, my companion in sentiment, must be too," he said. "Good boy, Cheery Chap. Sit, sit. It is out of the question that I should treat him as less than myself. The pain, the loss, the anguish would leave me prostrate, bereft, disconsolate. Totally unable to be of service."

"All right," I said.

The idiot spaniel slobbered gently.

"Thank you, thank you," said Far Ch Char Nce, quite as though he cared what I had to say. Apart from the Liskan commonality, who rely on the Ch for stimulation too much to cause much trouble unless they absolutely have to, only the Hereditary Arbitrator could command him to keep the peace among the Nation, and he wasn't bothering about it until the negotiations were over.

The dog came and sat on my foot. After all, I come from the same planet.

"There you see, he understands," cooed Far Ch Char Nce. "Look how nicely he is sitting down and breathing heavily. His little mind — a very limited mind, I agree — is filled with a peace and contentment beyond the understanding of all so-called Intelligences, except us of course."

Most of the Liskans simply induced their dogs to bury their own messes and to bathe and perfume themselves, but not Far Ch Char Nce. He cared for his dog personally, from a Liskan almost a degenerate degree of intimacy.

Esborne thought it was funny. At first. After all, now his Tenuous Relationships were over he had nothing special to do except outline Interplanetary Law to some bored Liskan official who knew what he was going to say before he said it, and anyway had already read the book.

"The negotiations are breaking down," I told him, even before the Liskans realised it. Human Intelligences may not be telepathic but we have some measure of foresight. Or anyway, True Born Isolates do, or we would all be dead.

But that had been the same morning, shortly before Far Ch Char Nce had come to tell me in other words that since peace was so boring they were prepared to set up a little interplanetary slaughter, to see how that was. And I had killed him.

Now we were going to renew negotiations, but what possible chance did anyone have of achieving anything worth doing?

"We'll have to remove the discussions to the Capital," I said.

"Not a hope," said Esborne. "We suggested that and they turned us down."

I took the Conference Room coffee table and shoved it out into the Meditation Gallery next door. It was crowded wall to wall with Liskans standing staring at the door I had opened. In turn they shoved the table the length of the Gallery and dropped it out a window. I don't think one of them looked away from me for a second.

For once I sympathised with the Admiral and his staff. I felt sick. I stepped back into the Conference Room, gently closing the door, and went to look out the window. The entire area around the building and the windows and balconies of all the surrounding buildings were crowded with Liskans. Staring.

I went back and sat down.

"Tell me," said Esborne cosily, "about being a True Born Isolate."

So I did. For the first time. Not that there's anything secret about it for anyone who knew who I was. There's nothing secret in relation to Mother. But I hadn't discussed it before.

"I think it's because I'm a woman," I said. "I mean Before Space and the development of the working Cluster there were billions of True Born Isolates, and most of them were women."

Esborne snorted. Whatever else he is, he's masculine. And probably human.

"Farmers, fishermen, cowboys, test pilots ... all women?" he said.

"In fact most men worked in teams, if not permanently, then from time to time," I said wearily. "The great majority of True, Working Isolates were women, housewives, and so on. Furthermore they resented and resisted efforts to make them work in teams. Read the statistics."

"Statistics compiled after the event," said Esborne.

And that is undoubtedly true. Before Space the question of isolates had no importance whatsoever. Some people lived or anyway worked by themselves. Some people dived into every available crowd like porpoises into the ocean. Some people created crowds, groups, working organisations and clubs where they didn't already exist. No one was aware of any compulsion about it.

And then came Space and the great distances. It was no longer a question of living by yourself among your own kind, or travelling or working alone in familiar or unfamiliar areas of your own planet. Now it was a question of going alone among Beings to whom your very species was unknown, among Intelligences whose values and desires were incomprehensible and whose behaviour was almost totally unpredictable.

Human Beings stopped travelling or working alone. The Working Committee from being a more or less derided feature of human life became the central effective unit. Most people felt good and virtuous about this until a gravel-voiced Nelian sociologist counted eight million terms for various kinds of human associations, and for convenience' sake called all the stable and predictable ones "Clusters". No complaints about discrimination served to convince other Beings that it wasn't the most serviceable term going, and within fifty years of Space humanity referred to itself as various "Clusters".

Mother even made a speech about it when she was running for President of the Association of Democratic Planets:

"Human beings have discovered through our long and chequered history that we work better and remain more healthy and more effective when we are members of a group or, as those Intelligences who discriminate against human beings say, — as members of a Cluster.

"We have always been intensely social beings, but since our active life span has been increased by approximately eight times its first recorded length in the past few hundred years, the bonds with our work groups and our living groups have become more intense and more important. We share our work, our ideas, our terrors, our joys and sorrows — and in the sharing, suffer less.

"Intelligences who discriminate against human beings have sometimes said that the habit is evidence of cowardice, proof that we are afraid to venture among other beings alone.

"To those critics I say that there is not one corner of any galaxy, however distant or savage, or lonely, where you will not at any moment see at least one human working group!"

"Did Mother get elected?" asked Esborne sympathetically.

I stared at him. Stupid sort of joke, I thought. It hadn't occurred to me that a fellow member of the Service wouldn't know the truth, but in fact he hadn't realised it.

"She is serving her eighth term, and is expected to be re-elected," I said.

"My God!" said Esborne, sitting down. "My God! You know, when you come to look at you, you're the image ...

"But my God! What are you doing out here? Doesn't the Service realise the mess it could cause if anyone, er ... Well I mean! What if Far Ch Char Nce had stayed dead? That's just one instance ..."

"Oh, shut up," I said.

For, of course, when you think about working Clusters you think about Humanity's vision of itself: normal, healthy, cooperative Human Intelligences.

51

But there have always been others who for reasons totally unknown have preferred to be alone for much of their lives. The condition appears quite unexpectedly among children whose parents are devoted members of valuable Clusters, and whose families have shown no signs of such a condition throughout the records of genetic history, right back to the beginnings of modern technology.

We are the True Born Isolates. We leap into Space, and strange species, and even isolation itself, like porpoises leaping into water. Many of us stay within the major human civilisations, forming tenuous or even sexual bonds with normal members of society. We are one form of the Friendly Stranger who is often amused, even pleased, to help an unhappy member of a group overcome his or her difficulties. But we are never really members of a group, even when we pretend otherwise, and the fact is resented.

But I was content to serve the Association alone in Dead Sector. I was a True Born Isolate.

"And your mother is the President of the ADP with an immediate working Cluster of 6,000 intimate friends," said Esborne. I shuddered.

"Well, it might have something to do with that — beating the telepathy factor, I mean," said Esborne doubtfully.

I sat and looked at him. It's quite impossible to describe a Solar Flare Regeneree except in terms of size. See one, you see them all. He was a big one.

"Not that I care," I said carefully. "I mean, I can spend my life caring, or I can forget about it and get on with living, but she isn't my Mother."

"What?" said Esborne.

"She's my twin sister. Or I'm her clone. My real parents are a pair of nice old microbiologists whom I met once by accident far, far away. And they weren't thrilled — I've heard of people leaving town to avoid someone, but they left an entire galaxy.

"I think that after bringing up Mother they felt they'd had enough of me."

Esborne twitched in an embarrassed way. "But you must have had someone ..."

"Oh yes. All my stepfathers, and my brothers and sisters, the rest of Mother's immediate family. And Mother in a way. She took an interest in us, you know. And she didn't make that speech about the disappointments of private life until I was grown, and already an undoubted Isolate, a candidate for the Service."

He continued to twitch.

"I like being me," I said. And it's the truth. Who wants to spend their lives knee-deep in "What the Chair said to Martha?"

Everyone else perhaps, but not me.

The door opened firmly, and stayed open. Esborne moved over to me. Nice of him, but a bit too much just then. I gave him a little pat and stepped forward.

Che Nce Ch, the Hereditary Arbitrator, came in with other members of the nobility. It was only the second time I had met him. Even interplanetary negotiation is regarded as rather beneath his notice.

"You have two privileges, Madam," he said to me. "Which will you use?"

"I fail to see how committing suicide or taking a bribe that I can't spend will have any effect in this situation," I said stiffly.

"No effect at all," he said in astonishment. "We were offering you consolation. Human Beings usually enjoy the very fact that they have privileges, whether they are pleasant or not."

One of the entourage bowed soundlessly before him, and he nodded. You don't telepath with the Hereditary Arbitrator without his express permission.

"Oh yes," he said. "And, of course, we would regenerate you if you chose suicide."

I wondered how it would turn out. Mother had been attempting something like continuous regeneration when she invested a few million life credits in four children and a clone.

And look at me. The exact opposite of what she had intended.

"Humanity is a highly variable species," said the Hereditary Arbitrator. "But I feel that you reject your privileges."

We looked at each other. "Please sit down," I said, against all etiquette, but he sat. "After all, you want to renew negotiations, that's the main thing."

"No," said Esborne.

The Liskans stood and stared.

"For the first time in our recorded history a noble Liskan has been injured without realising the intention of the attacker," said Che Nce Ch. "That is what matters. We will be most grateful, to the extent that I will give strict orders that no one may become bored in the continued negotiations, if you tell us how you did it."

I sat down. It was going to be a bribe after all, but one that I could use. I thought about Esborne and Far Ch Char Nce continuing the negotiations for the rest of the two year period, while I went off to Splinto for new boots and then wandered off to catch up with the latest developments, in the rest of Dead Sector, where I had never shown the badge to a single Intelligence; I could work in perfect discretion, my work was allowed to speak for itself and I was really free, in places crowded and in places solitary. "It's lonely out here."

The Liskans began to turn mauve with pleasure. A few of them danced. Such a small thing, to a Human — it hadn't been worth remembering before, while everything stopped and started again.

"I didn't know that I was going to do it," I explained. "It's an old, old human habit, one that we've been ashamed of for most of our history. We call it 'acting before we think'."

"Impossible," said Che Nce Ch with conviction.

"Commonplace," I told him.

Esborne shifted uneasily. "No working Cluster does it, of course," he amended.

"Working Clusters explain everything before, during, and especially after they do it," I said, getting up. "Working

Clusters may have had their place in the human entry into Space, but they have had their day.''

I danced. The Liskans danced. Che Nce Ch watched for moment, and then rose and shuffled about in a stately way for a moment himself.

Esborne stood and watched with no joy at all. ''I suppose this means that you're going off and leaving me here alone?'' he said querulously.

''It does,'' I said. ''It does indeed. This is the dawning of the day of the True Born Isolate, the only human beings who can beat telepaths, the only human beings who actually get out and DO anything under a year's notice of intention.''

And it was. The Liskans even flew me to Splinto themselves.

However, you can't defeat the Liskan urge for sensation. They tell me that Far Ch Char Nce has fully recovered and has applied to enter the Service as soon as the Liskans have been admitted to full Membership of the Free Planets. He wants to study me.

fairytale

A N I A   W A L W I C Z

once upon a time there was a king he had three daughters one
was very pretty but the two others why they were ugly as hell
so he preferred the ugly ones because they were very smart they
were very clever indeed he said to them don't worry about
getting husbands i mean all right if you want i'll arrange that
no problems but you should think about studying first the
beautiful one was dumb you see so he didn't like her at all not
at all why don't you like me or something she asked him sorry
i don't like you because you are stupid so she cried then this
fairy heard her and felt sorry for her she better be sent to
remedial classes or something the fairy said so she was to help
her improve her spelling and stop paying attention to how she
looked and all that so all the sisters were all right with the king
after that and all getting good marks and scholarships to
university because that's very important but the ugly ones
started to worry about just how ugly they were so the king
arranged for them to have plastic surgery so they looked a lot
better after that and were all all right i think but then they
wanted to get married after they got their doctorates only after
that so that was a problem because they didn't meet many men
because they were too busy at their study so the king had to
think about what to do because they were driving him crazy all
the time talking about getting married and worrying about
being old maids so he advertised in the aristocratic gazette for
handsome princes to apply so they did but the princesses didn't
like them you see they were much too smart for these princes

and laughed at them and so forth so that was worrying the king who was getting old by then you see he married late so by that time he was in his eighties and maybe would die he wanted to see the daughters settled so this time he advertised for very clever princes and they came but the princesses found them too ugly and said these men are very good to talk to but as far as looks are concerned forget it wouldn't touch them with a ten foot pole and the thought of kissing them just makes me sick well that was a problem what to do now what was the king supposed to do what were the princesses supposed to do and what were the poor unfortunate rejected princes supposed to do the king suggested maybe you could marry two princes apiece a good looking one for sleeping with and a clever one to talk to but that wasn't such a good idea so the princesses thought we got to think of something to do after all we got doctorates and they decided to produce perfect men for themselves the kind that could cook and be polite and wash dishes and be willing and able to tell good stories and the kind that wouldn't annoy them so they set out in the laboratory to combine all the parts of various princes to make good husbands and they worked all night but they didn't mind you see they enjoyed their work and were used to using their heads so lo and behold they made these perfect husbands by sticking all the pieces of various princes together if one had good eyes then they took his eyes too bad for him they had to do it and that was that and some prince would wake up blind too bad they said or take some prince's legs if they were nice legs they took them they would take them by special force of their minds and they took them and these men would wake up sometimes dead but it was all right for the princesses they didn't mind so they took what they liked and took brains and eyes and legs and shoulders and took hair and took feet a lot of princes died as a result and everybody thought that there was a plague and in the end the princesses had their husbands but they got bored with them and killed them because they enjoyed working in the laboratory more than marriage

Odd Man Search

C H E R R Y   W I L D E R

A hot wind blows in from the desert and the witch in the end room is crying for water. Brick fills up the blue dipper and heads for the little visitors' lounge. The office block is dilapidated. There are gaping holes in the interior walls that he can't explain and others that he kicked and gouged himself to make a kind of covered way between his rooms and the lounge. There was too much glass; little shatterproof turds of the stuff are crunching under his feet. The sky has forced itself in through the gaping frames and at night great sheets of moonlight fall and shatter on the sandy floor.

Shreds of paper cling to his legs as he clears admin and comes to the edge of the typing pool. Last week he wheeled the desks into a phalanx and covered the keyboards with drapes. The pool is quiet: a rock in the corner, a sandy bottom, darting fish shadows, a can Brick flung into the pool.

The lounge is intact and dim; Brick remembers — he surely was not told — the jokes about "little visitors". The main visitors' lounge across the street shares a fake western storefront with the canteen, labelled Saloon and Barbershop. Both places make him queasy; the one-armed bandits are horrifying, with all their arms outstretched, one or two marked with a scarf or a handkerchief. Sturdy and staunch they stand. There are the tables in the canteen and he recalls how the girls and men stood in line, sliding along their pink trays.

The witch Arada is lying on the couch in the lounge,

her eyes fever-bright in the gloom. She drinks greedily from the dipper.

"Thanks!"

She rests her hand on his arm and it is burning hot: a square, unkept, childish hand, scratched and scarred from her fight with the desert. She was the only one who came and for three days Brick thought she was going to die.

Twink had sensed her on the perimeter and when they crept up she was sprawled on the burning sand in her black weeds, scrawling a last desperate pentacle. He name was written on the bosom of her black gown: ARADA; she had been forty kilometres away with two ring-pull cans of Diet Cola. She travelled by pentacle all the way to the centre. The rest of the coven were lost; they had cast lots on which direction to drive the dune buggy and had picked wrong. Arada wouldn't go along. She sat in a pentacle — what else? — and watched all day and all night turned into day. Those poor mothers had pulled down some heavy working.

Now, on moonlit nights, she sings for thanksgiving. She has had Brick put out pentacles in blue masking tape all over the centre. They are inside one now, laid out on the carpet of the little visitors' lounge.

"Feeling better?"

"Sure. This is just some crazy reaction, you know."

"I know."

"In this dream the sand gets in my throat and I scream out for water."

"And I bring it along."

"Brick, where's Twink?"

"Isn't he around?"

His alarm bells are ringing and flashing already. More people coming?

"I think he got a call."

He feels hope; his heart is ready to burst with hope and he cannot conceal it from Arada.

"*No!*" she says in exasperation. "No, honey, none of your folks checked in."

Brick turns aside in embarrassment and confronts his own reflection in the mirror behind the bar. Sees a young red-haired man in jeans and a disposable T-shirt peering out anxiously from behind antique gold lettering. A thin-faced girl with seaweed hair floats in the depths of the mirror; Arada waves to him behind the "a" of Salem.

The old-time tobacco ads on the glass are as phoney as the anodised brass rail below the bar; the decor is late dude ranch. Brick gazes sadly at his reflection: some late dude. Ms Todd, the director, has left instructions — explicit, brutal — for handling survivors. In *his* dream she comes back again, with the department heads, right up to the wire. The counters scream and the strips in Twink's housing turn black: deadly contamination. Brick shoots them all with a six-gun and cannot ask the question: why was this red-haired specimen left behind to do the dirty work?

He drags aside drapes and a slat blind over the empty window frame and looks for Twink in the street. Tumbleweed and tumbling coke cans. Twink will have to go on clean-up detail. Brick remembers the lumber they disposed of in Block A, beyond the canteen, and shudders. Arada is watching him.

"Did you look at your file yet?"

"No," says Brick, "I told you. Ms Todd had it locked away."

"I'm sick of hearing about that Boss Lady!"

Brick clutches a handful of fibreglass drape so hard that it squeaks.

"Lay off!"

"It was a routine evacuation!" cried Arada. "Everyone cut out ... everywhere ..."

He catches a gleam of metal in sunlight at the end of the street. Arada is leafing through a promotional pamphlet on Todd-Gorman Research Enterprises.

"Cybernetics ..." she jeers. "They thought they had it made."

There is a familiar tapping, followed by a bleep.

"Hey, he's back!" she cries joyfully.

Brick smiles too. He cannot help smiling; he is programmed for Joy as Twink comes tapping and bleeping and dancing down the broad street.

"What's he say? What's he say?"

"Nothing," says Brick. "He's just happy."

He shouts: "Hey Twink, over here! LVL topside, pronto!"

Twink pirouettes, taps "wilco", and Brick holds aside the blind so that he can scramble in through the window frame. The lounge is dark after the street, so Twink puts on two upper lights; he finds a clear space and starts reporting.

"You're sure?" says Brick. "He says there's another."

He watches Arada in case she comes down with an attack of hope for her coven. But Arada is immune.

"Only one?" she asks Twink.

"Tap-tap."

"Like me? Female, human and all?"

"Tap. Tap-tap."

"Well, not female, but human. A man."

"Tap-tap."

Twink adds a whole slew of information so fast that only Brick can interpret.

"One man with vehicle. Man in bad shape. Unarmed."

"He said that?"

"Sure. Say 'unarmed', Twink. Repeat."

Twink draws in the two flexible upper limbs on his central housing and taps once for No, with colour code lights flashing for emphatic and peaceful.

"That's a pretty spooky thing to program him to say," says Arada, "unless . . ."

"I told you," says Brick, "it was a planned withdrawal."

"Okay, okay. Ms Todd knew what she was doing."

Twink, a prototype Todd-Gorman Sensor Terpsichorean, reacts sadly to the name with a blue light and a fluid movement of the lower limbs.

"Come on," says Brick, "we'll take a look."

"Can I . . .?" Arada sits up, hacking fingers through her hair.

"Better not."

"Are *you* going to be armed?"

"Twink is prepared," he says. "It's precaution, that's all."

They are trailing warily through the broken rooms, eyes on the street.

"Go down to the Rebus," he says, "and put this into the tapes — report of man with vehicle. You know, just type, the way I showed you. And get the bed ready. The one you were in."

"Brick" — she takes his arm as they swim through the typing pool — "does Twink have a counter?"

"Sure," he says, "and a test strip and all. Show Arada your radiation test strip, Twink."

Before she goes down the stairs Brick says, casually as possible, "You can watch through the periscope."

He catches sight of her witch face, taut and afraid; she scrawls a pentacle in the dust on the stair rail. He wishes, in case there is bad trouble, that they had made it, even once, in the moonlight, the way Arada swore they would do, once he got his head right.

Brick takes one side of the street and Twink the other; they move towards the west. It is long past high noon; every cactus casts a shadow as long as a man. Brick comes to the perimeter. The high wire has been flattened and twisted by windstorms until it resembles a barbed-wire entanglement. The gatehouse is an empty pillbox; he strolls across and takes his place in the slot between the two lanes where Velma, the gateperson, used to stand.

He can see in every direction: the level sands stretch far away. The Todd-Gorman Research Centre has become part of the desert, a handful of ruined, weathered structures, grown into the wilderness. You could not even tell there was water; as an oasis it makes a great ghost town. Brick thinks there should be palm trees and some more green, more shade.

Twink bleeps off to the southwest behind the tall shattered billboard that read ... ODD- ... MAN ... SEARCH. Brick sees a man in ragged clothes inching his way around the perimeter; he is exhasted but he comes on, grips the sagging wire, and half crawls the last few metres. Brick lets the man come by himself; he cannot touch or assist him, although Twink has signalled "Test strip clear". You can't drag a marathon runner over the line.

When the man reaches the slot of the gatehouse, Brick comes out holding his canteen of water. The man is dried up, desiccated: there is sand caked on his sunburnt lips; from his throat comes a grating sound. He clutches at Brick and the canteen; they sink down together in slow motion. Brick feeds him water, very slowly. It is Arada all over again, and he is afraid the man will die. The man gulps, his limbs twitch; he comes alive at the touch of water, like a brine shrimp or a Japanese water flower. As Brick pours in another few drops, the dry mask changes to the bony, ordinary face of a middle-aged male caucasian. The man opens bright, bloodshot blue eyes.

"Cook ..." he croaks, between sips. "Harry Cook."

"Brick Kennedy."

Brick hates and disbelieves his own name but he is willing to oblige the man.

"Thanks. Saved m'life."

There is something strange about the man's speech; perhaps the sand has stiffened his upper lip. Brick, still feeding him water, begins to smile.

"Hey ... You're a Limey ... an Englishman!"

"Bullseye!" says Cook.

He stays Brick's hand with the canteen and hoists himself into a sitting position. His eyes widen in terror and he scrunches back against the wall of the gatehouse.

"Relax!" says Brick, "It's only Twink. He's a robot."

"Jesus!" breathes Cook.

He takes another small snort from the canteen.

"Sorry. Not m'self."

Twink, all solicitude, bleeps, taps, flashes a series of questions.

"Sure he's okay. You did fine, Twink," says Brick. "This is Harry Cook. Got it? Give him a few seconds, then break out the transporter."

Cook peers out from under eyebrows thick with sand; his laughter is dry.

"The dancing language, eh?"

"Yeah," says Brick, "and a whole range of electronic responses. See the light bands? He's very smart. Say something — ask him a question."

"Why is he ... er ... why are you called Twink?" enquires Cook indulgently.

The reply is cheerful and succinct.

"Afraid you'll have to translate," says Cook.

"He says, 'It's short for Twinkletoes.'"

"Of course." Cook raises the canteen feebly, saluting Twink. "I should have known."

Twink begins to extrude the silvery framework from his central housing; Cook squints at it uncertainly.

"This is his transporter," explains Brick. "Kind of a mobile stretcher. You can ride on it back to ..."

He gestures vaguely up the main drag, unable to find a word for the place where he lives. Rooms? Quarters? Home?

"Back to base," he decides.

The exchange of pleasantries has exhausted Cook; he is in a watery coma, just smiling, as Brick rolls him onto the transporter. Twink offers more data.

"The vehicle!" says Brick. "Okay, I'll buy it. A Rolls-Royce?"

Tap. Bleep?

Brick steps outside the wire and looks along the curve of the perimeter. He experiences a mirage; it comes towards him, lifting the ungainly pads of its feet. Slowly Brick extends his arms in a shooing movement. The camel marches stiff-legged through the gateway and proceeds at a jerky trot down the street. It waits, knowing, smelling the water, outside the shell of the admin, footsore and a little thirsty. By the time Twink has wheeled Cook back to base, Arada has abandoned her periscope; she comes rushing out with a plastic bucket. The camel, bewitched, allows her to stroke its neck while it is drinking. When Twink and Brick come too close with the inert form of its rider, the beast coughs angrily. Arada is weeping and trembling; she clings to Brick.

"Alive! A man and a camel! Too much!"

Twink wheels the transporter into the admin lobby and they all go down in the freight elevator. It is very clean and quiet under the ground. The sweet-smelling greenish rooms are spotless; you could eat your meals off Ms Todd's floors.

Arada and Brick seldom pass beyond the third bulkhead; behind it lie the dismantled workrooms. Once in a while, according to the schedule, Brick passes through and checks the generator, throbbing in its cell. The place they use most is a utility room with a sink, tool cupboard, and the food dispenser. Brick still dials all his meals from the dispenser, but Arada explores the huge cold store, and tries to tempt him with apples from the crisper bins.

There is a dormitory with four bunks and they roll Cook tenderly onto the bottom bunk by the door. Twink enfolds the transporter and Brick gives him the high sign for the medi-reckoner. He wheels the unit across and they check out Cook.

"How is he doing?" whispers Arada.

"Your readings were a lot worse. This guy had transport."

All three of them set to work to clean up Cook with wet towels and a fresh-up blower from the admin washroom. Then they set up the glucose drip.

"It's funny," says Arada, gazing at the clean, creased face of the sleeping Englishman, "he looks a little like Harry Cook."

"That's his name! That's Harry Cook!" Brick is nervous. "How did you know?"

For the first time Arada gives Brick a very curious sidelong look: as if he might have been born yesterday.

"Where you been, boy? Harry Cook is in pictures."

She rattles off a string of titles, and one rings a bell.

"Yeah ..." says Brick. "I saw him as Philby."

Brick recalls Cook in action in what must have been a definitive portrayal of that sad cad, the twentieth century master spy. Cook, like Philby, is a first-rate actor whose cover is completely blown. His occupation's gone.

"They must have been on location," says Arada. "Only reason anyone would bring a camel into the desert."

Brick sees again what he alone did not see, and hears the crack of doom that he did not hear. The cameramen toppled and the expensive sets turned to chaff. The last picture show. In the last reel Cook, clinging to the camel's neck, rides off through the light of setting suns while the fringes of the desert sand are fused into glass.

Brick stares unseeing at Harry Cook, and experiences the guilt of a survivor. He envies Nero, fiddling while Rome burned ... participating. Not sleeping, not tranquilised in the green shade of the bunker, with a mind curiously blank and only Twink and the Rebus for company.

Abruptly he turns aside and blunders into the computer room. The Rebus is dreaming on half-power; the room in which the system is housed is warmer than the rest of the underground installation. Brick goes to the nearest keyboard and types:

WHAT DO WE FEED THE CAMEL?

There is a brief alteration in the timbre of the background noises; the Rebus prints out:

COWCAKE FREEZLOCKER ZP349, CEREAL MIX CAN124, VITAMAL ADDIT CAN130B, REFER ADTP709.

THANK YOU. PLEASE PRINT OUT THE REFERENCE.

There is an inward riffle on the other side of the narrow room and a card drops into the AD slot.

UTILITY BOX 9. ASSORTED GRASSES, FERTILISER, GROWTH TRAYS.

Brick grins. They will have that oasis after all.

While Cook is mending, Arada spends more time underground. Brick has a big program going topside; he circles the perimeter in person at dawn and sends Twink out during the heat of the day. He tries to stable the camel in the canteen, the main visitors' lounge, the garage, but it will not cooperate. The skittish beast lurks in patches of shade, and erupts from between the buildings. The centre is full of camels going thataway.

He keeps the eight silvery growth trays by him in his own pad, Ms Todd's executive suite, monitoring the green grass. He flakes out in the long afternoons when the hot wind blows from the desert, and half-wishes Arada would holler for water. The monotony is so enormous and safe and deadly that it carries him along like a warm wave. Who would, who will ever lift a finger to switch on a cassette book or even scrawl a pentacle?

On one of these long afternoons he flops a hand clumsily across the intercom trying to call Arada in the bunker. Before he can ask a question Harry Cook's voice comes in loud and clear; the channels are open.

"Won't read his own file?"

"No ..." Arada has a faint, scratching voice. "He's afraid."

"Strordinary!"

"Can't remember very much."

"And he thinks this suggests ...?"

Brick can feel Cook considering his odd case.

"Of course." Arada sounds harsh and distant. "Cybernetics ... big thing around here ... Ms Todd ..."

"I've heard of that lady."

Brick is rigid, unable to speak or switch off. He curses Cook for a spy, an infiltrator.

"Other possibilities ..." says Arada softly.

Before she can explore them, Cook's voice cuts in: "Don't believe it! Boy's deluded. Dammit all, he has a name ... Kennedy. His name is Kennedy ..."

"He thought it might be a phoney," admits Arada, and Brick finds himself nodding in agreement. "You see, it's a president's name ... Lincoln, Washington, Roosevelt ..."

"I see," says Cook, still considering, like Holmes on his

third pipe. "But what about bodily functions — surely he couldn't ...?"

"Ms Todd could build anything," says Arada. "And there are the heavy trauma cyborgs — wiped right out, then rebuilt."

"I still don't believe it!"

"Brick had a bad time," she whispers, "waking up, all alone, programmed ..."

"You're sure?"

"Seemed like it. He had to complete certain tasks. Burning up" — her voice fades like static — "incinerating the remains of Ms Todd's projects."

"Let's get this straight," says Cook briskly. "He was instructed to burn ...?"

"A whole mess of humanoid robots," says Arada flatly. "Half-complete" — her voice dwindles again — "lifelike ..."

It sounds like nothing; Brick and Twink on clean-up detail. But Arada comes in again, to the heart of the matter.

"What really burns him up," she is saying, "is that he missed everything. He didn't *share*."

"Bloody fool!" growls Cook. "Can't he see it's what we count on every time? Someone has to miss the end of the world."

Brick beats a retreat; leaves the lines open and tiptoes away through the drifting paper and sand and grains of shatterproof glass. He goes down later for his meal and talks with Harry Cook about planting out the grass. For two days all hands tear up the floor of Block A and prepare a roofed enclosure, camel-proof. They bring in topsoil by the cupful from the indoor planter boxes and the ruined garden beds. Arada brews a cauldron of vile mulch from the fertiliser — blood and bone — laced with fruit peel and camel dung.

The camel draws closer and closer to Arada as they sit out of doors in the evening, and finally muzzles her boldly, asking to be groomed.

"Put a spell on him?" asks Brick.

"Poor beggar had a girl trainer," says Cook.

Brick and Cook loll in the shade while she currycombs

the beast with a scrub brush from the broom closet. Then it kneels meekly before her; she climbs on its back and rides down main street.

"Rides a sight better than I did," says Cook.

Arada, firmly erect, with black rags over her ragged hair, is a tuareg, a weird desert creature. The sight of her leaves Brick blinking, dry-eyed, as if he wants to shed tears. All of us. All. The thought leaves him faint and empty.

The sun begins to settle into a bank of cloud that rides forever above the western horizon. Twink comes tintinnabulating through the red sunset light and Brick knows there will be some action.

"More survivors?" demands Harry Cook.

The signal Twink has picked up is "distant", on the limits of his equipment.

"Fifty, sixty kilometres," explains Brick, "depending on the transmitter. It's a repeater. That's right, Twink, play back ... You see there? I'm pretty sure it's a rescue beacon — type used on planes or small boats."

Arada has persuaded the camel to let her down.

"How do we get them?"

She looks at Brick and looks down at the sandy street, clearing her throat. Her big toe starts to draw a circle in the sand. Brick is ahead of her. Arada cannot be spared; Harry Cook is in precarious shape.

"My turn," Brick says.

"Twink ...?" pleads Arada.

Brick shakes his head; Twink is a function of the Centre; he cannot leave.

Once he has made the decision Brick is seized with impatience; he has to go now, right away. As they fuel the Safari DE and check the supplies, he trots out all sorts of good reasons, from the cool of the evening to the possible condition of the survivors. He cannot bear to spend the night with his friends, knowing he must leave them. He is already gone, burning up the desert, and then in less than two hours he *is* gone. Arada has kissed him on the lips, Harry Cook has thumped him on the back, he and Twink have exchanged a last bow. He is burning across the sand, watching the heading on the beamfinder.

Brick remembers Cook's last words: "I'll take good care of her." He sniffs at his own diesel fumes, polluting the wasteland, and feels an extraordinary emotion. He is jealous.

The desert night is cold and brown beyond his searchlights. He strikes out across the sand directly to the south-west, then follows an empty desert road. The intensity of the signal scarcely increases — thirty kilometres, forty, forty-five. Brick sees the road ahead turn downhill. The signal fades; rock shapes are thrusting at his lights.

He parks the wagon and steps out, drinking the silence, staring back at the stars. There is something in the unchanged landscape much stranger than all the routines evolved at the Centre. If he could stay here, leaning on the gritty hood of the wagon, he could remember everything. He can see the lights of the instrument panel through the windshield. He climbs back into the cabin and swivels the finder until the signal comes in, much stronger than before. The land falls away from this point; roads lead down into the canyon. Brick breaks the silence with a laugh like a coyote; he has come to the badlands.

The air seems warmer as he follows a turn-off into the ravine. This might be an illusion but it is so persistent that Brick runs a finger round his neckband, and glances at the wagon's detection gear. The radiation levels have risen since he left the Centre but are holding safe and steady. The signal fades, wavers, then blares out; he rounds a ragged butte and sees a single light ahead.

His instinct is to bring up the searchlights onto full beam, but this is not part of the drill. In any case it is not necessary; the mid-beam quickly discovers a light source . . . a one-eyed combivan. It is drawn up close to the wall of the canyon with its front fender almost touching a rock. Brick, afraid and excited, sends the wagon sweeping round to the blind side of the van. He thinks of the two vehicles as animals, meeting at night in the desert.

The van looks brand new in contrast to the dusty wagon, and at the same time shockingly mutilated. A gouged furrow, deep in the metal, reaches down the exposed flank to the shattered headlight. The windshields are out and there is an odd blistered burn spilling over the roof of the van. Brick stands on his brakes. There is more light: a blinking light above the gaping rear doors. It is the signal: like he said, a rescue beacon of the type used on smaller boats. A scatter of dark objects on the sand. Suitcase. Carton. The body of a young girl, flimsily dressed, almost naked, lying on her back. The body of a child not far away.

Brick goes through his security drill inside the van, clumsy with haste; he snatches up the emergency packs and the geiger. He runs to the girl and has time to reach for her pulse before they jump him on all sides. A heavy weight sits on his back; he is rabbit-punched and roughly frisked by more pairs of hands. He tries to talk and gets a salty mouthful of sand. He feels the decoy girl slip her live hand out of his grasp as she leaps to her feet.

"Please ..."

He lashes out with his left arm and feels contact with a human midriff. He cannot hit again.

"Help you ..."

Words are squeezed out of him; adhesive, thick as a re-tread, is clamped over mouth and wrists. He lies like a rock, listening. Five maybe, all ages, at least two women. Brick aches for a confrontation; he longs to see their faces. They keep up a steady flow of work phrases.

"Key ..."

"Got it ..."

"Over here. Johnny ...?"

"Put the ... sure ..."

"Ruth?"

There will be no confrontation. All they want is the wagon. Not one of them will look into his face, ask a question, kick or kill him. Some are hurt, panting, limping.

"Okay?"

72

"Yeah, sure ..."

"I can manage."

"Hey, Dad ..."

Their attack is impersonal; he might be in the hands of automata. Brick feels hot tears stinging his cheeks; he chokes behind the gag. There is a light slap on the sand inches from his nose; then they start the wagon with the searchlights on full beam.

Brick is surprised by his burst of energy. He vaults upright and charges at the wagon. He slithers dangerously along the hood, grunting like a madman, and hooks his bound wrists into the open window on the driver's side. He clings backward, half-running; over his shoulder he sees blurred faces, eyes in the darkness. The driver shoves him between the shoulder blades. Brick is falling away; he feels a tearing, like the adhesive, then more pain. He falls; some heavy object falls after him; the dust cloud is yellow from the searchlights. The wagon drives off, unwavering, down the canyon. Brick finds that his right arm is free and rips off the gag.

He lies where he has fallen and moves into an uneasy dreaming state, full of faces. A family, were they? Dad, Johnny, Ruth. One time they went on a camping trip ... Pick-up broke down and they called the highway patrol. His mother said, Andy, stand off the road.

Or maybe they were a Family. Marked, half-naked girls, hey Ruthie, Squeaky, driving helter-skelter into a death valley. None of the electronic equipment in the wagon was any use to them, even if they understood it; there was the automatic locking device.

I have to report the loss of one Safari DE tracker, Ms Todd. Lieutenant, your leave is cancelled forever. You must tend the Centre. It is in your hands. Ms Todd, the thing won't work. Tush, Andy, it works. See how you grasp the tennis ball. Brick tries to flex the fingers of his left hand, fails completely, and falls asleep until the dawn comes up like thunder.

He is cold and thirsty but clear-headed. He has remembered enough. He turns his head and sees the scarred

73

van, still in deep shade; a thread of sun is reaching down over the rim of the canyon. Maybe this is part of the conditioning — a little at a time, nothing too harsh. The conditioning came first, then the accident in the shuttle, and Ms Todd undertook repairs. No loss to the taxpayers. He might have gone back into space but the program ... terminated. He cannot look at the sky above the canyon. It is too bright, with a few trailing wisps of reddish cloud. He hears Arada's voice — "Some crazy reaction"; he smiles: time to get home. No one better conditioned, better qualified to inherit the Centre.

He is still unwilling to sit up; he exhorts himself in the person of Harry Cook: "Bear up, old man." He wonders, holding up his good right hand against the light, if Arada has read his file yet. He laughs and sits up, lopsided, thinking of his name, Andrew Jackson Kennedy. His right hand is scratched across the knuckles and the blood has dried. His left arm has been torn off, disarticulated at the shoulder joint; it lies on the sand, still and perfect, Ms Todd's finest work, with only a wire trailing. He scrambles to his feet and goes after it, feeling only an urgent desire to salvage and protect a precious object. He even knows, suddenly, how to replace it. Better check the Rebus for diagrams of the refit.

He rescues the arm and sees with a thump of fear and gratitude that the poor bastards last night left him his canteen of water. The only other thing left behind, besides the van, is a small pile of sand and plastic sheeting, half covered with stones. He lifts the corner and finds the body of the child, lying where he saw it, not far from the girl decoy, in a shallow trench in the sand. The child has a burn on its cheek. Brick kneels down and finishes the heap of stones. He sees it for a moment as a kind of ordeal, a choice — maybe if he had gone to the child first, instead of the girl, they would have made contact him. He discards this as fantasy. They were burying the child and they had the beacon out in the hope of a hijack. They were ordinary people turned into something else, between survivors and predators.

He figures the van must still have some life in it, but there is no way he can make it run. It is a Duo, with trannies removed and gas cylinders. He faces a fifty kilometre walk home; maybe Twink will pick him up sooner if they're monitoring the area. Brick looks at the sky light-hearted; he could run there, he could fly. He has a canteen of water and he recalls shade rocks at a bend in the road. Hell, he could make those rocks now, before noon.

He thinks better of it, through his own good sense or the good sense that has been laid on him. He climbs up awkwardly into the back of the van, placing the bionic arm and the canteen in the best shade. The van has a warm, stale smell; the doorway gapes like the mouth of a cave. He can see the child's grave and the sky above the rock wall. He sits patiently, waiting for nightfall.

The Truth About Oscar

YVONNE ROUSSEAU

"My dear Miranda, do invite me again soon for another of your charmingly wilful arguments!" And Hildebrand left a sample of his most popular, sweetly bewildered laughter behind him, as he wandered off into the night.

Left alone, Miranda whirled to confront the mirror, which reflected back her flushed cheeks, her black, recently cut curls, her amaranth eyes, and the wonderful green of her costume. Seldom had she disrobed so rapidly as she did now, and more seldom yet had she subsequently dressed herself as a young man of London 100 years ago. When she had done, Sherlock Holmes himself could scarcely have observed a more convincing slim youth in an ulster.

Little did Hildebrand guess that tonight she would act in support of the view she had (surely so unanswerably) argued.

"O, but (Hildebrand), the waste of it!" had she not proclaimed, clasping her slender hands which were pale as white camellia petals in the moonlit water. ". . . If only Oscar Wilde had never embarked upon his libel case against the Marquis of Queensberry! If only he had torn up the Marquis' card — it was so ill-spelled, after all ('To Oscar Wilde, posing as a somdomite'!) — and ten days old before he even saw it . . . O, Hildebrand, think of Oscar Wilde's life had he never been sentenced to those two years' hard labour; had he not afterwards been exiled and hounded about the Continent. What divine plays he would have written! What an age he would have attained! Why, he was eleven years younger than Sarah Bernhardt, and yet he died three years before she had recorded her voice for us — that divine voice, which thrills through one's nerves as if one's own soul had become audible. Only think, if Oscar Wilde had lived to speak to us in this way! If we, too, could have enjoyed his famous conversation — that conversation so often, and so convincingly, reported to us as so altogether unrecapturable. O, Hildebrand, how can *De Profundis* — how can *The Ballad of Reading Gaol* — ever compensate for our loss, and for Oscar's misery?''

Ah, but how unworthy of her emotion was Hildebrand's reply ...

"My dear Miranda, what makes you suppose that Oscar Wilde could, in any case, have written another worthwhile play, after *The Importance of Being Earnest*? Surely, he was going horribly downhill. How do you know that his disgrace did not avert some still more terrible catastrophe? Something, even, so dreadful as his dwindling into a gross and pathetic old bore?''

Miranda was stung into launching a topic she had resolved strictly to avoid. "But, Hildebrand, supposing that one had a time machine — of course, the idea is absurd (but you may remember, Hildebrand, that Wells published *The Time Machine* in the very year of Oscar Wilde's disgrace ...). Supposing that you could travel back in time, and alter Wilde's decision to sue the Marquis: surely you would take the opportunity, Hilderbrand? It would not be like tampering with a world war; it would not alter the human genetic materials available in the world; and yet it would increase human happiness so greatly. Of course, the case is purely hypothetical; but I am sure you could not hesitate!''

"To alter the past! My dear Miranda, whatever can you suppose the past to be? I am afraid that your ideas are sadly unscientific. And for all your admiration of Wilde, I am afraid that even your ideas upon art are very shallow. Do you not see that some more of Oscar Wilde's plays (not to mention the lack of *De Profundis* and *Reading Gaol*) would utterly change the universe?"

Well, Hildebrand was gone now. He, to call her unscientific! She, who had penetrated Wells' pretence of writing fiction; had divined the true identity of the Time Traveller; had perused the documents preserved by his family, and mastered the cipher in which he had secreted his plans and principles! (How thoroughly, if she had cared for such pleasures, she could have publicly discredited that bungler, Einstein . . .) She, who had refined the Time Traveller's methods of manipulating higher Euclidean space; she, whose own time machine was infinitely more elegant — indeed, all but as simple as a Möbius strip! No awkward monstrosity, hers, to be insecurely stowed beneath some bush; the light metal could be folded so ingeniously that, when she had slipped over it a curious black sheath, the observer beheld only a clumsy (but undeniable) furled black umbrella . . .

No, Hildebrand was not the superior being he supposed himself. Black sheath in hand, Miranda settled herself astride the machine, and activated it; her destination was Hyde Park, at 10 in the evening of Thursday the 28th of February, 1895. So she fled on past the nights and days — black, gold, silver, blue and grey; and then came the brownish void of maximum speed, when she seemed so heavy, so small and remote; and now the flickering changes again, the familiar lightness of body, and the sudden wincing alarm of arrival. No, she had not landed in the foliage of some unremembered elm tree. Unobserved, amid the brown folds of the February mist, she disguised her machine (tucking it under her arm), scanned her luminous pocket-compass, found her way out of the park, and set off eastward along Piccadilly.

As she approached the Avondale Hotel, Miranda thought she noticed (passing in single file, through the fogbound glimmer of a street lamp) the faces of Aubrey Beardsley, George Bernard Shaw, Thomas Hardy, Rudyard Kipling, Max Beerbohm, Henry James, George Gissing, "Lewis Carroll", and

W. S. Gilbert all out for a walk together. She might have been mistaken, however; it might have been another nine gentlemen. Between the hotel entrance and the door of "Mr Oscar Wilde's suite", on the other hand, she seemed to notice nothing.

Miranda was alone with Oscar Wilde (the hotel staff member, who had conducted her, being dismissed again); she was damp from the fog, she still clutched her "umbrella", she was calling herself "Sebastian Melmoth", and she had no idea what she should do with her hat; but, even more, she was overwhelmed simply by her first encounter with a great man — for great he was, in the most literal sense. He loomed before her, lighted cigarette in hand, while his large lucent eyes, beneath their heavy lids, surveyed her with enormous — though kindly — sagacity. He was (so evidently) bigger than her, stronger than her, lazier than her — and are not these, in women's eyes, the three invincible marks of masculinity?

"Mr Wilde, I apologise for this intrusion, but I come on behalf of the theatre — not St James's, I mean, but Theatre itself ..."

But where was the magnificent calm (where, even, were the words) with which she had intended to proceed? Was she not obvious? Uncharming? In imminent danger of being turned out (before she could even begin her all too indelicate errand)? Miranda dreaded to see the good-humoured curve of those sensual lips hardening into disdainful affront; to see in those beautiful light eyes (where, even now, she momentarily detected fatigue and preoccupation) the green blaze of contempt. What balm it was, when his slow, courteous voice (which someone had once described as "pure cello") seemed not altogether to discourage further explanation ...

"From Theatre itself, you say, and yet not from St James's? Ah, I suppose you mean the Haymarket; you mean *An Ideal Husband*. But do you really prefer it to *Earnest*? That is certainly not very trivial of you; but, you know," and he paused to discard his cigarette, "it is not very like a journalist, either."

"No, I am not a journalist, Mr Wilde. I am here with an advance payment (a payment on account, if you like) for your next play — the one you will write after *Earnest*." Miranda was hastily (without letting her "umbrella" fall) unfastening her moneybelt, which was loaded with the appropriate coins — how heavy it was, and how numismatists would have clawed her, had they known. "There are 150 guineas here. But, Mr Wilde, forgive me; I am going to reveal knowledge for which I can offer no explanation; there is no person living at this moment who is responsible for my information — not the porter at the Albemarle, not the Marquis, not even Mr Robert Ross. I swear it on my honour — on your own honour! I beg of you to hear me out. Let your reverence for youth intercede for me — call my words clairvoyance, if you will — but I know of the card the Marquis left for you; I know that Mr Ross is to meet you here, in little more than an hour; I know what you intend to say to him. O, Mr Wilde, please reconsider! Please use this money to pay your bill here, and then go to Paris, as you would have done already, if the hotel had not refused to release your baggage until the bill was paid. Tear up the card; ignore the foolish Marquis; live long and happily! Believe me, Mr Wilde, if you prosecute the Marquis (as you now intend), a life of misery lies before you, and an early and most painful death. You will never write another play — your great genius will henceforth be silent. O, Mr Wilde, you are at the verge of a most terrible abyss!"

Miranda had moved herself almost to tears — but distressful tears must not, she knew, be shed in the presence of Oscar Wilde. Exquisite youth that she appeared (the colour fluctuating in her cheeks, her eyes wide with emotion, her lips parted), Miranda breathlessly awaited the effect upon Wilde of her surely impressive intellect.

"My dear boy, you do seem to have a quite improbably lavish acquaintance with my personal affairs." Miranda noticed now how he placed a bent forefinger before his mouth as he spoke (a mannerism, as she had read, designed to conceal his unattractive teeth); she noticed how carefully waved was his dark hair, how flabby his hands were — and she felt for him that surge of yearning love which is aroused in a woman by the deficiencies of a man (since these, alone, are essential; in these, alone, she knows that she will never prove to have been mistaken).

But Oscar Wilde was continuing. "Your clairvoyance, however, is wonderfully inexact. You are altogether at fault, I assure you, in supposing me resolved on a criminal prosecution."

"O, Mr Wilde, you cannot deceive me in this way, however kindly your intention. I know that you have resolved to prosecute; I know it absolutely, quite beyond any power — even of yours — to persuade me otherwise. Take heed of my words, Mr Wilde — think how it will be, to descend from the heights, into the very abyss!"

Miranda wrenched the door open and fled from the room, utterly discomposed by this cherished being's frivolous denial of the awful step he contemplated. The controls of her time machine had already been set (when she landed in the park), and she was able to unsheathe and erect it on the run; thus, Miranda was gone before either Oscar Wilde, or anybody else in the hotel, had any chance of witnessing her departure; she was in her own room again, a quarter of an hour later than when she had left it.

In the rush of her travel, Miranda suffered unexpected qualms; what if Hildebrand had been right, and she returned to a world that was unrecognisable? But as she changed costumes, very slowly, Miranda's distress had become different; would she now be forever out of touch with her own world's reality? For in her memory was no alteration; Oscar Wilde's imprisonment remained, and the number and names of his works were unchanged. Yet she knew that such words as hers could never have been fruitless — and that the money had given him must have been spent.

When she heard the voices of Hugh and Viola at her door,

Miranda sighed, and sprang to admit them; her contact with reality was not irretrievably lost, then. There must have been, as her expectations promised, a performance of *The Importance of Being Earnest* that night; Viola and Hugh, having been among its audience, were calling on her afterwards, as she had arranged. From the observations they would let fall, she could surely gain some notion of the plays, unknown to her, which Wilde had written; and how she would enjoy herself in the library tomorrow, bringing her knowledge into step with the world around her — which she, singlehanded, had changed!

"What a play!" was Hugh's greeting. "What a genius Oscar Wilde possessed! Such a gift for creating happiness! Ah, if only he could have gone on writing; if only he hadn't taken that ghastly Marquis to court!"

And Viola shook her head, in tragic affirmation. "Why — why did he ever do it? Utterly incomprehensible! Always, for all the world, completely incomprehensible!"

Robbie Ross was in full agreement with her, on a Thursday evening in 1895, when he uselessly urged his friend to change his mind again.

"No, dear Robbie." Oscar Wilde was adamant. "You don't understand. It is true that, after I had written you that desperate letter, I decided for myself that it would be folly to embark on a criminal prosecution. But now I have been assured that I am *fated* to go ahead; a most beautiful personality has come to tell me so. I attempted to protest — but he would have absolutely none of it; he assured me that it was written already in the book of destiny. Ah, what genius it is to be young! Without his coming, I should certainly not have proceeded; but, with the subtle voice of the omnipotent Tempter, who attracts the sinner to the fruit by proclaiming it forbidden, he has promised me, even, the descent into the Abyss! Ah, you don't know how he has inspired me, Robbie! I shall make the most beautiful statements in court ..."

Miranda was desolate — she would never understand her failure — but she did feel a strong instinct that she must never confide in Hildebrand, and ask him for his explanation. Even if his thinking did not, as so often, prove to be quite absurdly circular — what could his opinion alter? After all, is the past not past?

Creator

DAVID LAKE

Real are the dreams of Gods

Keats, *"Lamia"*

It was a fine morning as usual on the planet Olympus, and Jay
Crystal was just finishing breakfast in his private palace when
the robot butler announced the arrival of the Installer.

Jay rose at once, and almost ran to the cleared room. He
had never been so excited in all his immortal life. When he
reached the room — yes, there it was — the gleaming machine,
like a medium-sized light-smell-sound concert organ, was being
rapidly assembled by the red-and-green painted robots of the
Creation Corporation; and there beside them — not super-
vising, for the robots knew their job perfectly, but as it were
giving them his blessing — stood the Installer.

The Installer was a dark Olympian, as dark as Jay was fair.
His thick eyebrows were now bent in a slightly quizzical smile.

"We took the liberty, sir, of starting before you arrived.
We thought you would like the job finished as quickly as
possible."

"Yes, yes," said Jay. "Fine. How long will they be?"

"Another minute or so; and then — Mr Crystal, we are
so glad you decided to have one. I do admire your work for
public kinematron — those delicate, civilised sketches, but you
know, the creatron represents the future in the entertainment
industry. Besides, using this you can really get inspiration for
your kine work. Ah . . ."

The robots were drawing aside.

"They've finished. There now, sir, you have your creatron! Would you now please throw the master switch yourself?

That's not just a piece of ceremony: it's essential for the working of such a personalised machine ..."

Jay moved to the red button-switch on the wall. He touched it lightly with his right index finger, knowing as he did so that the switch was picking up his personal emanations, as it was designed to do; and in milliseconds the creatron sprang to life. There was a faint but profound humming sound, and on the display screen high above the console there appeared a jagged track of greenish light.

"That's your brain monitor," said the Installer, smiling gently. "It's basically an insurance device. We don't anticipate you will have any trouble, sir, but just occasionally a client gets so emotionally involved in his creations that we have to — er — assist. All creatron monitors broadcast to our company headquarters, where they are under constant surveillance. At the moment, all the monitor is showing is that you are pleasurably excited. As you should be! You want to have a session at once? Yes, naturally. I'll send the robots out, and then ..."

And then they were seated together at the creatron; or rather, the Installer was seated, but Jay lay forward, comfortably semi-prone, his body supported by the harness, his hands lying lightly on the control panels, his head nested in the sensitive helmet. Before and below him, through the great window, lay the void that would be his world — when he created it. At the moment it was only a grey amorphous chaos. The Installer was explaining the controls.

"Under your left hand, sir, you have the fundamental law dials and buttons. Those four in the bottom row are the dimensors, for length, breadth, depth, and the large graduated knob which you twist is for time. Above is the row for forces: analogues of nuclear, electro, weak and gravitation; and above those again is the pseudo-mass setter. It'll all be clearer if you create a world now, for practice."

"Er ... can I erase it afterwards?"

"Surely," smiled the Installer. "There, on your extreme bottom left is the annihilator. Yes, the red button. Or, if you

don't want to destroy your world without trace, above that is
this amber button marked 'Store'. That will remove your
universe from the working area, but with its whole history
recorded, so that you can replay it or return it to the working
area for further development. Using 'Store' you can create
several different universes. The corresponding button on your
right hand — the one marked 'Hold' — that merely suspends
time while the working is in progress. The creatures in the world
don't notice a thing, of course, because there is no time for
them to notice *in*. Among other things, 'Hold' lets you insert
a special move if you want to. And the graduated knob below
'Hold' is the Limited Time Cancel; it erases the recent past, and
lets you insert a whole new sequence. And those buttons nearby
on your right are the initiators, for just such insertions . . ."

Jay frowned. "I've heard of them. Miracle buttons, they
call them, don't they?"

"I believe some people do," said the Installer. "Very
popular they are, too, with some of our customers. They make
creation as easy as sketching with a pencil and rubber."

"And about as artistic," said Jay scornfully.

"Quite so. I can see you are a bit of a purist, Mr Crystal.
Well, I like that; so am I. You can get some quite comic effects
with the miracle buttons, but it *is* more satisfying to let a world
be self-consistent. That's like not cheating when you're playing
patience. You lay down the laws at the start, and then you abide
by the consequences. You will have enough degrees of freedom
anyway, through the wills of your creatures; or, to put it another way, they'll be self-willed enough to surprise and amuse
you. Now, would you like to start?"

Jay set the time control, then pressed "Run" and one of
the dimensors. At once there was a white line running across
the world-space; or rather, space now existed as one dimension
of length isolated and lonely in the midst of chaos.

"What happens if I don't press any more dimensors?"
he asked.

"Then you get a one-dimensional universe. That's quite
possible; indeed, you can have an amusing, rather classical

world with One-D. Of course, all your creatures will have to be line-masses, and they won't be able to cross or pass each other ..."

Jay hurriedly pressed the second dimensor. At once chaos vanished, and the world became one vast sheet of pale grey.

"Now you have Flatland," said the Installer. "One of our clients, a Mr Abbas, achieved a notable creation in two dimensions ..."

"With circles and squares for characters," said Jay. "Yes, I've heard. But all that's a bit limited. Lacks human interest." He touched the third dimensor.

The pale greyness changed subtly. He felt a thrill of vertigo: it was as though he were looking down an infinite height, frightful, fathomless — utter emptiness forever. He clutched desperately at his armrests.

"Realistic, isn't it?" said the Installer. "Don't worry, you can't possibly fall *into* it. That space is totally unreal in our terms; it has no more existence than a space described in a work of fiction. Or, to put it another way, it is *inside* you, — in your mind. It will be less frightening when you've filled it with something. Now, go on, Mr Crystal ... give your world some laws. May I suggest, if you want something realistic, the following settings, just to start with."

Jay followed his instructions, and punched the buttons. The next moment he couldn't help shouting with amazement. All at once, through the window, there were shining sparks in a blackness, like a silent firework display.

"There now," said the Installer. "You have just created light and matter, and your universe is exploding. If you turn the Time control anticlockwise, the explosion will become a sedate expansion ... yes, so. Those sailing blobs are galaxies. Now, if you want a close-up view of one, this View control above the depth button ..."

For half an hour of real time Jay manoeuvred, fascinated. He seemed to plunge into the heart of a galaxy, which was now condensing into stars. He watched a solar system form about a young yellow star, and then he followed a small planet through its evolution until the asteroids stopped falling on it, and the cratered surface spewed out air and water, and nearly the whole surface was a steaming, cloud-wreathed ocean.

"Now is the time to create life," said the Installer softly.

"Doesn't it arise automatically?" asked Jay, surprised.

"Nothing really arises 'automatically', Mr Crystal. The whole machine only works because your mental impulses are being implemented. And there are certain crucial stages which require a special impulse from you. This is one of them. But all you have to do is *will* it, and it will happen. Say 'let there be life', if you like ... the verbalisation is sometimes a help."

"Let there be life," said Jay.

And there was life. At this setting of the Time control a billion years passed by in a minute. In two minutes there was a fringe of green around the shores of the growing continents. In four minutes, there were vast forests, and amphibians floundering through them. Then Jay touched a control under his left hand, and slowed down created Time with respect to the Olympian viewers.

Now it took a few minutes to evolve giant reptiles, birds, mammals. And Jay began to feel increasingly strange and uncomfortable. He squirmed.

"I ..." he began.

"Not to worry," said the Installer, one eye on the monitor-screen, one hand on Jay's arm. "This is normal, sir. You are creating higher life forms, aren't you? They are beginning to have a clearer and clearer consciousness. And of course it's *your* consciousness in every one of them. Tell me how it feels to you."

"As if I'm being torn apart. Divided in a million pieces. And being stabbed with a million needles."

"Quite so. You can control that two ways. First, mechanically — that grey dial on your right, marked 'Empathy', turn it anticlockwise and the pains will fade. But so will the involvement. Experienced creators damp the pains without losing involvement, by a technique of mental relaxation. I can show you that, if you like, but it will take a bit of time. We'd have to have another session, perhaps several. There's no extra charge for that, if you wish it. It's part of installation service. I always use relaxation myself, I may say."

"You mean, you — you practise creation too?" said Jay.

"Of course, sir. I have my own 'tron at home. I have to be an experienced practitioner, you realise, otherwise I could hardly advise clients."

The next moment, Jay uttered a yelp. The Installer leant across and twisted the grey dial to the left.

"Pardon me, sir: you can turn it up if you like, but I wanted to shield you from emotional insult. What *was* that, if I may ask? My guest-viewer here is not so finely adjusted as your master one."

"A primate," said Jay shakily. "It was caught and slowly crushed by a huge constricting snake. I could feel its fear, its horror, its pain." He pondered. "Say, this is *my* creation, isn't it? *My universe*! Why do I have to have pain in it? Isn't there a setting, or something, that I can introduce to stop all that kind of thing?"

"Well," said the Installer, with a slow, dark smile, "if you feel that way, you have several possible strategies. Number One: you can slightly alter the fundamental laws. With a different ratio between the four forces, you could make sentient life impossible anywhere in your universe, as you said. Strategy Number Two: use one of the miracle buttons. Actually, you can insert a set program, so that life develops with no sensory nerves, hence no pain — but no pleasure either. That way, you'd have to program for another series of miracles, to keep the things alive at all — because of course with no pain they'd always be getting killed. They'd have no incentive, you see, to avoid falling over cliffs and so on. Wouldn't you agree, sir, that that would be, well, rather an inartistic universe? Your creatures would be zombies; and you couldn't get any kind of kick out of them. Believe me, I know; I tried that once myself, as an experiment. It was only good for laughs. Well, there remains Strategy Number Three — discreet miracles."

"What do you mean?" asked Jay.

"You can punch the Hold button at various critical moments — for example, you could have saved that primate by pressing Hold and then annihilating that snake. That button on top left — the orange one — that's the Selective Erase. You can even program the machine to make that happen every time, in defined situations, so that you don't have to sit up all night working a billion separate miracles an hour. And you can even interfere with evolution along the same lines — this is a little more complicated, but I'll show you how — and wipe out the breeding stock of reptiles which would develop into snakes. And so on."

"Inartistic," said Jay dully. "Isn't there any other way?"

"I'm afraid not. There is no way to have pleasant things without unpleasant things except by miracles." He paused, and half rose. "Well, sir, if you'll excuse me, I have another appointment in half an hour — another installation. Business is booming, you see. But if you like, I'll come around tomorrow to see how you're making out."

"Yes, yes," said Jay absently. He had pressed the Hold button, and his universe, though it didn't know it, was in stasis. For one of his primate species had descended from the trees; and now he was thinking about the creation of Man.

Next morning, when the robot butler emitted a discreet electronic cough, Jay was deeply engrossed in the creatron. At the third cough, which was as loud as that of a large carnivore in the world of his private creation, Jay finally looked up.

"Mr Harriman, sir."

"Who?"

"The Installer, from the Creation Corporation."

"Show him in, show him in right away," said Jay irritably. "I need him now."

Harriman glided in with his usual faint dark smile. "Well, Mr Crystal, how are you making out?"

"Not too well," Jay admitted. "In fact, I'm having trouble developing a humanoid species at all. I ... I've tried with likely primates on several planets, and ... well, I've had to use some miracle buttons ... I thought that mightn't matter just for practice. I picked the likeliest looking species, and then killed them off ... I mean annihilated ... its nearest rivals ..."

"What, individually? That must have been a colossal task!"

"No, I looked at the instruction tapes and I ... er ... set up a program. The program identified any over-violent, over-aggressive primate species ... giant carnivorous gorillas and such like ... and automatically wiped them out."

"That was clever handling, I must say," said Harriman. "I thought I would have to explain to you about programming, but I see you've beaten me to it. Well, sir, what happened after you wiped out those monster primates? Can I ... er ... inspect?"

"Sure," said Jay; and they both bent over their viewers. Harriman showed Jay how to increase the specificity and magnification of the guest viewer; and now they both got a good look at a sylvan scene.

The planet was much like Olympus, with a yellow sun and a blue sky, but of course much wilder, with huge forests and tropical savannas. And there, on the fringe of a warm forest, they saw a troop of primates. There were some fifty individuals of both sexes and all ages, a good deal hairier than humans, but with bare flat faces, and delicate features. A few were strolling among the trees, unhurriedly foraging for fruit, some on all fours, others on their hind legs. They were clearly able to walk bipedally, but they were not being purists about it. It sometimes happened that two foragers came up to a luscious fruit about the same time: when this happened, each blinked at the other, and then backed away with a curious little simper. Neither got the fruit: both went off to look for pickings elsewhere.

All of a sudden another troop of the creatures emerged from the depths of the forest.

"This should be interesting," said Harriman in Jay's ear. "A crisis situation. Now, in my worlds I've always found — hey, what's wrong with them?"

The "crisis situation" was resolving itself very simply. The invading troop infiltrated the earlier arrivals, who blinked at them and simpered. The invaders simpered back. They took one look at the wide savanna ahead, whinnied or whimpered a little, and melted back into the deep forest.

"Well!" said Harriman. "Is that what always happens, when two groups meet? No battles, no defence of territory?"

"No," said Jay sharply. "I'm happy to say, my people are not violent types. I chose the most peaceful species I could find. I wanted to avoid the unhappy history of our own early development."

"I see. And do your peaceful 'people' never go out onto the savanna?"

"Never, you see, there are large carnivores out there."

"Aren't your people carnivores themselves? I should have thought ..."

"Certainly not," said Jay. "They're strict vegetarians. I want to develop a decent civilisation, without all the outmoded barbarism. You know that's the kind of ideal I have been promoting in my kine sketches — civilised interaction between individuals and species. Surely it's important to start right?"

Harriman took a deep breath. "Yes, it is," he said. "Tell me, how long in their terms has your species there been living at that evolutionary level? Semi-bipedal forest-living fruit-eaters, with no weapons ... er, perhaps I should say tools?"

"Twenty million years," said Jay disconsolately. "And in that time on this planet my program has eliminated four cousin-species, all savage hunters."

"Well, Mr Crystal," said Harriman, "that was your mistake. You have obviously, through your program, eliminated four very promising candidates for full humanity."

"Humanity?" cried Jay. "They were murderous beasts ..."

"So were we all, once," said Harriman, with a gleam in his dark eyes. "And the beast still lurks in us; our civilisation is just a veneer, necessary perhaps, but at bottom, for many of us, rather *boring*. Hence, largely, this boom in the creation business. The big Box allows many people to indulge harmlessly in delicious savagery. Wait till I've shown you the full scope of the empathy techniques, Mr Crystal. Then perhaps you'll change your ideas a little as to what's desirable and undesirable in a sub-world. Wouldn't you like to be, say, the savage leader of a mighty horde of magnificent barbarians, roaming through the jungle and the desert, the mountain and the plain, sacking towns and cities, holding at your mercy your cowering enemies and their equally cowering but much more attractive women?''

"I would *not!*"

"Oh never mind," sighed Harriman. "But look, sir, whatever your ultimate ideals, let me tell you that you'll *never* create a human-type species this way, out of these nice guys. Nice guys come last. In fact, they don't even run at all. Two things you need: meat-eating, for a start; and aggression, selfishness, sheer death-take-the-hindmost competition as well. Hunting skills, brains, and the competition with other members of the same species ... that makes for real *ambition*. Ambition is what got us to Olympus in the first place. You remember how space travel began? It was a space race that put our race in space.''

"There must be another way," said Jay stubbornly. "Look, Harriman, we may have made it to Olympus, but ... I've read history too, you know ... we wrecked our original planet doing it, and damn nearly exterminated ourselves in the process. The damage we did to the universe! I'd like to explore a better way, to see if I can't create a race without our evils. This is not just a game; if I succeed, I may have some vital message to give to all of us in the real world.''

"All right ... try," said Harriman, shrugging. "I'll teach you all there is to know about the machine, all the techniques of programming, empathy, and so on. And then it'll be up to you. I might make one suggestion, though.''

"What's that?''

"If you have to use the miracle buttons to favour one sub-human species over another, pick the meanest, the cunningest, the most bloody-minded one that the planet offers, that way you'll speed up the evolution of true humanity very much. Oh, all right, all right, I know you won't ... in that case, why not merely let things take their course? Keep off the miracle buttons, and see what evolution throws up. When they're wearing clothes — and swords — then you can take them in hand, and try to tame them. There are techniques for tampering even with intelligent species, you know, to make them milder or fiercer. For instance, you do this ..."

By the end of that session Jay was handling the creatron so expertly that Harriman decided he could be left to get on with his experiments for several days. In fact, it was a whole week before the butler announced him again. Jay had not been actually on the creatron, but pacing beside it. When Harriman entered, he went forward, almost running, to meet him.

"Harriman, I ... it's overwhelming ..." he flustered.

"It *is* rather exciting, once you get into it, isn't it?" said the dark visitor, smiling. "Well, tell me all about it. You know, Mr Crystal, we will soon be able to cross you off my list of *new* clients, and then the maintenance departments of the Corporation will be officially in charge of you, not my team. After that, I hope we can be just fellow practitioners of the great art; and — why not? — friends. Well now, Mr Crystal ..."

"Call me Jay," said Jay. "Please."

"All right, Jay, if you'll call me Sam ... short for Samael. All my friends do."

"Sam, I've created Man."

"Congratulations, Jay. What did you do?"

"Nothing really. I let evolution take its course, and humanity arose! They became very like us."

"What, those silly good-natured ape-men in the forest?"

"Oh, hell no," said Jay, waving his hand as though brushing away an insect. "I got rid of them. In fact, I decided not to cheat any more — no more miracle buttons — so I started from scratch. I erased my first universe ..."

"Your whole *universe!* Why not just the planet?"

"I had messed about too much," said Jay contritely. "I wanted to start over, clean. So I did. Set up the four laws, and the mass-constant, and ran up the new universe at top speed. Then I chose a middling-sized galaxy, and began to watch various promising yellow suns. I just *watched*. Many of them developed the right sort of planets, and I created life over and over, just by willing it, as you showed me. And then I let the Life behave as it wanted to. I used the middle empathy band ... it was a really weird sensation."

"It sure is," said Harriman, with a reminiscent gleam in his dark eyes. "You feel it coming out of your gut, don't you? All of them: the sharks, the snakes, the dinosaurs, the tigers. I like to use the micro-focus sometimes, and feel myself giving birth to the little fellows, the bacteria, the viruses. Hell, I've fissioned myself into a billion bugs: syphilis, rabies, cancer cells, and also into the leucocytes that go for them. I've killed myself, eaten myself on all levels. There's no kick like it."

"Yes, well, it's certainly disturbing," said Jay, passing his hand dazedly over his fair hair. "So much horror, so much evil — it becomes evil, after all, when you reach the highest animals — and every bit of it was *me!* Out of the darkness of my mind, the things I hate took form. To be frank, I nearly went crazy from time to time: I had to fight hard not to reach for the miracle buttons and exterminate monster after monster. But I didn't touch the buttons; I let those nightmares do what they wanted to do!" He paused, shuddering.

"You *did* practise the relax-withdrawal, didn't you?" said Harriman anxiously. "Things might get rough if you didn't."

"Oh, sure, I withdrew," said Jay flatly. "What else? Do you think I could stand deep empathy, or even middle empathy, with a *massacre*? When I was all the victims and all the killers at the same time?"

"Okay, okay," said Harriman. "So ... what did you come up with?"

"Civilisations," said Jay, "many civilisations, on many planets. Not all were humanoids. Great Olympus, I've been centaurs, I've been dolphins, kangaroids, octopoids, but in the end it was the humanoids who fascinated me most. So *like* us!''

"And were there any meek and mild races among your civilisations?''

"Not one," admitted Jay sadly. "All carnivores and killers, like you said, Sam. I suppose it had to be that way at the start. Paradise was never lost, but maybe it can be found. That's what I want to work towards. Meanwhile, meanwhile, I must say, some of my races have done the most astonishing things! Why, they've even produced *literature*!''

"They frequently do," nodded Harriman, smiling. "In fact, a lot of the kine-writers plagiarise from the works of their own creatures. You might think of that yourself, Jay. It's not really cheating. After all, your creatures are *you*. They're a part of your mind which you're liberating, putting to use.''

"I never imagined I could write anything like *this*," said Jay. "I transcribed it onto tape." He flicked a switch. "Listen! Of course, this is only a translation into our language, from one that my creatures invented. It sounds much better in the original, which — great Olympus! I understand perfectly. It's from a huge long poem.''

The remote, impersonal voice of the speech-synthesiser began to chant:

"Full well I know in my heart that the sacred city will fall,
The day shall come when Troy and her king will be laid low,
Priam and Priam's people, the folk of the strong ash spear:
Yet not for them do I grieve, the queen, the king nor
   my brothers
Many and brave, who will fall in the dust before the foemen,
But for you, dear wife, in the day when some bronze-
   coated Akhaian
Shall lead you away a slave weeping for your lost freedom.
Then in some foreign land will you bend to your master's will
At the hard toil of the loom, or under the burden of water,
Bearing your load from enemy streams to enemy houses.
Some man shall say as he sees you, 'Why, that was the
   wife of Hektor,

The best of heroes in war, when men still fought
  about Troy.'
So shall one say, and bring fresh grief to you, friendless
  and widowed;
But let me be dead in that day, and let the heaped earth
  hide me
Before I hear your cries, as they drag you into slavery."

The voice passed into silence, and Jay switched off the
tape. He said, "They don't write poetry like that nowadays,
not in *our* universe."

Harriman shrugged. "Of course not. How can they ...
how can we? We have a comfortable civilisation, and the im-
mortality pill, and wars are banned by the United Planets
Organisation. Just look at what makes up great poetry — for
instance, that extract you taped, which I agree is pretty good:
death, war, slavery, the blackest of evils. Sheer tragedy.
Without that, no brilliant poetry. And no kicks. You have to
go to your sub-universes now for those. Say, by the way, what
race produced that poem? They must be pretty good, even by
my standards."

Jay shuddered. "They're the most frightening of all
humanoids. Not much to look at. In relative measurements
rather small, in fact nearly all specimens are well under eight
feet —"

"The runts!" said Harriman, grimacing.

"— but they make up for that in their fierceness, in grim
determination, in sheer ingenious *cruelty*. When I realise that
they're *me* ..." He shook his head. "I must do something
about them. They're a challenge to all I love and believe in."

"Why not just press a certain button?" said Harriman.
"Jay, it's not worth upsetting yourself."

"No ... no more annihilations," said Jay firmly. "I promised that to myself. These people are *mine*. I must help them,
change them. I'll think of something." He seemed to change
the subject. "Sam, can you tell me one little thing? What's that
knob for, on the extreme top right of the control panel?"

"What knob?"

"This," said Jay, touching it. The thing was a small projection, a metal hump on the main body of the panel.

"That . . . oh, nothing," said Harriman, with a quick little laugh. "That shouldn't be on there. In one version of the machine there was an extra control there for a special kind of empathy, but we found it too dangerous, and the control was discarded. It's surely not functional on yours."

"Dangerous?" said Jay slowly. "*Can* the creatron be dangerous? In the real world, I mean?"

"Not if you use it sensibly," said Harriman, "but in the early days of the development we had a few accidents with people who *weren't* sensible. In one of the worst accidents . . . well, we never could find out *exactly* what happened, because you know if the creator *dies*, all his universes are automatically erased. Their being is his being, and when he goes, so do they."

"Somebody *died*?" said Jay, huge-eyed. "On *Olympus*? How is it that didn't make the newscasts?"

"It wasn't on Olympus, luckily," said Harriman. "It was on Amentet, which is practically owned by our Corporation, so luckily we were able to hush the matter up. Anyway, it was the guy's own fault — he got hooked by the Box, and we didn't have enough experience at that time to read the signs of addiction. He was a Corporation employee, name of O. Siris, I believe — he kept muttering that he was being torn apart, and then finally he *was* torn apart. He had been bleeding from more than a dozen wounds when they found his body, still strapped to the machine. You see, some dreams can be deadly, if you let them take hold of you. Now, Jay, you have been warned. These present models are much safer than the early ones, but that monitor is not there for nothing. And if you feel you're getting into any kind of trouble, don't hesitate to get me on the laserphone."

"All right," said Jay.

The fine Olympian days went by. Jay was now thoroughly absorbed by his hobby, his creatron; no longer did he write for the big 3-D screen, but then he didn't need to: he had an adequate income from his royalties on former works plus the basic salary paid by the United Planets to all citizens as of right, the Existence Benefit. The cut-down in his work hardly mattered: he felt that he was deepening his understanding of human nature so much with his new dream-box that when he returned to kine-writing he would produce masterpieces. What was perhaps more serious was that his absorption in the sub-world was sapping his social life in the real universe. His current girlfriend, Aphra, complained about it. One early morning, as they lay on Jay's anti-gravity bed, Aphra swallowed the pill which rendered her at once immortal and sterile, washed it down with a shot-glass of nectar, and said: "Jay, I'm leaving."

"Yes," said Jay vaguely. "I suppose it's time." He slipped off the other side of the bed and reached for his robe, his eyes unfocused.

Aphra sat up sharply on the foam force-field, her long yellow hair waving like angry snakes, her usually soulful blue eyes for once contracted in irritation.

"No," she said, "I mean, I've had enough. Pay attention, will you? Your mind's not on it when we make love any more. Well, you aren't the only fellow who ... Sam, for instance, now he's more fun to be with, there's a bit of spice to him! And he can take that box or leave it. If you want to see me again, Jay, give me a lase at his place."

Jay let her go, nodding absent-mindedly. He was not jealous. Besides, Sam was now his best friend. He would take good care of Aphra.

And Sam came round almost every day now, to swap yarns about sub-universes. Their dealer-client relationship was now officially at an end: they were merely two fans together. Sam seemed to be much more relaxed about the possible dangers of the creatron.

"I checked with the Corp," he said, on one of these visits. "The Total Empathy control is *not* functional on your machine. For some reason the button's still there under that metal cap, but the technicians assured me that there's no connections under it. All new models, from now on, will have no button there at all. Anyway, I know you can't do anything foolish like that guy Siris." He smiled, and nodded at the creatron. "How's it going in there, Jay?"

"Terrible ... and wonderful." Jay swallowed. "Whenever I take it off Hold I've got the Time control set for scanning at a year an hour on that planet I mentioned to you. Yes, I know that's slow, but I'm following their civilisations in detail now. I've moved on about two centuries from the time of that poem I quoted, and ... strange things are happening, Sam. They're developing philosophy, *religion* ..."

"Yeah, they usually do," said Harriman, grinning. "I always enjoy my creatures' religions. Every one of them involves humanoid sacrifices — some of them very ingenious in their methods — and quite often the sacrifices are offered to Guess Who? Me, yours truly, the owner and maker of the universe, Samael Harriman himself!"

Jay shuddered. "There's some of that in my world, too. It's horrible. But ... I have hopes. It's decreasing, especially in a belt about the middle of my world's greatest continent-complex. Over the last two centuries, there have been some brilliant men arising, in several different cultures. One little tribe gave up human sacrifice long ago, and substituted animals. Then, recently, one of their best men denounced even that. Curiously enough, he claimed to speak in *my* name. He told his people that I wanted 'mercy, and not sacrifice'. And in other countries, other men have been saying much the same thing. Look: let's get on the machine, and I'll show you."

When they were at the viewers, Jay swept the scanner down through the clouds of that blue and white planet. Below them lay the peaks of a towering mountain range capped with ice and snow. Jay swept southwards, at decreasing altitude, until they seemed to be hovering with an eagle's-eye-view over a wide river-plain — a warm area, with jungles and narrow clearings where a brown-skinned people were growing rice. Here and there the clearings became wider, and in their centres, on the banks of the rivers, rose walled cities, cities that looked well laid-out, with busy markets, gorgeous palaces, richly adorned temples, and spacious parks.

Finally, Jay narrowed the view to one city, and in that city to a beautiful park. In the distance, tame protected royal deer were wandering over lawns and between flame-of-the-forest trees. Closer up, between the scattered trees sat, squatted, stood or strolled a large crowd of all kinds of people: little clusters of the bejewelled nobles and merchants, with their bodyguards and slaves of both sexes; shaven-headed priests; and a large ragged rabble of common folk, men, women and children, with a fringe of dirty and diseased beggars. Towards the centre of this crowd was a cleared space around a great green-leaved tree. Before the tree, in the front rank of the crowd, sat a handful of gaunt men in yellow robes: and facing these and the whole crowd, there sat under the tree another yellow-robed man, a man less gaunt, with an imposing presence and handsome, composed features.

That, at least, was the scene as Harriman saw it. For Jay, it was different: for he not only *saw* the scene, he *was* it. He was that hot earth, that grass, and his were the branches and green twigs that swayed in the warm breeze. These sensations were relatively dim; much more strongly, he felt the life of the deer browsing in the distance, and of the crowd milling in the foreground: he was proud and well-fed in the nobles, he was seductive in their dancing girls, he was lusty in the young farmer come into the city for the day, he was in dull pain in the old beggar with the crippled knee.

But above all, he was in the man under the tree.

He felt a vast compassion rise in him, as he looked through the man's eyes at the crowd. Suffering ... all the world was suffering: birth was suffering, old age was suffering, sickness was suffering, death was suffering. Contact with unpleasant things was suffering, parting from what one wanted was suffering. And only he knew the cure, only he could teach that best way out, the Middle Path ...

And so he, the Enlightened One, taught them. The Four

Noble Truths, the Eightfold Path, the Five Precepts. All life was sacred: therefore abstain from injuring any living creature. And all life was *one*: the idea that you had an individual, eternal soul was the great illusion from which you had to break free. If you clung to that illusory self, you would remain bound on the wheel of suffering existence.

"*Sabbe sankhăra dukkha.*" The words of that warm country's language came fluently out of his mouth, sonorous but not strange, since he had the gift of all his creatures' tongues. "All compounded things are suffering ..."

The crowd were impressed. A few of the people plucked up courage to ask him questions. A priest:

"How should one sacrifice to the gods, O Enlightened One?"

"The best sacrifice is that of right moral action, of mercy to all living thing. As for the gods, they too are fellow creatures: they too need enlightenment."

"O Holy One!" cried a woman suddenly. She was a new arrival; she bore on her hip a baby which ... no, not a baby: the only life in it was on the microscopic level of decay. The corpse of a baby. To this personal grief she clung; and was therefore bound. "O Holy One, you know all secrets: grant me a charm, a medicine to bring my son back to life!"

And he answered her: "Go woman, to every house in the city where there has been no death, and ask of them one mustard seed."

"But," said the woman, stricken, "the city is old: in every house there has been death."

"That knowledge," said the man under the tree, "is the only medicine for death."

At this point Jay began to withdraw from the scene, his viewpoint rising till he was looking down on the deer park through the eyes of a brown hawk that glided and soared, uttering mournful, tinkling cries as it scanned the earth in hopes of prey. He pressed the Hold button.

As they both got off the machine, he translated for Harriman the message of the man under the tree. He felt astonished and elated. He finished: "I didn't know I had any such things in me! Me, the Enlightened One! Why, Sam, on the strength of that I could set up as a philosopher in *this* world!"

Sam yawned. "I could tell it was *your* world all right, Jay. *My* bright boys don't come up with teachings of that kind. Currently, my people are going strong for Zapism."

"Zapism?"

"Yeah. The First Noble Truth of Zapism is stated like this: Zap a rat before he zaps you. Thus spake my Zapathrustra. However, Jay, I'll hand it to you: your world there is brilliant, complex, *artistic*. I liked your whole crowd, the beggars, the prostitutes, the bully boys, the nobles. You've really got tremendous talent — no, that's too weak — I should say, genius. My worlds are cruder, simpler."

"Sam," said Jay, "what did he mean by saying 'the gods are our fellow creatures, they too need enlightenment'? He was talking about *us*, wasn't he?"

"I guess so," said Harriman. "Why not?"

"But . . . but he sounded as if he *knew* about us, as if we were on the same plane of reality as himself!"

"Again, why not?" Harriman smiled darkly. "After all, that guy is really a part of your mind, Jay, so in one sense he *is* on the same plane. And our creatures *do* get inklings about us. That's a thing we fans discovered pretty early in the game." He laughed, shortly. "Before he had that accident, that guy Siris said something that gave us all in the Corp a bit of a jolt. See what you make of it, O Enlightened One! He said, 'We made the sub-worlds, but who made *our* world? Maybe the sub-worlders did. We invent them, they invent us. You scratch my essence, I scratch yours. Mutual make-believe! It's creative writing that makes the worlds go round . . .' How about that, huh?"

Jay muttered, "Herakleitos!"

"I beg your pardon," said Harriman. "Is that a new swearword, or something?"

"No," said Jay. "Herakleitos is one of the philosophers of that planet in my sub-universe. He has ideas very like the one you mentioned. He lives in a country a bit to the north-west of the one we were looking at; they're a brilliant people too. You would like them: very artistic, but very bloody-minded. Herakleitos is one of the bloodiest minded and the cleverest of them. He says that gods and men live in a mutual relationship — each produces the other. He also says that all existence depends on conflict, strife, war: if conflict were to cease, the whole universe would disappear."

"He's dead right," smiled Harriman. "At least, he'd be right in *my* universe, because if the battles stopped in my world I'd press the erase button. Eternal peace is just too boring to be endured. Jay, I like the sound of your Herak guy much better than the one you just showed me: he's really on the ball."

"I must prove him wrong," muttered Jay. "Oh yes, I've learnt now that *some* aggression is necessary, in the early development of humanity. But not so much, not what is actually going on in most places of my world! War, massacre, slavery, torture . . . surely that *doesn't* have to go on."

"Oh yes it does," said Harriman crisply. "It has to go on *somewhere*, Jay, or we'll go nuts. You don't realise it, but we of the Creation Corp, we really saved our civilisation from a general breakdown. Before the Box was invented, you should have seen the figures for intakes into mental hospitals, attempted suicides, even *murders*. Poeple must have kicks, you know. Now they get 'em in their private boxes, that's all. That's why we can afford peace and painless living in the big world, the real world."

"The other worlds are real, too," said Jay. "You've already admitted that. And I know it's true. When I am *in* there, it's as real as here. To think that I once annihilated a whole universe!" He shuddered.

Harriman laughed. "Why, that's the biggest kick of all. Only, it's best not to erase it all simultaneously. If you do, they're all gone without knowing about it. If you erase selectively, *then* you can have fun, as the poor saps see their suns and moons disappearing, and then the next county, and so on. I always end a game that way."

Jay looked at Harriman, appalled. And from then on, their friendship was not what it had been.

For many days after that, Jay buried himself completely in the world of his creation. He did not leave his palace; he did not even leave the room that housed his universe, but had his robots serve his meals right there, on a small table beside the great machine. He ate hurriedly, and then returned at once to that terrible and wonderful blue and white planet.

He still kept Time going at a year an hour, which allowed him to cover a sub-world generation in a couple of Olympian days. Subjectively, when he was in middle or deep empathy, his time was the time of the sub-world, which meant that his solid dreams packed what seemed to be the experience of a lifetime into three or four "real" days.

Gradually Jay concentrated his attention on the culture which had produced the terrible philosopher Herakleitos. These people were rising to a peak of glory. Few in numbers, they nevertheless defeated a huge eastern empire: and Jay was there when they did it. He entered the brain of a fully-armed warrior, in a sea-fight by a rocky island, and felt the exultation of his host-creature as he leapt ashore and drove his spear again and again through the cowering enemies. It should have been horrible, but it was not — the man was in love with what he was doing, namely exercising one of his best skills, and doing so without personal hatred in defence of his beloved city. And, as the fight ended with the enemy all dead or in chains, words were forming in the hoplite's brain; for, Jay found, he was also a great poet. He would write a tragedy for the next festival, and this fight would be in it. But it would be no boast of his city's prowess: rather, it would be a poem of awe at the justice of the gods, how they smote down overweening pride, the lust for conquest; and the enemy king would be the tragic hero. But their own war song would have a modest place:

"O children of Hellas, onward! Now make free
Your fatherland, your children, wives, your fathers,
Gods and graves: now the fight is for all things ..."

Jay was also in the theatre on the day when the play was given. It was a great play. Best of all, the audience wept for the sufferings of the *enemy* ...

Yes, thought Jay, there is a greatness in this people. Perhaps they will transform this world into something better.

He followed them for one, two generations. And now the city which had fought so nobly was itself an Empire, with all the overweening pride and lust for conquest which the old hoplite had denounced. Quarrel after quarrel they picked with their neighbours, until they roused a whole coalition of enemies against them. Any friend of these enemies they attacked, even neutrals.

Jay watched with horror as, in time of peace, the forces of the city besieged a small neutralist island town. Traitors within opened the gates; and then the invading army rounded up the whole population, women and children in one great herd, men in another. Then the soldiers began methodically cutting the throats of the men. The women and children were screaming; but the soldiers made them wait there till the massacre was over before they drove them down to the ships and the slave markets.

One of the city poets made a play after that business, too. But this time the play was bitter and ugly with horror. It was set in legendary times, but the story was much the same: the burning town, the killing, the captive women. The enslaved queen cried:

"O God, our maker, begetter: do you see?"
And the other slave women replied:

"He sees, but the flames still burn ..."

Jay hurriedly pressed the Hold button, and withdrew. He even withdrew from the creatron room, and for several hours lay in a stupor on his luxurious bed.

When he arose, he had given up all hopes of salvation from the cities of Hellas; and he was also suffering from a profound sense of guilt. *He* was the callous god to whom the slaves cried in vain; he was also all the killers, all the slave masters, all the torturers. Somehow, he must expiate. He thought of the miracle buttons; then shook his head. No, that was merely cheating. And it solved nothing. The evil was in himself; in himself he must destroy it. He would save his world, if it killed him ...

He felt a burning desire to get down in there, to do something effective, to commit himself utterly. Then he remembered something. No, it wouldn't work — Sam had said there were no connections. But it was at least worth investigating.

Back in the room, he searched round the back of the creatron, and found the instruction tapes. He had never played them right to the end: now he did so. And finally the robot voice said, tonelessly:

"Total Empathy Control. Extreme top right, coloured purple. Not, repeat not, to be touched unless an assistant is at hand to watch the brain monitor and if necessary to impose Hold and end the empathy.

"Total Empathy produces total illusion. The operator will lose all consciousness except the consciousness of the host-creature: subjectively, he will be that creature until the creature dies or until Hold is imposed. It is advised that the operator should select a host-creature which is in good health and safe from external dangers; and also arrange with the assistant to have the Hold control activated after a very limited period. The operator should also check that he himself is in perfect physical condition before attempting Total Empathy.

"Repeat: Total Empathy Control. Extreme top right, coloured purple ..."

Jay switched off. Then he summoned his butler.

"That metal cap," he said, pointing. "Can you remove it for me?"

"Certainly, sir," said the robot. He put his metal fingers to his metal chest, opened the small window there, and took out an instrument which had hardly changed in a thousand years — a screwdriver. Then he bent over the creatron. A minute later, the butler straightened. He was holding up a small rounded piece of metal.

"Order executed, sir."

"All right, now leave me," said Jay.

"Sir." The butler left.

There it was ... a purple button, no different in size or shape from many others on the great machine. It wouldn't work, of course, Jay told himself, but it might be a help psychologically. When he was in middle to deep empathy, and had selected a worthy host, he would press it, and then follow that man through his life of striving for justice and mercy. It would have to be someone like that great Enlightened One, but perhaps more active, more impassioned. Not in the East, not in Hellas. How about that little tribe in the area between, whose prophets had so long ago denounced sacrifice?

He pressed the Run button, and history resumed. Jay located the tribe he wanted. They had passed through various tribulations, but they seemed to have emerged from them: and their faith was firmer than ever fixed in a just and merciful God. Now the Hellenes were expanding all over the middle of the planet, and they were lording it over that little tribe, too. They were trying to turn *them* into imitation Hellenes, acceptors of the world as it was, in all its sensuality and cruelty.

But the tribe resisted fiercely. Persecution merely spurred them on to greater efforts; and now the Hellenes were overthrown by a power from the West. These new overlords were a grimmer people. At first they favoured the little tribe, but surely this could not last. For the newcomers, now a great Empire, were thoroughly infected by Hellene values. They were the biggest slave masters of all time, rich, arrogant, merciless. The massacre of the island town was repeated again and again, all round the coasts of that middle sea, until the Empire was unbeatable, and Jay was thoroughly sickened.

It was now late at night. He pressed the Hold button, went to his bed chamber, and did not sleep well.

Next morning he rose a little later than usual, had a light breakfast, and threw himself upon the creatron. He pressed the Run button, and found his favourite little tribe. Yes, it was as he had expected: they were seething with righteous anger against their masters, the holders of a cruel Empire.

And everywhere among them was the feeling: the hour is at hand.

On the bank of a river stood a wild man, a prophet. A stream of pilgrims was coming to him, and he was ducking them in the river, pouring water over their heads, in token of purification.

"Prepare ye the way of the Lord!" he cried.

Jay explored the prophet's personality. Fire, yes, and indignation, but a certain narrowness, a lack of balance. Could he not find ...?

The next moment a pilgrim approached the river bank; a young man with a short neat beard and shoulder-length hair, poorly but cleanly dressed.

Jay did not need to explore. Already he felt the attraction, the greatness of soul, the burning pity.

He reached out his hand, and pressed the purple button.

The room was bright with light of Olympus' noon when they found him. Aphra was in the room a little ahead of Sam, and when she saw the inertness of the body stretched out on the machine, she uttered a shriek and rushed forward.

"Sam, he's bleeding!" she cried.

"Hope so," muttered Harriman. He ran to the right side of the creatron, and punched the Hold button. Then he turned to look at Jay.

Blood was running along his forearms. Aphra was feeling his chest, touching his lips.

"He's alive!" she whispered, brightening. "Oh, Sam, what happened?"

"I can guess," said Harriman grimly, looking at the exposed purple button. "Those idiot engineers assured me ... but never mind that now. Let's get him off of that, but carefully: he might have some bones broken. Damn lucky thing you insisted on coming today. I don't believe they even had anybody in the Corp watching the monitor. No, don't try to move him yet: I'll call the help."

The robots came, and following Sam's instructions got Jay Jay onto a stretcher and finally onto the soft anti-grav bed. At this point he groaned, and opened his eyes.

"What ... where ..."

"Take it easy," said Harriman."You'll be okay, Jay. You had a little accident, but we got here fast, you were much luckier than that guy Siris. You've got some wounds — the one in your side is the worst, but it seems to have missed all the vital organs. Don't talk yet. We'll get the auto-doc onto you in a couple of seconds, and then ..."

They did just that. Jay's wounds healed in seconds, and after two minutes he was through the sedation period. He breathed deeply, and sat up.

"Okay, now, spill it," said Harriman, eyes wide and eager. "In one way, Jay, I'm glad this happened. We've never had such a chance before: no one who got into a really dangerous, physical-effects emergency in TE has lived to tell the tale. What did it seem was happening to you?"

Jay told them.

"Say!" breathed Harriman. "You know, that's one method I never dreamed up? Jay, you have the most *creative* ideas! Now, of course, I'll be able to use that in my worlds. Pity it had to happen to *you*, though ... subjectively, I mean. Well, I hope you've learnt your lesson. Mind you, I've already lased to the Corp and they've got a team in your Box room already. That purple button is coming off right now — that's as a public precaution. After that, if you like, we'll give you a new Box. We owe you at least that. After all, it was our carelessness that landed you in this mess."

"No," said Jay. He scrambled off the bed. "Tell your men to stop ..."

He was rushing for the door. Harriman blocked his path.

"Take it easy. What ..."

"I don't want them to erase my universe!"

"They won't," said Harriman. "That's your privilege. I guess you'd like to erase it slowly, beginning with those guys who ..."

"No," said Jay, "I'm not going to erase it at all. I'm going to continue it. Oh, I won't try Total Empathy again ... I don't need to. I know what it's like now to be a man in a world of pain and death and cruelty. I also know that you can't eliminate pain and death and cruelty — we haven't eliminated them even from *our* world, we've just tucked them away from our godlike selves, into such places as these box-universes. The pain and the evil has to be, because pain sharpens pleasure, and evil brightens good. What's important, though, Sam," he said, looking at Harriman steadily, "is to know which side you're on."

From that day onwards, Jay's life on Olympus became more normal. He once more wrote for the kine-screen: and the art circles hailed the appearance of a new master dramatist, no longer a writer of delicate little sketches, but a poet of such passion as had not been seen on Olympus before. Some of the Olympians were puzzled; but others acknowledged his greatness. Jay, in short, was a success; he was even popular socially.

And Aphra was once more sharing his bed.

"I like you *much* better than Sam," she said, with a shudder. "Jay, I had to find out the hard way. You know what? He's a *sadist*."

And Jay also spent many hours at his creatron, though he was no longer addicted to it. He watched the Empire crumble; and then, to his astonishment, he watched himself being hailed as a god, and a new sort of Empire rising in his own name. An Empire that paid lip-service to universal love and mercy, and at the same time embarked on crusades, on massacres of unbelievers and heretics.

Jay smiled sardonically, a little wearily. It was always the same story: all victories over cruelty quickly became cruel themselves ...

And that new sort of Empire passed, too. Now the planet

was split among several great nations, all making progress in physical science, all beginning to devastate their world.

"At this rate," thought Jay, "they'll soon be turning into *us*! Then who will be the gods, and who the creatures?"

From time to time, he had company at the guest-viewer; not Harriman now, but Aphra. Aphra hugely enjoyed all of Jay's world — she was the perfect audience. She loved the sinners as much as the saints, the villains as much as the virtuous. She had a special weakness for world-conquerors.

"Isn't he *cute*?" she breathed, gazing down on a young artillery officer who had made himself an Emperor, and was tumbling old kingdoms as fast as his men could march.

"Do you think he's cute *now*?" said Jay, as the great army died in the snow, while the Emperor fled at top speed for his distant capital.

Aphra tossed her yellow locks.

"Not any more," she admitted. "Besides, he's *middle-aged*, and getting a paunch. The young Emperor on the other side, though, and that funny stiff general, they're really fun!"

Jay smiled. He was getting used to Aphra's point of view, as she presided like a spirit of beauty over his world. Yes, pain and evil had to be there: and many of the beasts of prey had a certain terrible beauty — even the human ones. You still had to choose goodness, but you could choose it whole-heartedly only because goodness could never win out completely. And so the great game went on ...

Did this make perfect sense? He wasn't sure. At times he thought it did, but at other times he was overwhelmed by the mystery of it all.

And he still sought for wisdom among his sub-people on the blue and white planet. Their science was crude, but their philosophy and theology often quite subtle. They had a good deal to say about *Jay's* nature — things that thoroughly surprised him.

Finally, nearly two thousand years of sub-time after the accident with the purple button, a new idea had arisen among the philosophers and the churches. In medium empathy, Jay entered the minds of his former worshippers, and heard them think it and say it. Gravely they repeated: *"God is dead!"*

Jay smiled as he pressed the Hold button.

"How wrong they are," he murmured to Aphra, "luckily for them! But it's true, they and I had a close shave, once ..."

Stiletto Inheritance

HUMPHREY McQUEEN

For Peter Curtis

"We'd like you to tell us how you got this knowledge." I'd become their prisoner on a Tuesday, the day after I'd found out Alfred Deakin had been murdered. I'd been so excited by the results of my research that I'd entertained the staff club bar with my discovery about Australia's early prime minister. Next day, on my way to university I'd stopped my Saab to pick up a hitch-hiking student, a willowy boy with Titian-tinted hair. He said he was feeling sick and asked me to drive him home. I'd helped him inside and put him to bed when three men and two women came into his room. My first thought had been that they were the police and I prepared to say nothing. Then the one who is now cross-examining me had said: "Good", and I sensed blackmail. No one else spoke. Not even after one of the women walked across to the now-standing, naked boy, slipped a long-bladed knife from her sleeve and stabbed him through the chest. He looked towards me, opened his mouth a little, and fell.

What the hell was this, I thought, some vigilante gang of a moral majority. That's when I began to fear for my life.

"Through here," the other woman said as she led the way down a passage to a larger room.

The man who had spoken before spoke again: "We'd like you to sleep for a while."

The second woman took a syringe from her bag. "Please roll up your sleeve," she said.

115

If they planned to murder me, an overdose would be less painful than a knife so I lay down on the couch, put out my arm and looked up at the three men gathering around us. As the one who had spoken bent over me I noticed that he had a smear of mascara on his left eyelid.

"We'd like you to tell us how you got this knowledge."

I've been awake for some hours but I don't know how long I slept. I've been fed quite well, allowed to shower and given some clean clothes.

"Our patience is inexhaustible, Professor, but our time's limited. Please help us to clear up this little matter. You know that Deakin was murdered. We just need to know how you found out."

So hard do I peer into my interrogator's eyes for some sign of make-up that he backs away.

"No mock heroics, please," he says. "As you've seen not all my colleagues are as polite as I am. You can stare me down easily enough, but she will draw the eyes from your head and give them back to you to eat. The others are quite uncivilised and cannot imagine torture without hatred. If you prefer I'll leave and they can ask our question. How did you find out about the murder of Deakin?"

There seems little point in not telling them since my answer is entirely innocent.

"Well," I begin, "as you possibly know I'm completing a biography of the Victorian politician, John Murray. A full-scale life and times really, but in one volume. Interesting times. Murray had twice been Chief Secretary and I thought it would be worth my while if I got to understand the workings of the police force. So I set about tracing the life of a typical policeman. By chance, I'd asked for a file at the archives about a certain Constable Bramble whose name I'd picked at random. Well, instead of getting his file I got another man's file by mistake, a fellow by the name of Brumbie. But as a mistake is still random, I decided to use what I'd been sent. Brumbie turned out to be a rather untypical officer. An Ulsterman and graduate of Glasgow University who joined the Victorian force in 1905. He'd been sent out from England to keep an eye on Tom Mann the British union leader who set up a Socialist party here and led some of the biggest strikes Australia has ever seen. There was one at Broken Hill..."

"Shorter, Professor," commands the knife-lady.

I look towards the mascara-man: "I'm just doing what you asked. Do you want me to go on?"

"Of course, Professor. But try to recount only your recent researches and not the whole book. We'll read that later." He moves towards me as he speaks and now stands behind my chair. None of the others show any reaction and they obviously accept his leadership. If I can content him I might yet be allowed to live. The knife-woman raps her hands on the back of a chair so that I can see ringless fingers with roughly trimmed nails and thickened joints. My chances against her are non-existent.

"Get on with it," she drones.

"By the time Mann left Australia, Brumbie was married to a Ballarat girl and promoted to Inspector. When war broke out in 1914 he was attached to the Governor-General's staff and helped his aide to run British military intelligence in Australia. That was how he came to investigate Deakin's death. As you know, Deakin left politics a wreck. His mind had gone. In the last months he began raving. His remarks were lucid in one sense but the oratory ran on ridiculous lines. He seemed obsessed with his childhood and referred to himself as 'Alice'. After he died, his son-in-law, Herbert Brookes, used his own intelligence network to obtain copies of the coroner's report. That report contained nothing unusual. But in Brumbie's file there's a pencilled draft of another report to Brookes which rules out assassination by the Sinn Fein while acknowledging that Deakin had been poisoned."

"Did Brumbie's report give any reason for this extra-ordinary action?" The question comes from the mascara-man who has been waiting for a pause rather than an opportunity to ask it; it is as if he is reading from a television interviewer's clipboard.

"To keep him from raving. That was all." I hear my own voice hysterically high and fast.

"Did it suggest in any way what Deakin was raving about?" This time his question sounds almost spontaneous.

"No. No. We know from La Nauze's biography what some of Deakin's obsessions were and we can surmise that these preyed . . ."

"No suppositions," my interrogator breaks in, more impatient than uninterested. "Just your facts please. As if your life depends on it: do you know what Deakin raved about to so alarm the government that they murdered him?"

Nobody else in the room reacts to this question. The two silent men stand near the door, the knife-lady by the window and the other woman is sitting at the table where I'd eaten. If the government murdered Deakin, what hope is there for me? My right leg is shaking and I can't unclasp my hands. My mind is having too many thoughts for my brain to form words into an answer. My interrogator, and even the knife-lady, say nothing. I know now what to say.

"I never said the government ordered his death. You're trying to trap me into admitting things I know nothing about. That wasn't Bramble's report."

"Bramble!" interjects the knife-woman. "Brumbie. Not Bramble."

"What's it matter whose report it was. It said nothing about my government. I'm telling you what I read."

"That's the problem. What you read is our problem," and the interrogator goes and sits on the end of the bed where I had been drugged. "Even before we . . . we enticed you here we'd checked back on your research activities and found Brumbie's draft. There was such a document. What we can't decide is how soon you will join that draft in the past tense. You'll appreciate that such a matter isn't treated locally and could take a little time. We suggest a little more sleep."

This time it is the knife-woman who produces a syringe and my terror catches the interrogator's eye.

"Don't be afraid. Charley won't hurt you." I lie down and Charley stands over my bed. From that angle she seems over six feet tall and the last thing I remember after she gives me the injection is a hair growing out of her right nostril.

I wake up a second time to find only my interrogator in the room. He says nothing as I dredge myself from the bed and try to walk towards the table where he is sitting.

"You'll be all right after you've eaten" he says as he stands up and moves around to pull a chair out for me. "A full stomach'll dilute the drug."

For some minutes I sit still, thinking about how I will cut up my meal and how heavy it will be to lift to my mouth and how exhausting to chew.

"Allow me," volunteers the mascara-man and he holds a forked piece of potato near my mouth. I take it in and allow it to slide down my throat. A spasm shoots back and I realise I'm hungry, anxious for the next offerings which will give me the strength to feed myself.

"I'd offer you some wine but that would fog your recovery."

For the first time I see my interrogator for what he is, a clerk, fifty-four, fifty-five years old, but the worse for wear.

"Do you have a name?" I venture.

He draws in air, and dares a truth: "My colleagues call me Monte." The expression on his face shifts a fraction before freezing somewhere between a wink and a smile. I can think only that I am going to live. I know it. I know it. I keep saying that over in my mind. His intimacy is my life sentence.

He pours Maxwell House coffee from a thermos. Sitting opposite each other saying nothing, he waits for me to finish eating.

"I sense that you sense that you are going to leave us happily." He hesitates and I wait for him to begin the explanation. "There are certain conditions, certain promises required."

119

"I'm in no position to bargain." I stand up and walk to the armchair. The food is helping to revive me but there are shudders of exhaustion.

"There's no rush," says my companion. "It's important that you're alert when I explain the conditions. Neither of us would benefit from a misunderstanding."

His language avoids the clichés. He says "now" and not "this point in time." Yet it is no less bureaucratic in its choice of words, in its avoidance of immediacy. He flirts with elaborate double negatives, "Neither of us would benefit from a misunderstanding." Is he telling me that his life would be in jeopardy or is he simply being polite about my murder?

"I'll tell you if I'm tired and don't follow."

He pushes out his tongue, running it along his top lip before smearing the spittle on the bottom one by drawing them together back over his teeth.

"The proposition is simple. We'll tell you all the truth and if you promise to publish all of it, or none of it, you will be able to go about your work. But you can't select the bits you want. The credible bits. It's publish all, or nothing, or be damned."

"That's fairer than most sources allow me."

"You haven't heard all of the story yet. You might prefer to publish none of it." My interrogator is becoming my confidant. He pours himself a cup of coffee, sugars it, and walks across to the window intending to raise the blind but then not doing so. "Deakin was a transvestite. That's what he was raving about. That's why he was helped along. He wasn't alone. He was part of an organisation." My confidant pauses to stop himself smirking. "Australia is run by transvestites. Always has been. Well, ever since federation." He is no longer talking to me. What he's saying is meant for me but his voice is aimed beyond this room, defiantly.

"The office of prime minister has always been in the organisation's gift. All Australia's prime ministers have been transvestites. From Barton to Fraser. All of them. Deakin endangered the secret. That's why. That's why what you found out had to be done. And that's why you're here." I stop myself laughing by coughing and sneezing into a handkerchief but my informant does not notice. He is too intent on his fantasy to acknowledge disbelief.

"Are you part of the organisation? I noticed mascara the first morning."

"I also serve. But in an attendant capacity. Waiting upon the prime ministers." He stands up straight, pushing his chest forward. "We are waiting for one now. They knew your trained mind wouldn't accept my word. So one of the prime ministers is coming to tell you what I've prepared the way for you to comprehend."

What can I say to him? He's obviously more than a little unbalanced. No matter how friendly he feels towards me it's obvious that he is not amenable to reason. Not that I am capable of rational argument either. All I can think to say is that I am tired: "I'd like to lie down again. So that I'll be alert when your prime minister arrives."

"By all means. I'm sorry if I've overtaxed you. One has so few opportunities. The truth is not always ours to protect." He draws in his lips again, several times quickly, biting more than pursing them.

His problem is already mine. To whom could I tell what is happening to me? I could amuse dinner parties with an extravagantly fabulous and embroidered version. No one will believe me or my story. It will be like my account of Archbishop Gough's departure. Even people who know I am telling the truth about his affair expect me to make it up as I go along.

The door opens unannounced and there he is, outframing the doorway. Unmistakable even in a tweed skirt, blouse, sensible shoes, make-up and wig. "We met in Adelaide on the 164th anniversary of the battle of Austerlitz." He moves towards me, takes my hand and squeezes it till I wince. "I'm looking forward to reading your biography. Biography is my favourite form of fiction."

There is no mistaking him; no possibility of a double.

"You've heard about my double life. My task is to convince you, to make sure that you aren't game to tell anyone else for fear of being made a fool. The easiest way to do that is to take my clothes off.''

He begins to undress and reveals a woman.

"Don't tell me I've surprised you? Did you expect a man? How old-fashioned you gays really are. We have kept up with the times. Our group has contained women since 1904 but we were never considered eligible for the prime ministership. Fraser and I put an end to that prejudice. And, I might say, encouraged us all to be a little daring. For as long as the PMs were men they'd confined their dressing-up to private gatherings. Once our sisterhood secured control we demanded the right to appear in public. That's why Fraser goes to fancy dress balls in dinner suits. People think he's being dull or cautious whereas she's laughing up her tailored sleeve.''

He is almost dressed again and I'm keeping my eyes lightly closed.

"Do you agree?''

"To what?'' I respond.

"To our conditions.'' He is sitting in the lounge chair, pointing at the coffee, knowing that Monte will interpret his finger. "Our condition is that you publish nothing in which case no one will be any the wiser. Or, that you publish everything in which case no one will believe a thing you say. Either way we win. Only partial truths threaten us because people can accommodate the bits and pieces. Do you accept?''

"I don't follow. You want me to tell everyone that Australia is run by a conspiracy of transvestites.''

"No.'' The fullness of his breath turns the letters into syllables. "We'd rather you said nothing at all. But we've nothing to fear from the whole truth. We always tell people the truth; all the truth and nothing but. That's how we confuse you. We ourselves, of course, never function on the truth. All our decisions are made on the basis of gossip and rumour.''

I cannot think of anything to say. He is the proof of what he is saying but I cannot accept the evidence of my eyes.

"Do you agree to our conditions?" he repeats. "Or are you having some difficulty?"

"The difficulty is that I don't believe you. All my training, experience, research has taught me to reject conspiracy theories. And now I'm confronted by the most bizarre and impossible story I've ever heard. Or seen. I simply can't accept that transvestites rule Australia."

"You accept that politicians run the country."

"But you are those politicians. You appear as one thing but you've been something else."

He crosses his legs, lets one shoe drop to the floor and wiggles his toes. "We manage only the government side of things," he confides. "There's more to running a country than that."

"That's what I mean. How do you get away with it? What about the power of the press? The banks? The Jews? The Masons? Don't any of them have a say in running the country?"

"I see that our black propaganda has been very effective. You rattle off all the old conspiracy theories. A man of your learning would recognise the name of Zaharoff."

"The armaments king."

"Quite so. And one of our English circle's finest creations. He took the blame for the great war."

"You're not trying to tell me there's an international gang of transvestites running the whole world?"

"There is an international body but we don't run anything. It pains me to admit it. I once had ambitions too. I found out that our function is purely decorative. We are, so to speak, the costume jewellery of power. The diamonds, not the crown itself. We dazzle. That's all."

I sit up and press my thumb and middle finger against my temples, trying to see the traps.

"Aren't you frightened the press will expose you?"

"They do, and we encourage them. Particularly the cartoonists who have always pictured us as women. Barton and

Reid were two old washerwomen; Billy Hughes as a little elf; Menzies as Queen Victoria. The iconography distracts attention from the substance. If it's been in a cartoon it can't be true, can it? So the more exposure we get the safer we are. A little truth, on the other hand, is a dangerous thing. So you must agree to all or nothing." He is standing over me lopsided on one shoeless foot.

"I can't trust you to keep your word. It's not the Deakin business or the transvestite thing. It's the boy. I saw Charley kill him. I'm a witness to murder. Not just the discoverer of a murder that happened sixty years ago."

"Don't waste your time being sentimental. The boy means nothing."

"Then why kill him? He'd done nothing. Knew nothing. Seen nothing. You obviously knew his hair was my colour before I went bald. That's why you picked him as bait. There was no need to kill him. I'm easily frightened if that was your aim."

"To frighten you, yes. But we didn't kill him. The knife had a retractable blade. It was stage-managed. He's alive." The ex-prime minister waves his hand in front of his face to wipe away the words. "He's alive. It was a trick. To frighten you."

"Then let me see him," I repeat. "I can promise nothing till I know he's alive. I don't care what happens to him, but if he's dead then so am I."

Mascara-man sorts through the files of his mind to find an answer. "We could put him on the seven o'clock news. Have him interviewed in the street. You'll see him live on television." His eyes stopped blinking.

"That will do." I relax at the thought of seeing the real world again. The television news will orientate my mind, let me know the date, let me relate to people and events. I'm out of touch. That's why I'm so vulnerable.

"So glad you've agreed." The leader wrings my hand again, and walks out, one shoe on, and the other in his hand.

I lie down and consider the possibilities. Monte serves tea and leaves me with a dozen magazines and newspapers. One of them has a report of an accident involving me. I am in hospital and my condition is stable. Monte returns with a portable television set.

"We couldn't manage the news so he's on a current affairs program on one of the commercial stations."

The program is about toothpaste and advertising. A street reporter is stopping people asking them to smile into the camera. The Titian-tinted boy appears. He smiles a set of perfectly white but slightly uneven teeth.

"Do you believe advertisements?" the reporter asks.

"They're the best things on telly," he laughs, and smiles at me.

Monte turns off the set, and turns to me. "An ambulance'll take you home and a nurse'll stay with you for a day or two until you're fully recovered."

I stand up, gently nodding agreement, but not moving.

"You're free to go."

I am about to say something like "Thank you" when he opens the door and adds: "I'll see to it that your book is favourably reviewed."

I pass him and get to the end of the passage when he calls after me: "I must caution you against spreading rumours."

Albert's Bellyful

FRANCIS   PAYNE

This is the story of how I finally got my inheritance out of
Great-Grandpa Lennox, and so bought the mill and married
my beautiful Janie. And I suppose I'll have to say a bit about
the rest of the family, too, such of them as came into it, 'cos
they all played a part, except possibly my sister Susie, who
never plays much of a part in anything, anyway.

At the time I'm thinking of, we all lived in the farmhouse
on the Mallee: me, my Mum, brother Albert, and sister Susanna. And out in the shed at the back, up the hill a bit, lived
Great-Granddad Lennox, who hadn't seen the light of day for
twenty years. He was a strange old coot, Great-Granddad,
and we all knew it even then; but I'll have more to say about
him later.

Mum was almost Standard herself, 'cept for her left eye,
which was all sort of funny and no good for seeing with at all
(so she said). Still, it would have stopped her from getting the
Rijansky treatment, even if she'd had the money: so she'd had
ten kids before Dad got killed, and only three of them lived.

I was born eighty-two years after the War, when everyone
still had the CT19 virus hidden in their cells, screwing up the
genes and making most of the kids come out all wrong. The
Rijansky treatment came in when I was nine, and Dad scraped
up the money to have me cleared of the virus and immunised.
Mum says that he had to go over and relieve the Harrisons of
some of their surplus pigs to raise the cash, too, which I don't

doubt, knowing Dad. He was always a pretty horrible sight, Dad was, and I reckon anyone'd agree that they could spare him a few pigs for a worthy cause.

I guess the story begins when I finally broke up with Louise Northby, whose family held the farm on the other side of Three Dingo Creek. I was fifteen then, and thinking about getting married: and, being a Standard and CT negative since my Rijansky, I was a pretty good catch. Louise was Standard, but she hadn't had her Rijansky because her people couldn't afford it. I had thought for a long time that it would be nice to have Louise as a wife: we could start a farm of our own, raise chooks (this being my family's line since Dad died) and one day we'd have her treated and we could start having kids. And there wasn't anything against it, really, if we didn't want to wait that long, in risking having a few nice but dumb Defects around.

Now it so happened that one day I had been sent by Mum to scrape around in the old ruined village for metal, and I found Louise on the same errand. So I popped the question to her. And would you believe it? She turned me down.

"No," she said. Turned out she had pledged herself to some Country Law Enforcement official. Now I thought that was pretty low, since our family has always had a running grudge against the CLE, and more so since they shot Dad. Now I don't want to reopen an old argument, but I reckon that when they killed him Dad was just quietly minding his own business, collecting road taxes, like he'd done for years, and like Granddad and Great-Granddad had done before him, all the way back to the War, almost.

And, although they claimed it wasn't his road to collect taxes on, I reckon he had as much right to it as anyone else had, and more than most, since road tax was the family trade. And he hardly ever shot anybody. He'd just come out from behind the Rock with his machine-gun and collect the tax from travellers. Then one day the CLE staged an ambush and made a widow out of Mum and orphans out of Albert, Susanna, and me.

And now my darling Louise was going to marry one of them.

"But why, Louise?" I asked her. "What's he got that I haven't?"

"He's a lot more mature, Jonathan Fewkes, let me tell you that! He's eighteen and more of a man than you are."

"Is he a Standard?"

She blushed in replay.

"You mean you're going to marry a fellow who isn't even Standard?" I was really shocked at this. It was a waste of good genes. Why, a girl like Louise could have all her kids normal, with the right husband.

"He's not far off. His left arm — it's a bit short — but he's got two eyes and five fingers on each hand, which is more than I can say for some members of *your* family. And he's rich. You'll never be rich. My mother says that all you Fewkes . . ."

Now Louise had a terrible sharp tongue in her head when she got stroppy, but I reckon that she must have known from the look on my face that she'd gone a bit far with that last remark, 'cos she shut up suddenly. I stopped arguing and went on collecting metal for Mum.

By the time I had finished, I was feeling pretty sad, what with getting rejected in marriage and having my family insulted all in the one afternoon.

When I got home, brother Albert was sitting on the verandah skinning rabbits. He's pretty bright for a Defect, Albert, and can talk a fair bit, though all in all he does less around the place than Susanna, who's downright stupid. But he has a messy and nasty way of skinning rabbits and knows that he shouldn't do it on the verandah.

"Hey, Albert!" I said. "You better get this mess cleaned up before Mum sees it, or you'll get a thumping."

He looked at me out of that one eye of his, and rubbed a bloody hand over the funny nose up in the middle of his forehead.

"Aw, dah have to?"

"Yes, Albert, you have to."

He started to gather his pelts and rabbits and, as I climbed the steps, I got a good look at the mess he'd made. It was shocking.

"Albert, can't you kill them first?"

"Nah. More fun alive."

There were times when I'd belt Albert if he really knew what he was doing. But, like most Defects, he doesn't, so it's no good complaining.

I trudged into the house and dumped the metal onto the table.

"Mum!" I yelled. "I'm back."

She came out of the kitchen.

"G'day, Jon. Got much?"

"No. There just isn't much these days to get."

She sorted over the rusty old scraps, then looked at me. "What's getting at you, son? You do look unhappy."

So I told her the whole story: how Louise was going to marry a CLE man, because he was older, and rich.

"But, pig's bum, son, you'll be rich too one day!" she replied.

"Eh?" I asked, feeling pretty stupid.

"Don't you know about the cash your Great-Granddad Lennox has stored up in that hut of his?"

I shook my head.

"Hell, that man has a fortune. Remember he collected road tax for years: since before your old Mum was even born. I don't know how much he has, but he's got gold and firearms and ammunition . . . I reckon you'd be richer 'n' any CLE man when you do finally inherit."

"When will that happen?"

"When your great-granddad dies."

She scratched her head, frowning, then finally came out with, "He's old."

"How old?"

"I don't know! Well, I'm not as young as I used to be,

130

anyway, and he's your father's grandfather, and your father was forty-two when he was murdered: so he's probably over eighty. Reckon you won't have long to wait."

I thought for a while. I was wondering why he hid himself in that hut. I'd never even seen the inside of it. And I'd never even seen the outside of Great-Granddad, either. His voice I had heard a few times, thanking me for food when I brought it to him, and that was all.

I asked Mum why he hid himself.

"He's crackers," she replied cheerfully. "He got religion before you were even born, and quit tax collecting and took himself off to that hut to pray. He was always a bit ..." She tapped her head meaningfully. "He used to collect them funny paper things."

"Books," I suggested.

"Yeh, books. Dunno what good they did him, but he claimed he had a use for them. Used to open them up — you know how they fold open in the middle, I think you've seen one — and he used to spend hours and hours just looking at the paper bits. Bloody queerest thing I ever saw."

My sister Susanna looked Standard, but she wasn't. She was really quite pretty, with blonde hair, blue eyes, and pale skin, though she was usually red and flaky from sunburn: she couldn't stand the sun at all. It was a pity she smelt. She had this really queer animal smell, and it had nothing to do with washing and not washing: she couldn't help it.

And she was stupider even than Albert. She couldn't talk at all, and it took a lot of coaxing to get her to sweep a floor or even to fetch and carry. She did it, though, when she got the idea, which was more than Albert did.

One thing she did beautifully was catch chooks. It was sort of intuitive. If we wanted a chook caught, we just put Sue in the chookyard, and she'd chase and chase until she caught one. Since the chooks fled screaming from everybody, it saved a lot of effort.

One afternoon, about a week or two after Louise turned me down, when Mum wanted a chook caught for tea, Sue was having fits, which she does sometimes and I hadn't mentioned. So I had to go fetch it. I unlatched the gate, and the chooks all ran to the other side of the yard. I closed the gate behind me, selected a good big one, and ran at it with the axe ready to chop. But the darned things were faster than I was, and the moment I chopped they'd be somewhere else.

After about a minute of this, I heard somebody laughing. I looked up and saw two faces peering at me from over the fence: two girls, so alike they must have been twins. Strangers.

And then I boggled a bit, because it wasn't two girls. It was one girl, with two heads. Funny broad shoulders, two necks, and two identical heads.

"G'day, girls," I said, a bit quietly, and also a bit annoyed, 'cos I didn't like anyone laughing at me being made a fool of by the chooks, not even a Defect like that.

"Haven't seen you around before," I added, to make conversation.

"No, there's only one of me," said one head. "And you haven't seen me before because my family only just moved into the area. My name's Janie Paluszak."

I shook hands. "You're Janie, too?" I asked the other head. Both of them laughed.

"Yes, yes, there's only one person inside here!" said the head I had spoken to; and, "Despite appearances," added the other. From the way she said it, it sounded like a joke she went through every time she met somebody new.

"Having trouble with the chooks?" she asked.

"I am a bit, yes."

She let herself into the yard, then knelt down and stared hard at the one I'd been chasing. A nice four-eyed stare. The chook shivered a bit, then started to walk towards her. When it was standing at her feet, she straightened up.

"You can chop its head off now."

I did, and it started to run in little circles, flapping its wings

132

just like the way any headless chook will.

"How'd you do that?" I asked.

She shrugged — and that was something to see in itself.

"I just do it. My father can do it, too, and he's Standard to look at. So I must have inherited it. I just think about worms and seeds and things that you'd expect a chook to like, and it comes."

"Can you do that with other animals?"

"If I know the sort of things that they like." She smiled, on both sides. "What's your name?"

"I'm Jonathan Fewkes."

We chatted for a while, and then she left to go back home while I took the chook in. I would have invited her inside, but Mum doesn't really like Defects, for all the fact that she's not quite Standard herself. Especially she doesn't like the really bizarre ones. Even Albert gets it rough at times, and I just couldn't see her taking to anyone with two heads.

Well, the next part of the story should be easy to guess. Janie came over a few more times, and we talked. I went over to her place, and we talked. Finally she invited me in to see her parents.

I had to swallow twice before I could say hello to her mother ... or perhaps "mothers" fits it better. She, or they, were a pair of Siamese twins, joined in the middle but, unlike Janie, definitely two people. She had three brothers; one Standard, one who didn't have any arms, just hands growing out of his shoulders, and one that I didn't see that day. They had him locked up in the back room.

"He's a dwarf," she said. "Usually he's pretty good, but he sometimes goes funny and we have to lock him up for a while."

I didn't realise how far things had gone until the father started asking me serious questions — about what my prospects in life were, whether I could support a wife, things like that. But when I did realise, I didn't really mind. I liked Janie. There was only one problem, which was that Mum would never agree.

133

A Standard, Rijansky negative at that, marry a really defective Defect? No way! As I had said myself to Louise, it would be a waste of good genes.

As you can imagine, this problem of Janie versus my mother preyed on my mind quite a bit. I just couldn't decide what to do: to stop seeing her and save my genes for a Standard girl, or to defy Mum and go for the one I liked. What a decision!

And, perhaps to give myself something else to think about, I found that I was wondering again and again about something completely different; namely, my Great-Granddad Lennox. It's odd to have a relative live not 200 metres from you, when you've never seen him all your life. Especially when he holds a fortune that you'll inherit as soon as he dies.

I was tempted, right from the start, to hurry him along a little ..."

The money would solve all my problems: I could marry Janie no matter what Mum said or thought. The money would go to me, of course, coming down in the male line where possible, Dad being the son of Great-Granddad Lennox's daughter, and both Dad and my Grandmother being dead. Albert could not inherit, being deficient.

The question was: how could I kill him? Ten years before then, I'd have said "with a shotgun"; but the CLE were poking their sticky beaks into everybody's private business these days and I'd never get away with it. Busybodies! Their interference meant that I'd have to do it on the sly, and hope that no one guessed.

Janie agreed. She's a very practical girl. One of the brightest people I've ever met. Far brighter than most Standards. Must come from having two brains.

"You'll have to get the money out of him somehow," she said.

We were sitting in the bushes up by Three Dingo Creek, holding hands, and we'd been talking.

"I don't really like the idea of killing him," I replied.

"Mum would guess, you know, even if we did hide the body."

"She wouldn't do anything," she smiled. "Your mother wouldn't turn you over to the CLE. She really wants the best for you, you know."

This embarrassed me, 'cos it was a reference to the fact that Janie and Mum had met, by accident, at the Meat Market a while back, Mum with a barrow of trussed chooks and Janie with some of her people's pigs. They'd had some sort of talk, apparently, but neither of them would speak of it afterwards. Mum just seemed gloomier than ever, and Janie finally accepted that my parent would never allow us to marry.

"Yes. But she wouldn't like it at all," I said.

"There is another way out."

"What is it?"

"Ask him for the cash."

"Are you crazy?"

"He'd probably give it to you."

This seemed nonsense to me. "Why?"

"He's old and he lives all by himself. What good is it to him? If you went up and asked him, telling him why you needed it now and what you needed it for, he might well give you some."

What an idea! It never struck me that folk might voluntarily hand cash over to someone else. I guess that's what comes of being in a road tax family.

Then Janie kissed me. For those of you who haven't had the pleasure, being kissed by a girl with two heads is quite something. It's a bit like being kissed by two people at once; but each knows what the other's doing, and they can coordinate things. It beats being kissed by a Standard girl any day.

So I kissed Janie and she kissed me, and we decided to ask for the money.

Luck came my way that night, 'cos Sue was having fits again and Mum was cleaning up, so I was asked to take Great-Granddad Lennox his tea. Now perhaps I haven't pointed it out before, but we kept him, though he did nothing whatsoever for his keep. Every week he got a sack of supplies and every night he got a hot tea.

On his side, he didn't even come down for his food; we took it up to the hut and left it there. He wouldn't even eat until we'd gone away. Sometimes he'd call a "thank you" from behind a closed window, usually not even that.

I half believed that he was fooling us and didn't even live there all the time, because we'd often find yesterday's tea untouched on the verandah for several days running. Mum said, no, it was all part of his "getting religion", and he had a habit of screwing himself into odd positions, shutting his eyes, and just plain thinking. Taking no notice of what went on around him, for days sometimes. Mum had seen him at it, of course, because he hadn't retired to his hut until a few years after she married Dad; she knew all his habits.

So I was wondering, as I walked up the track to his hut, if I'd get any answer from him when I knocked at the door. Half a chance I wouldn't. Even if he refused, it would be interesting to see his face.

I put down the tea and knocked on the door.

"Who's there?" His voice was cracked and old, like it had always been, but at least he was there.

"It's me."

"My great-grandson Jonathan."

"Yes."

"Good. Well, leave my tea, and thanks."

"But I want to speak to you." It shocked him. It was twenty seconds before he answered.

"Why?"

"Can I come in?"

"No!"

"Why not? I can't stand outside and talk."

"I don't talk to people."

"Why not?"

"I don't. *Go away.*"

"But I've never even seen you!"

"You never will."

"Why not?" He didn't answer.

I tried the door. It was locked.

"Why don't you talk to people?"

He still said nothing.

"You're not a Defect. You're a Standard, like me, and you're not too bad to look at. Mum even said that you didn't look your age, that you were handsome. Why hide yourself?"

But he'd shut up on me like a rabbit trap, and I didn't get another word out of him. So after a while I quit talking to myself and went back to the house.

He wasn't going to hand over the money: no doubts about that.

It was going to have to be the other way.

I told Janie about it, and she thought a while, then told me what to do. It was like that already: she was telling me what to do and I was doing it. I didn't mind. I was head over heels in love with her: she had two of the prettiest heads you ever saw and in 'em was more brains than I had in my one, so it was commonsense that she made the decisions. Surely?

My first job was to get a look at him and check that he really was there all the time. If, as I thought, he left sometimes, it would be easier to rob him than to kill him.

We waited until one night when Mum came back with a cold dinner and said that Great-Granddad had gone thinking again.

I wanted to go up to the hut and look inside. If I were right, there'd be nobody there: if Mum were right, he'd be curled up like a snake in a knot with his eyes shut.

Next morning, after feeding the chooks and Albert, I set off up the hill, telling Mum that I was going to check the rabbit traps. I took my crossbow with me, to make it look right — I didn't intend to kill Great-Granddad with it, 'cos of the CLE.

It was broad daylight. One little chink in the hut would be enough to let me see all of the inside without any trouble. But in daylight I would be visible from the inside, too. I walked around the hut out of sight, approaching it from the back, where there were no windows or doors.

It was an old, old house, pre-War, and looking as if it hadn't been repaired since the bombs fell. It was weatherboard, of a sort, and must have been painted once, though it looked bare wood now. It wasn't difficult to find a loose plank and look under it.

He was there, all right. There was a bed and he was sitting on it, with his back to me. I could see everything in the room, and there wasn't much to see. The bed, a table, some chairs, and shelves with books on them: quite a collection, at least two dozen of them. Not much else.

My great-granddad was sitting with his legs all curled up, so that the soles of his feet were pointed at the ceiling. He was sitting very still, and for a minute I thought he might be dead, until I saw him breathe ever so slowly.

After a while I got tired of watching nothing happen, and decided to creep around to the window to see his face.

His curtain was loose, and part of the window was broken. So I peeped through.

His eyes were shut, so he couldn't see me. I'm glad of that. Because I was struck so rigid by what I saw that I couldn't have moved for a minute, even if he'd stared straight at me.

The man on the bed wasn't my relative. Couldn't be! My great-granddad was at least eighty. This fellow was closer to thirty. Quite Standard to look at, but not a sign of age on him.

Then I started thinking. A man who hides and won't let himself be seen. Why not? Because, if anyone who knew Old Man Lennox saw him, he'd know that it wasn't he. I had planned to kill the old man for his money; someone else had beaten me to it! And, for God knew how many years, we'd been feeding a fraud. Keeping him, day in, day out — keeping a murderer and a thief!

I was bloody angry by the time I got back to the house. If he had stolen the money, that put an end to all my plans. That rankled even more than the thought of how we'd been had.

"Mother!" I called as soon as I got back.

"Yes, Jonathan?" She came out of the kitchen, all covered in flour from the baking.

"You think you'd recognise Great-Granddad Lennox if you saw him again?"

"I reckon I would! I'd know him anywhere. Even after all these years. He was a handsome one, he was."

I told her what I'd seen, and suggested that we both go up for a look. She agreed. I took Dad's old machine-gun down from the wall. The trusty old family weapon. If we had a sponger on our hands, I was going to get him, CLE or no CLE.

My mother's reaction on seeing the man in the hut was the very last I expected. She took a good long look, then grabbed me by the arm and stalked off into the bushes. Her face had gone all white and she was trembly, like she was cold.

"I thought it might be," she said, then nothing else.

"You know who it is, Mum?"

"I should."

"Who is he?"

"That, Jonathan, is your Great-Grandfather Lennox."

She started to bite on her lip.

"When he first locked himself up, I can remember your father saying . . . that he was about sixty. I couldn't believe it. He looked just like he does now. Jon, he hasn't changed at all in the twenty years since then. Maybe not quite twenty years . . . but since that man locked himself in his hut, your father and his brother have both gone, and they were his grandsons. His own daughter's died of old age; and, so help me, he hasn't aged a day to look at. I don't understand it, but that's him all right. That's him."

There was, of course, only one person to take a problem like that to. So I visited Janie.

Had I said that her father was also a very brainy fellow? He seemed to know the answers to most questions, and it was he who solved the problem of the Old Man.

"I came across someone like that in the last place I lived," he said. "In fact, I'm surprised that you haven't heard of them here. There's been quite a stir in some centres, especially recently.

"Basically: your great-grandfather is not Standard, though he may look it. He was born just after the War, right?"

"I think so," I said.

"Then he is a Defect. But he's a Defect like your sister Susanna. His shape is the same as everybody's, but his chemistry is wrong.

"Did you know that ageing is artificial? That we should go on and on indefinitely, but that an actual mechanism exists to make us age and grow old, because it has to be forced on the body?"

I shook my head. I hadn't known that. It was a funny thought, though.

"Your grandfather ..."

"My great-grandfather."

"Whatever he is, he lacks that mechanism. It's the only bit of him that the CT19 mucked up."

"Does that mean he'll never die?" I asked, my heart sinking.

"He can die by violence. Most of them did, when people found out about it. And — well, I don't know it for sure, but I suppose he can get cancer or have a stroke, or die from disease of one sort or another. If he doesn't, he'll just keep going on and on. There's no saying how long for."

Most people had decided that these long-livers were unnatural and were lynching them whenever they were found.

I liked that idea. It wasn't fair that people should go on like that, stopping the next generation from inheriting. If some fellows refused to die and step aside — well, others would just have to take matters into their own hands.

I explained all this to Mum. I asked her what she intended doing. She looked very thoughtful, then said she wasn't going to go killing her own husband's kith and kin, and that she'd keep feeding him as long as he lived. That night she took the meal out to him as usual, and came back with a cold one, but he was apparently up now and had thanked her for tonight's.

I did a lot of thinking when I got to bed. I finally decided that he wasn't going to hand over the money, and he wasn't going to die and let me inherit, and it just wasn't right that he should go on living when everyone else was dying around him. So it was my right and proper duty to murder him and inherit.

I met Janie again the next day. We had a kiss and a cuddle and talked. We had both come to the same conclusion. The old man had to go, and we were going to do it ourselves.

When?

"Well, there's no time like the present," said she. "Anything against tonight?"

I hadn't expected it to be so soon. But there are some things that there's just no point in putting off.

We met at sundown in the thicket on the corner of the abandoned farm by Three Dingo Creek. I had my crossbow and my knife. I would have liked the family machine-gun, but Mum would have noticed it gone. Janie had a nice heavy hatchet.

We started off when it was dark.

Janie knocked on the door. We had been hoping to get some sort of response out of him, since it might have been his tea. But there was no answer.

I looked through the hole in the window.

"He's thinking again," I told her. "Up on his bed like a trussed chook. We'll have to break our way in. Let's have the hatchet, honey."

She smiled with one head, in the cute way she has, and tried the door handle. The door opened.

"It helps to see if doors are locked before you chop them down," she said.

I was a bit annoyed at that, but then she can't help being right, since she's so smart.

There was a funny smell in the hut: an old smell, which sounds odd, but that's the only way to describe it.

The room lit up: Janie had lit one of his candles. Great-Granddad Lennox still hadn't moved a muscle.

"Where's the treasure?" she whispered. "If we can find it now we can just take it off with us."

Well, we searched that whole hut, as quietly as we could, trying not to wake the old man, but there wasn't a thing to be found. Not a thing.

"There'd be rather a lot," I said. "Fifty years of road tax! A cartload, maybe two. He must have it hidden somewhere else."

So she walked over and shook him.

He didn't wake up very quickly. It was like a drunk coming out of a snooze. He blinked, shook his head, blinked again, and opened his eyes slowly. And when he spoke, his voice was very dull at first.

"Who are you?"

"I'm your great-grandson Jonathan, and this is my wife."

A good look at Janie woke him up. "How in hell did you get in here?"

"You left the door unlocked," she said.

"But ... oh, pig's bum." Then he put on a sulky expression. "Well, now that you've seen me, what do you intend doing?"

I started to say, "Kill you", but Janie cut in.

"We want to know where you've hidden your road tax."

He turned his face to the ceiling. "I don't know what you're talking about." Then he closed his eyes again...

... and what happened after that gets a bit difficult to tell. The shortest way is to say that the room vanished. There just wasn't an old man or a hut any longer. There was a cave.

I was suddenly in a very dark cave, and there was a monster, a Thing all slimy and horrible and slavery, about twenty metres away.

I was petrified! I didn't know what had happened. One moment the hut, the next ...

The Thing turned and saw me. I still had my crossbow,

cocked, so I put an arrow in it quick smart and made ready. Its eyes lit up, and it roared. I took careful aim and fired.

The bolt went right through it as if it had been made of paper. It gave a sort of gurgling laugh and raised a paw, all horrible steely claws, at me. I tried to run ...

... and bumped into the wall of the hut.

"What happened?" I asked.

"Fantastic!" Janie was laughing. "He's far better at it than I am."

I turned, all shaky still, and saw that Great-Granddad Lennox was lying on the bed. There was a big cut on his forehead and Janie was holding the hatchet by the blade.

"He can project images, too. But I've never taken over a person the way he did you."

"Was that what happened?" I still hadn't quite recovered from the change.

"Tell me — could you see his images and the room, or just his images?"

"All I saw was the cave."

"I could see both," she smiled. "Enough of him to lay him out, anyway."

There was a crossbow bolt stuck in the wall. It hadn't been there before.

"He didn't think quite quickly enough. If he had, he would have made you see me as the monster. And got you to kill me. That would have been nasty."

"Could he have done that?" I asked.

"I'm fairly sure he could. So next time, don't shoot."

She was standing beside the bookcase, and her eyes wandered to it.

"He has some very interesting books," she said.

"Eh?"

"Doesn't matter, for the moment. First we have to work out a way to get his money from him."

We thought about that.

"Mum should be coming up with tea soon," I said. "Do you want to be here when she arrives?"

Janie shook her heads.

"Then what do we do?"

"Move him somewhere else, and leave the door shut and the candle out. Your Mum'll just think he's meditating."

"Meditating?"

"That's the name for what he does when he just sits there."

He was starting to come to by now, but he was very sick-looking. Janie must have hit him really hard.

"We're going somewhere else," I said.

"You might be. I'm staying here."

I reloaded the crossbow and pointed it at him.

"I am ready for death," was all he said.

Then he shut his eyes again. I think he was trying to breed another illusion, but he just groaned and put his hand to his head, so I guess he couldn't do it with a headache.

But Janie hit him over the head again just in case. Nice and solid. It gave me a sort of sick feeling in the stomach, though, to hear the sodden thump. He fell forward onto the floor.

"There's an empty sack here," she said. "Let's put him into it."

It was his weekly provision sack, lying folded up in the corner. We finally got him in it — he was half-awake and groaning by the time we'd finished — then put out the candle, and I carried him, in the sack, down the hill.

It would have been a funny sight, if anyone had seen us: the moon was out nice and bright, and here was Janie, with her two lovely heads, and me, bent down under the weight of a groaning sack, walking together in the moonlight down the hill from the old hut.

"Hey! There's someone coming!" whispered Janie, and she vanished into the bushes.

It was Mum, carrying the tea.

She eyed me curiously. "What have you got in that sack, son?"

"It's ..." I gulped. "It's some stuff for the chooks."

She nodded absently. I was hoping she wouldn't ask me what, since "stuff for the chooks" was just the first thing that had come into my head to say.

She walked on. The old man gave out a long horrible groan.

"What was that?" she asked.

"I ... stood on a bloody rock!" I said.

Before she could ask any more questions, I marched off down the hill. And kept marching, until she was out of sight.

Then I stopped. I didn't trust Great-Granddad Lennox, and I needed Janie to handle him.

I felt a touch on my arm.

"Janie! I'm glad to see you."

She kissed me with one mouth, keeping the eyes on her other head open to watch for anyone coming. Dammit, there's no arguing: having two heads is plain useful at times, and I won't hear anything said against it.

"Let's take him to your Rock," she suggested.

And so I finally dumped the sack on the Table. Now the Table is a low flat boulder behind the Rock, very nicely situated in the shade on summer afternoons. For years back, my family had used the Table to eat meals off while waiting for passers-by to tax, and counted their taxes on it afterwards.

It was an historic spot. In fact, the fellow in the sack had been the founder of the business, way back then: and just over there, on the road, Dad had died carrying on the trade.

A lump rose to my throat.

Meanwhile, Janie was bundling him out of the sack onto the Table. He looked horrible. Even in the moonlight, you could see he was pale, and there was blood all over his head.

"Well, Lennox," said Janie. "We've got you now."

"I'm not saying anything," he replied.

"I had a look at your books, and I know where you get your powers from." That stumped me, because I didn't know anything of the sort.

"You can't employ them against me; so you won't get out of this at all unless you tell me where you've stored your treasure."

"What treasure?"

"Fifty years' road tax."

"Oh. That treasure."

He leaned forward, and spewed all over the ground. It was revolting.

"Well, where is it?"

"Why should I tell you?"

"Because we'll cut your throat if you don't."

He shrugged. "I've lived long enough. Death doesn't frighten me. I know there's a life after death. Send me to it if you like."

Janie looked at him for a long time. Then she said, "You really want to die, don't you?"

He didn't answer, and she said something I found a bit surprising. She said, "All right. We won't kill you until you *do* tell us where the treasure is! An end to your life in exchange for your money! Fair?"

He looked startled. "What was that?"

"But if you don't tell I will hit you over the head again."

He looked very sad, then shut his eyes.

For a moment there was a kind of shaky feeling, like there had been when he made me see the cave for the first time. I shut my eyes, and then opened them again: and I was still at the Rock. But I was standing in a different spot. I was on the other side of the Table, so that Janie was on my left instead of my right.

Had I really walked round without realising it while my eyes were shut? How odd.

She leant forward. He whispered something into her ear.

"Good!" I heard her say. Then, "He's told us where the treasure is. Kill him."

I reached for my crossbow.

"No. Take your knife and jump on him!"

This puzzled me a little, but I did what she said. I jumped

at him. He twisted away, and I thought I heard a woman screaming somewhere. I had cut him, but not very badly.

Then the scene did change. I wondered why it had taken so long. I was back in the shed at our farm, and there was one of the pigs lying on the ground with its feet tied up. I had killed a pig like that a while before. I still had my knife in my hand.

"Kill the pig." It was Janie's voice, as close as if she were whispering in my ear. I started towards it, but the scene got all fluttery and for a second I was back in the cave again, but I ignored the Thing. Then it changed, and we were at the Rock and I saw Janie standing a few feet off, holding her arm, with blood flowing from a cut in it. It went funny and Janie became Old Man Lennox standing there: I heard something like her voice saying, "Kill him!" — but somehow I knew that it wasn't really Janie speaking. It was the old man fooling me by making me see him instead of her.

At last the pig scene came back.

I guessed then that Old Man Lennox and Janie were fighting with images, his against hers, so I willed Janie to win. The pig scene became clearer. That implied that the pig scene was her effort.

The knife that I'd been holding became the pig-killing knife. I grabbed the animal by his ears and slit his throat, good and proper.

He gave a horrible scream, a human scream, and the blood gushed over my hands.

The image went. We were back at the Rock, and on the Table in front of me was Great-Granddad Lennox with his throat cut. Janie was standing about three metres away, and her arm was injured. She had her eyes closed, and she was shivering.

"We've done it now," I said.

"Thank God," she whispered. "It was close."

"But how are we going to find out where the treasure is?"

"I got the image. That last set of pictures was just for you. But, since he wasn't consciously projecting anything at me, I got a lot of unconscious jumbled stuff. Including where the money was. It's buried in the back yard.''

She sat down. The cut on her arm was still bleeding badly.

We went back to her place immediately. Her father had been in bed but when he saw that Janie had been hurt he started to treat her without complaint. He didn't even ask me what we'd been up to. He guessed. Like I said, he was a bright fellow.

While he was putting stitches in Janie, I washed up and cleaned the knife. She went to bed, and her father and I had a little talk. He suggested that we dispose of the body somehow, and make it look as if the old man had vanished: then I could claim the treasure as mine by right.

I thought that was a good idea. So I said goodnight and went home.

Mum was still up. I didn't even need to see the lights; I heard her howling at Albert. Poor Albert often gets howled at. Usually when he's done something wrong, but not always.

"Greedy devil! You've had your dinner! There isn't any more! Out!"

"Aw, Mum!"

"No! No more!"

"Hungry . . .''

Albert's never satisfied for food. He's always after more, and sometimes he steals it from the kitchen.

The front door opened and Albert came bumping out onto the verandah. There he sat, looking hungry and resentful.

I had an idea.

Next morning, Mum woke me up quite early. She was furious. So furious she wasn't speaking straight.

"Your brother Albert! He's been at the chooks again! The bastard!"

She dragged me out onto the verandah. There lay Albert, asleep, his face smeared with blood, looking as if he had swallowed six footballs.

He'd done things like that before — getting into the chook-yard and eating chooks or, once, most of a pig.

"How many chooks are there?" she asked.

"'Hundred and seven," I replied.

"Well, we'll see how many he's had."

So we counted them. It's not easy when they keep running the way they do. But eventually Mum decided that they were all there. As were all the pigs, and all the crops. Nor was anything missing from the stores, nor from the kitchen, nor from the cupboards.

Mum never learned where Albert's bellyful came from. I never said, and neither did he. Later on, I went down to the Rock; I found a thighbone lying by the Table. Chewed. There were some broken spikes of bone on the road, and very little else.

He couldn't have eaten all of it in one go. I think he hid pieces all over the place, 'cos he kept coming up with odd meaty titbits for weeks afterward, and a month later they were stinking titbits. Then they ran out, and he took to stealing from the kitchen again.

It turned out that Janie really had learned about the treasure. We dug it up after letting Mum discover that Old Man Lennox had gone.

From the way she acted, I think that Mum guessed, roughly, what had happened to him. But she never said anything. She just looked at me oddly every so often. She never mentioned that sack again, either.

There's not much else to say. Janie and I went back to the hut for the books, and later on she taught me to read. I've never returned to the place since then: there's something queer about it, and I don't like it. As if there was something hiding under the bed, or lurking in the corner. I was glad to get out.

Well, with the money I bought a farm, and a mill, and still had loads left over. Three cartloads it came to. Fifty years' road tax! We're rich now.

Of course, Janie can't be Rijanskied, so our kids have all

been Defects so far. Eight of them, and only one still alive, a sweet little girl whose feet and hands aren't quite right and who's not that bright, really, when you get down to it. It's a pity. But then Janie has been a good and loving wife and a dear mother.

That's our story, and there's nothing else important. Except that I can't really understand most of Great-Granddad Lennox's books, even though I can read them. Still, I got a wife and a fortune from him, so I reckon that's enough.

Not in Front of the Children

G E O R G E   T U R N E R

Marianne shared two fears — call them psychopathic traumas and be not far wrong — with all the members of her wealthy, leisured social regnum.

The first was Death. The fabulously expensive antigeriatric treatments could not postpone the end for ever and — oh, fearful thought — could not guard against accidents. Accidental death of a coterie member was an unmentionable event, the disposal hushed up and hurried. Death, like Ageing, was a dirty word.

The other was the Generation Gap, a phrase that might have been invented for the Twenty-second Century wherein, as in Marianne's case, a family might have eight generations extant, all loathing each other, and not cordially. In particular, the young detested the old whose signs of age were flaunted on their faces, and refused to recognise kinship.

The eighth generation, the children, called themselves Liberated and endured their parents with offhand affection, boredom, resignation, screaming fits or open dislike, according to type. Nothing new there.

And God had visited Marianne with an additional personal plague, a daughter, Ellaline.

Awash with woe, she ran to her father who at seventy-one looked little older than herself. He heard her complaint with a patience that threatened to expire as her interminable circumlocutions refused to settle for an improper word. Her social regnum fancied itself as neo-Victorian and was capable of a stiflingly genteel prudery.

Finally a phrase bordering on indecorum penetrated his wandering attention. "What do you mean, poor? What poor children? Where — how could Ellaline meet *poor* children?"

Marianne was close to tears. "They go to the Lower Town ... groups of them sometimes ... avoid their tutors ... run wild ... actually *mix* with the — the *poor*. I think she hears" — her voice dropped — "abominable words."

He had no time for the neo-Victorian pretension. "A phase, dear, a phase. She'll grow out of it."

"That's all very well, but people may find out. The social disgrace!"

"Are you concerned for Ellaline or for your social image?"

Taken by surprise, she thought about it. "Both. There must be a limit. Poor people are as bad as Liberated permissiveness. The children shouldn't know about them."

He said brutally, "They have to, sooner or later. The knowledge didn't ruin your life."

Marianne bridled. "I was a grown woman, able to withstand social shock." She spent a second or two admiring her inner strength before reverting to clinging daughter. "Can't you advise me, Daddy?"

He paid little heed to the Liberated regnum which was, after all, some sixty years away from his own. He clutched at a familiar straw. "Why not talk to your great-grandmother, she's the brains of the, er, senior branch."

Marianne's ears burned. To speak of someone three regna distant was an indelicacy, even from one's father. Across a Gap so great there could be little communication.

And the signs of — of *ageing*, would be so evident.

She could not do it. What bizarre social mores might she not encounter in that withered regnum? And it was whispered on the prurient grapevine that they had no respect for sensibilities.

Her father said with unaccustomed roughness that the, er,

senior woman had more life experience than all her descendants put together and that Marianne, as a troubled mother, should steel herself to face unpleasantness for her daughter's sake.

The troubled mother, who had her full share of the cheap dramatic instincts derived from hypnobooks and holoplays, saw the challenging truth of this and rose to it with stern determination. Her regnum might nod and whisper but she, the dauntless mother, etc ...

Besides, if she managed it properly they might never find out.

Ellaline was thirteen, overweight, unpleasantly imaginative and a fine exponent of the resentful frown considered *de rigueur* among the young Liberated. Most of her age group thought liberation consisted of being rude and disobedient to parents, and they worked at it, but even the Advanced Libbers thought Ellaline pretty far out. She had begun to speak of matters not so much liberated as downright uncomfortable to think of. She was definitely Going Too Far.

Ellaline and her friend (actually the daughter of her mother's pastrycook — upper servant class, really, privileged so long as she didn't presume parity) sat on the grass in the park at the edge of the Lower Town, where the more venturesome *poor kids* sometimes came. She wasn't allowed there but that was part of the liberated fun, like the frowned-on but frantically expensive denims and sandshoes copied by tradesmen from patterns in the Historical Archive. (Marianne loathed them, but what could one do? Fashion decreed, and she couldn't have her child held to ridicule by her peers.)

Jennie had found her a poor kid to liberatedly mix with, in fact a distant relative not usually mentioned in the Servants' Hall.

Friend Jennie, being a servant, didn't have to follow fashion, which her parents couldn't have afforded anyway, and if her cotton overall was better cut than the ragged one-piece covering of the poor kid it was not otherwise very different.

Poor kid Jimmy Johnston, aged fourteen, eyed Ellaline's

denims with what passed for a lascivious leer and told her in his atrocious gutter whine that his Gang Name was Roger the Lodger. "Cause I got a beaut," he explained and waited for the customary, "Show!"

She was not interested.

"Doncher wanter see it?" She shook her head. He was affronted. "Why doncher?"

She shrugged, not intrigued by maleness. She did not know, any more than did Jennie and Jimmy, that her course of preparatory treatments, just begun, would delay the onset of sexuality for several years. In any case, her present curiosity centred on a very different human trait.

She said authoritatively, "I'm a Liberated Regnum product. I want to talk dirty."

"Like shit and piss? Everybody talks dirty."

Ellaline's blonde head shook violently. "That's just ordinary dirty. I mean like *dead* and *dying*."

Jennie put a hand to her lips and giggled nervously. Those words, unleashed in the home, would have stripped plaster from the walls. Ellaline wouldn't have dared because her mother would have had a megrim or at least a vapour; her father, who could himself use very masculine language at times, would have belted his daughter for such crudity. One just didn't! Even in the Servants' Hall, where nobody could afford the treatments, it was considered bad form to use so much as the periphrastic "passing on" or "ultimate condition".

Jimmy Johnston was puzzled. "What's dirty 'bout dead? Everybody dies." (No training, no upbringing, no sensitivity.)

Ellaline corrected him gently, observing good manners with one less fortunate than herself. "In my social class we do not."

He surveyed her as a freak. "Then it's true about the jections, is it?"

"I think you mean the treatment. It is quite true. Didn't you know?"

Jennie cut in officiously, "The gutterbums don't get told everything. It isn't good for them."

"You shut yer bloody trap," Jimmy told her. "You're not a Class Kid like Ellaline here. We know plenty." He turned back to Ellaline. "Would you live a hundred years?"

"Forever."

"Garn!"

"Yes! Forever!"

"My old man says you don't. 'E says you stretch it but in the end you cop out."

"That just isn't true! There isn't any end."

"You die!"

"Well, what's that? What is die?"

Jimmy stared, not believing his ears. Jennie murmured, "Like passing on."

"You be quiet, Jennie. I want him to tell me."

The boy said, "Everybody dies."

"You say so, but what *is* it?"

"You get old and you die."

Old? That was really dirty, really gutter dirty, but, "That doesn't tell me. What happens when you die?"

Jimmy had never looked on death but he had his ideas about it. "You go wrinkly all over an' yer hair falls out." He remembered his bloody nuisance of a grandfather. "You piss yerself and stink and get the screws and fall over dead. Not alive any more." The rich girl was plainly horrified and he felt triumph in his superior knowledge. Serve her right, not wanting a look. "Everybody falls over dead. Then you go rotten and they burn you in the deadshed."

Ellaline squalled at him, "You're a dirty liar! We stay beautiful and go on forever. You're disgusting!"

He promptly hit her, but she was solid for her age and hit back hard enough to sit him on his tail in sheer surprise.

"You're filthy!" She headed furiously out of the park, dragging the pertrified Jennie.

Jimmy, who was not blessed with courage and had an ingrained awe of the upper classes, yelled after her, "Well it was you what wanted to talk dirty!"

Wondering just what was dirty about it, he dragged his

three-score-and-ten-limited carcase to his feet, arranging a pugnacious expression for the benefit of any peer group gutterbum who might have witnessed the incident.

Marianne had never seen her great-grandmother. One simply *didn't*. The woman's name was Agnes and she belonged to the regnum of Intellectual Women, which must have been an *impossible* period to have been born into. How did ordinary fun-loving women *cope* with such a time? No wonder the fashion had swung against them into the Homeloving Mouse regnum, though that must also have been hard to bear with pompous men behaving as though they ran everything, not as tranquil and free-hearted as dignified neo-Victorian.

She might have dropped the whole idea if, during three days in which she dithered, news had not filtered up from the Servants' Hall (via her primly horrified personal maid) of the scene in the park by the Lower Town. It became impossible not to take some action. Such a word as "death" in the mouth of a thirteen-year-old was Not To Be Borne.

At the sight of Agnes' home — squarebuilt, no-nonsense, plenty of concreting, only a small and easily-managed block of ground — she felt a psychic chill. It reeked of intellectualism. Would the woman understand simple, direct speech?

The sight of Agnes herself destroyed Marianne's composure utterly. Her great-grandmother was — no doubt about it — *middle-aged*. Marianne had never been very sure what the word meant but now saw what it must mean: grotesque decay. Lines on the face. Grey hair at the temples. The beginning of wrinkles on the hand. A failure of uprightness in the carriage. *Was this the future for her, too? For everybody?* She struck the thought aside as morbid; Agnes had merely Let Herself Go.

"You're Mary Ann? I got your message."

"Marianne."

"All right — Marianne, if it matters. Don't stand there, woman, come in. I'm not a bloody gorgon."

Thinking, *Oh, yes, you are*, Marianne followed her into

the functionally square-cornered lounge with its sturdy, functional furniture and flat-toned walls. No multi-phase veneer for mood-change decor; no lighting console; no fleximoment flow in the design of the carpet. Everything the same and for ever. So much for the Intellectual Women! Couldn't they perceive their own dowdiness?

And the pictures! Twentieth-century originals, no doubt, and vastly valuable but — the angular man with both eyes on the same side of his nose! And the huge thing in three shades of white-on-white with a single, baleful red eye glaring from the top left corner, accusing through verdigris-coloured lids!

How could anyone live like this? She refused to see the room, removed it from her consciousness.

Looking at Agnes was little better. The absolutely decrepit woman sat with spread knees on her square-backed chair, openly staring, examining. "I see the family features transmit well."

Marianne muttered, "Do they?"

"Yes."

The one word, then silence. Did Agnes' regnum not provide for conversational gambits?

"Well, Mary Anne, what's the trouble? You're not the kind to break caste for the fun of it."

Caste! What a horrible way to express the GG. The solecism scattered her thinking. "My father said — he said —"

"He told me what he said, that he'd advised you to see me because I've lived long enough to learn some sense. So your teenager's been hobnobbing with gutterbums, eh? Do her good."

"*Good*!"

"Don't shriek at me. Won't hurt her to meet real people and see the rough side of a few facts."

Marianne gabbled, "But I've tried to protect her. I've tried to bring her up respectably. I've tried —"

". . . to keep her as ignorant and silly as yourself. And she resents it. Good."

Marianne stood. "You disgraceful, horrible woman!"

The disgraceful, horrible woman leaned forward, stretched a muscular arm and pushed. Marianne sat down and burst into tears. "You don't understand. It isn't just teenage libbing. It's the dreadful things she says."

"Such as?"

"She wouldn't dare do it in front of me but I've been told she talks about" — the word stuck firmly behind her teeth — "the Big D!"

"Death?"

Marianne jumped. To have it said straight at you like that! She nodded miserably.

Agnes said, "Well, talking about it won't kill her. Have you told her what the word means? No, you haven't; you wouldn't know how. Call yourself neo-Victorian! The Victorians were a pretty hardheaded bunch under their prissiness but your crowd are just a mass of pretensions with nothing under them. Send the kid to see me. Thursday. In the morning. Not later than ten o'clock. I'll straighten her out. Right?"

It did not sound at all right but how could you argue with a steel-thewed dragon who pushed you about?

Marianne agreed and fled.

She had, lately, a sense of being always in flight from somebody or something. She really must see her psycomforter.

Convincing Ellaline that she should waste a fine summer morning on some aunt (some grown-up, preachy, interfering bag) was not easy.

"I haven't got an Aunt Agnes."

"Yes, you have, dear." It was permissible to lie in a good cause; one shouldn't frighten the child with a GG of four regna.

"I never heard of her before."

Marianne said vaguely, "Perhaps not. Ours is such a large family. We don't always keep in touch."

"Anyway, why do I have to see her?"

"Because she has asked to see you."

"Why?"

"She has something to tell you."

"What does she want to tell me?"

Marianne heard the stubborn note and recognised battle offered. She should have thought this out more carefully. "That is for Aunt Agnes to say."

Ellaine had a practised ear for her mother's evasions. "I don't want to know, anyway. I don't know her. I won't go."

Marianne heard the stubborn note and recognised battle ladylike muscle growing under the puppy fat and wondered if beating was not becoming unwise. The solid Victorian beltings held to be suitable in cases of waywardness had lately produced, after the obligatory tears, a sullen and impermeable silence and a short-lived improvement. Best, perhaps, to take her psycomforter's advice and engage the child's interest, and that called on the resources in her devoted mother area.

"I think you should go, dear."

"But what *for*?"

"Because your Aunt Agnes is an education specialist" — this was true — "and she wants to explain something to you. I'm sure you'll be interested."

With her mother plainly in retreat it was only a matter of maintaining the pressure. "How do you know I will? What is it?"

Marianne said uneasily, "Something very important."

"But what?"

"It's not for me ..."

"I'm not going."

Marianne caved in because she had neglected to prepare positions for temptation and/or blackmail. "Aunt Agnes wants to tell you about —" With the strongest of intentions she could not break the lifelong conditioning surrounding the ultimate profanity.

"About what?"

"About," Marianne said desperately, "the Big D." A mother could do no more.

"You mean de-" Ellaline stopped the half-made word in time. Her mother's face promised that such a defiant indecency might unleash levels of violence so far unattained; her mother with a strap in her hand could at times lose all control, as though something in her leapt in a frenzy of release. Ellaline changed to judicial consideration. "That should be fun." She filed her mother's shudder as a triumphant memory. "Of course I shall go."

Marianne heard the irrepressible gloating. *I have brought forth a monster*.

With a smile of primal innocence the monster asked, "Is Aunt Agnes's hair falling out?"

The interview ended in blank stares.

Since the ancient beginning of slavery very little of Society's supposedly private doings has been hidden from the sharp ears and eyes of the Servants' Hall. Perkins, the chauffeur, knew more about Agnes and the further reaches of the family than did Marianne and he had a pretty accurate idea of why he was driving Ellaline to see her.

As for Ellaline, he thought her a rich bitch who needed regular belting. Being, like most servants, something of a snob, he did not approve her association with gutterbums but he admitted that she was sharp enough in her fashion. For instance, she observed quickly the changes in the ambient architecture and realised that she was being carried beyond familiar areas.

"Where are we, Perky?"

"On the way to Mrs Ballantyne's."

Ellaline frowned as she surveyed the smallish (by her standards), square-built houses of a past age; there were places like them in old pictures.

"She wouldn't live here. If she's my aunt she must be in Mummy's regnum. She wouldn't live in one of these boxes."

So that was the story; these "treated" freaks were so conditioned by their fear of time that the simplest truths became snarled in social taboo. "Maybe she's not actually your aunt.'' The kid would find out soon enough. ''Sort of courtesy aunt.''

''I see.'' She did not see, yet. ''What regnum is this?''

''Number four — Intellectual Women period.''

''I didn't know they had numbers. Is Number Four old?''

What a word! She had no business to know about people being old. Learned it from her gutterbum friends. ''Fairly,'' he said, cautiously.

''How old, Perky?''

''Hard to say.'' Oh, to hell with it! ''In their second century.''

''Shit!'' said Ellaline.

''I didn't hear that, miss. And the Fours like it that way.''

''Do they? Do you know all the regna, Perky?''

''Drivers know the whole city, miss.''

''How many are there?''

''Eight. Number Eight's yours. That's the lot, so far.''

''What do you mean, so far?''

''Since the treatment started. Don't you go saying I told you this.'' She might be a rich bitch and a brat but she could be trusted.

Ellaline was silent for a while. The flipper moved smoothly, gently, just above ground level, slowly while Perkins scanned for the right address.

''Perky, what happens if you don't get treatments?''

''You —'' It was tempting, but he played safe. ''After a bit you pass on.''

''What's that?''

''You better ask Aunt Agnes.''

She thought of asking was it the same as ''die'', but that wouldn't help since she didn't know what ''die'' was. She asked instead, ''How old are you, Perky?''

''Twenty-eight, miss.''

''Are you going to stay with us always?''

''Can't, miss.''

''Oh, Perky! Why not?''

''We don't stay after thirty.''

"But why?"

He glanced at her puzzled face. Rich bitch or not, she was better than most. "They send us away."

"Why?"

He said savagely, "Too old at thirty." *Because they'd have to see every day what's coming to them in the end.*

"Does your hair fall out then?"

He asked between gasps of laughter, "Wherever did you hear that?"

"A gutterbum told me." She continued, with deliberate intent to shock, "He said you piss yourself and stink and go sort of not alive any more. What does that mean?"

Perkins stopped the flipper with an unnecessary jolt. "This is the place. And about bloody time, too."

"Servants aren't allowed to swear," said Ellaline.

For Ellaline, born in the fountain of youth, only young people existed. Those looking as old as her mother represented the limit of ageing and appeared positively historical to her young eyes. That these people crossed three generations, maintained in changelessness, was peripheral information with little meaning.

She did occasionally see older persons. Now and then some decrepit unfortunate appeared unexpectedly in a street and there were peculiarly repellent individuals in that park at the edge of the Lower Town but her eyes registered them without understanding; there was something wrong with them and it was not necessary to think about it. In the flurry of circumlocutions, evasions and genteel usages which surrounded the concept of ageing she had little chance of comprehending what she saw. You grew to look like Mummy and then you stopped like that, what else?

So the apparition of Agnes with facial lines and loose skin and discoloured hair was daunting. She wanted at once to retreat, to have no truck with this *different* person — but she was also curious about novelties and not short of courage.

"I want to see Aunt Agnes."

"You are Ellaline?" A just-as-I-thought nod. "'Aunt', is it?" A snort. "Well, I'm Agnes."

Ellaline's thought was, *Mummy never tells me anything when she should*. She asked, as politely as her doubts could manage, "Are you unwell?"

"No, Ellaline, I'm middle-aged." The term did not seem to register. "Don't stand there on the doorstep; come in."

Ellaline took three adventurous paces into the living room her mother had tried to shut out of her vision and asked, "Is this a schoolroom?"

Agnes laughed, which took much of the grimness from her face, and told her, "It's my living room."

"But there's no furniture for proper living in."

"There's enough: chairs, table, couch, pictures. You're used to your home crowded with imitation Victorian junk, aren't you? Whatnots and antimacassars, by God!"

Ellaline's face hardened into the flat lines her mother recognised as trouble on the way. She said clearly, "Fuck!"

Agnes did not seem surprised, which rendered the exercise unsatisfactory. "Why do you say that?"

"You were rude about my house so I am rude to you."

"Fair enough," said Agnes, disappointingly. "Why don't you sit down?"

Mortified by the failure of one of her most effective shots, Ellaline chose the hardest-looking chair so as not to be seduced into relaxing; she needed to be on guard with this witchwoman. She asked, still seeking advantage, "Why do you look ill?"

"I don't. I look older than your mother, but that isn't an illness."

"Older?" The word took on some visible meaning. "That's more years?"

"Yes."

"But Mummy doesn't get — older."

"She does, just a tiny bit each year, but you don't notice because the change is small."

"But the treatments keep you the same."

"Not quite. They slow down the ageing — that is, the

looking older. I'm nearly a hundred years older than your mother.''

"Jeez!'' said Ellaline, to whom a century was some indefinable historical lapse. Curiosity was overcoming defensiveness. "When you were like mother was everything different?''

"Much better, I think. But everybody thinks their own regnum the best. Don't you think libbing is better than sticking to social forms?''

"Of course; don't you?''

"I think it's mostly sloppy manners, dirty language and bad temper but I agree that it's better than being a prissy imitation lady with your mind closed to facts and your life ruled by fear of the future.''

"I don't think I understand all that,'' said Ellaline.

"That's why you're here, for me to have a talk with you about the facts of life which your mother doesn't understand too well even if she could bring herself to speak them aloud.''

"The facts of life? My friend Jennie showed me a book about that. It's called, *How To Do It And Not Get It*.''

Kids don't change, Agnes thought, *thank God*. "I don't recommend that one and those aren't the facts we need to talk about. We are going to talk about ageing and death.''

"Yes!'' Ellaline's eyes sparkled. "What's death?''

She had quite forgotten that Aunt Agnes was decrepit and repellent and strange.

Ellaline tended to regard the next couple of hours as the most important of her life, which they were not. They may have been the most fascinating and absorbing but in nearly three centuries she encountered many concerns whose handling overshadowed her excited gulping of some shallow knowledge.

At one point she asked, "But why can't everybody have treatment? Is it sort of reserved?''

"Sort of is right; reserved for those who can afford it.''

"Can't the people in the Lower Town afford it? Or the servants?''

"Heavens, no."

"Are there many of the poor people?"

Agnes was for once taken aback; she had not realised how narrowly the neo-Victorians restricted their children's information about the world — in the sacred name, no doubt, of protecting their *innocence* from *nastiness*, that word which covered everything disturbing or, for comfort's sake, unseen. The taboos on discussion of age and death were understandable though stupid, but deliberate inhibition of knowledge of the structure of the world was criminal.

She said angrily, "About one person in a thousand can afford treatment. It uses expensive materials and expensive expertise and it must be repeated every few years. And each of us must be telemonitored throughout every moment of our lives. Anti-geriatry is the most expensive industry on earth."

Ellaline was trying to understand "one in a thousand", to absorb the idea of a world packed with people she knew of (as, mistily, she knew of the existence of other regna and, indeed, other countries) but had never needed to think about, people who lived only a little while. Unable to encompass huge numbers or the meaning of a little while, she thought of Jennie and Perkins and burst into tears.

Explaining why Perkins must soon be turned off from staff was not easy, but Agnes was an extremely efficient counsellor with a flair for reducing abstract terrors to graspable fantasy. She felt complimented when Ellaline at last gave judgement: "I think that's just silly, trying to pretend it isn't there if you don't look at it. It isn't the servants' fault." She examined Agnes closely. "I don't care if I look like you in a hundred years or whenever. You still have fun, don't you?"

Agnes agreed, with a straight face, that she still had fun and refrained from adding, *In ways you don't yet dream of*; explaining that would have meant treading minefields. Surely her mother could explain sex to her, in spite of *How To Do It And Not Get It*? Or could she? It began to seem doubtful.

The idea of death was impossibly difficult to clarify. The

child had never seen a dead animal of any kind, let alone a human being, and the example of a squashed beetle would not be the most engaging entry into the subject. Finally she hit on the stuffed animals in the museum, but it was still not easy. The idea of going to sleep and never waking up, of *stopping*, did not really get through to the girl. She accepted it as stated but did not understand; privately she thought that Agnes was holding something back and that you just got older and older.

Perkins said, "I thought you'd never be finished. Three hours!"

Ellaline was contrite. "You must be starving."

"Not me; I got lunch in the kitchen."

"That's all right, then."

She was pensive while Perkins drove. At last she asked, "Do you know about dying?"

"You aren't supposed to talk like that."

"Don't be pawky, Perky. Do you know?"

"Of course. Everybody knows."

"I didn't."

"And now you do?"

"Not really. Agnes makes it sound like being turned off like the holoviewer, or turned out like the light."

"It's something like that. Maybe more like running down until you stop."

"But what happens then?"

"Nothing happens then. Except maybe dreams. Nobody knows."

After a while she tried again. "Agnes isn't my aunt; she's my great-grandmother."

"I know."

"How do you know?"

"The staff know all about your family. It's in public records."

"Well, then, who's the very oldest?"

"Old Jock Higgins."

"Who's he?"

"Your five times great-grandfather. He's nearly 300."

166

"It sounds a lot." It didn't really sound like anything intelligible. "What's he like?"

"I wouldn't know. Nobody ever sees him. Perhaps he's too old to bother." Perkins allowed himself a mild piece of libber vernacular: "He always signed himself the Old Bastard."

"Why?"

"Dunno, miss. Maybe to spite his rich society kids because he was nobody important." He had been trash, even in a servant's eyes, but there were limits to expression. "He was the first person ever to get the treatment."

"First ever?"

"That's right. He was dying" — her interest heightened at once — "of cancer and he sold himself to a laboratory that wanted a human subject for experiments in total immunisation. That's fixing you so you can't get sick. Anyway, it worked and he's still alive."

"Was he rich?"

"Not him. He got his for free; the only one that ever did. He made his money letting doctors do tests on him as the Immortal Man; then he won a lottery prize and got a stock broker to handle his money and finished up with millions. And that's how little Ellaline comes to turn up in the eighth regnum."

"Now why the hell," said Ellaline, just to see Perky's lips twitch, "didn't Mummy tell me all this?"

"Maybe she doesn't know. Even if she did she'd keep it quiet."

"Why?"

"How many times a day do you ask *Why*? Your mother wouldn't want to know about an ancestor who was a sideshow boxer and con man who did a little breaking and entering on the side."

Then he had to explain the terms to her.

"He sounds terrific."

"He wasn't a nice man."

"Not nice — terrific. That's different." As Perkins pulled into the drive she said, "I'm going to say *dead* to Mummy."

"Don't you! She'll have a fit."

"Or a vapour or a megrim."

It was Perkins' turn to ask. "What's a megrim?"

"A sort of vapour, but noisy."

She thought that *dead* might be stretching her luck too far but couldn't resist retailing the scandalous history of Old Jock Higgins, careful to make it seem that Agnes had told her.

"Oh, dear God!" moaned Marianne, who did know the unsavory details and all of whose friends pretended (to her face) that they didn't. "Don't ever mention that name again. He is our family shame."

"But if it wasn't for him ..."

"I will not listen. And you will obey me! You will never again mention ..."

Ellaline sensed a lapse of control coming on and made a hasty promise.

Old Jock, banished forever from naming or allusion in the home, assumed special status in Ellaline's mind, ousting Jiggles the Werecat and Thorinda the Amazon Gladiatrix, her longest lasting holovid enthusiasms. She built in her mind a picture of Old Jock — hairless, canyon-wrinkled, fiend-ugly, piss-wet and rotten-fish stinky — on the general lines of a horrorvid puppet. She knew she had it all wrong, that the reality was probably ordinary and boring, but anyone whose mere name could drive Mummy into a tantrum must surely have something interesting about him.

She wanted to see for herself.

With what she thought considerable guile she suggested a further visit to Agnes (who just might be free-minded enough to help). The result was a why-must-God-persecute-me tirade about that dreadful woman who put unspeakable knowledge into the head of an innocent child.

Agnes was placed out of bounds.

The park by Lower Town was placed out of bounds.

In the home, young Jennie was declared a Pernicious Infuence and placed out of bounds.

Embargo on Jennie was the last straw. Ellaline became determined. Old Jock became a Project.

"You want to get me sacked before my time?" asked Perkins. "Forget it, kid."

Furious, Ellaline attacked below the belt. "Servants have to address me as miss, not kid."

"If I tell your mother what you're after your name won't be miss, it'll be mud."

"You hate me!"

"Not all the time," said Perkins. He thought that when he was turned off at thirty she would be about ripe for indiscretion. Pity.

It took Ellaline, not accustomed to working out practical matters for herself, a long time to realise that Old Jock could be located in the Directory — but there was nobody listed as "Old Jock". After considerable thought she conceived the idea idea of tracing her line back through Genealogical Records and bid fair to become lost in the tangle of ancestors, relatives and by-blows, but did at last arrive at the improbable Ian McIvor McAdam Higgins:

— the first treatee —

— born in ancient, unbelievable 1972 —

— which made him 278 years old, older than anybody —

— and living less than three miles away.

She studied the street map and decided that the attempt was feasible, cutting the corners of three regna and crossing one completely. The trek would itself be an adventure.

Her tutors, as she should have guessed, reported her absence. Marianne's first thought — her intelligent first thought — was to notify the police. Her less intelligent second thought was of the appalling places a rampaging Ellaline could get to.

Foreseeing public scandal she discarded all ideas of the police and despatched Perkins in the flipper to search, scour and ransack the streets and not dare return without her.

Perkins, like all the gossip-hungry Servants' Hall, knew where everyone lived who was anyone and set a course for Old Jock's home, the obvious first target, and found Ellaline in twenty minutes, two miles away, lost and hovering between tears and temper.

"Oh, Perky, do I have to go home?"

Perkins thought about it. The kid was, after all, only trying to come to terms with knowledge that 99.9 per cent of the race accepted without thought. Denying her indefinitely, he reasoned, would turn discontent into rebellion; the results, in the stupid regna societies, could be unpredictable and psychologically cruel.

"Soon," he said, not pushing his courage too far, "but we'll call on Auntie Agnes first. She's a sensible sort of woman."

Agnes asked, "In God's name, Perkins, what do you expect me to do? Take her to see the Old Bastard?"

"Why not, ma'am?"

Agnes recognised that as a good question, agreeing that such determined curiosity should be satisfied. But she did not fancy figuring in a family brawl of trans-regnal dimensions.

"It wouldn't take long," Perkins persuaded. "Ten minutes there and back in the flipper. Just a quick look is all she'll need."

"We might not be welcome."

"An eighth generation visitor? The Old Bastard will be tickled to death."

"But her mother ..."

Perkins held up an unservantly finger. "Why tell her? Make it quick and leave the excuses to me; she'll be glad to get Ellaline back and ask no awkward questions. Besides" — he turned to Ellaline — "you won't give me away, will you?"

Ellaline squealed, "You mean tell Mummy? She'd never

get over it. Old Jock is horrorvid to her. She'd go into a — a decline." She remembered tactics. "I'll be good, Aunt Agnes. I'll just look and that's all."

The nurse — middle-aged servant-class and afraid for her job — was undecided.

"You understand it isn't *him* I'm worried about. He's just about falling apart but he loves visitors. It's her. I mean, the regna and all that. It just isn't done, is it?"

"I am the girl's great-grandmother and with me it *is* done. If Mister Higgins enjoys visitors, why, we are visitors."

"But the little girl ..."

"She has seen old people before." Yes, Agnes thought — me.

"But not this old. There isn't anybody else this old."

Ellaline took on the expression that often upset Marianne's day. She said, "I'll write to the Old Bastard and say the servant wouldn't let me in."

That did it.

He was in a chair in the sun at the back of the queer old twentieth-century-style house, with only a lawn at the back instead of a Party Garden and Games Rink.

He was quite unbelievably tiny; he would be no bigger than herself, Ellaline thought, if you took the blankets off him. She'd bet his feet didn't touch the footrest.

His wrists had great bones on each side but the arms behind them were thinner than hers and the flesh on them slack and wrinkled and brown-spotted. His fingers had knobs for knuckles and their skin was shrunk tight round the bones; his hands lay on the blanket like semi-transparent spiders waiting to skitter.

His head was a skull with eyes. He had no hair at all, so Jimmy Johnston had been right about that, but his eyebrows were black and the eyes under them a sort of washed-out blue that looked as if they had seen everything that ever was.

She sniffed, cautiously, not wanting to be rude, but the

only smell was a sort of mustiness like an old empty cupboard. Maybe he wasn't pissing yet. She had no knowledge
of catheters.

Agnes and Perkins stood back while Ellaline went slowly
forward.

The ancient eyes did not blink or turn from her as she came
close enough to touch him. The pallid mouth opened to display
teeth that did not look real (they weren't) and a tip of whitish
tongue that licked the lips in preparation for speech. A
splintered sound of laughter came out of it like snapping
matchsticks and the sunken cheeks squinched up to make lines
round the eyes. A voice creaked out of the cavity.

"I ain't seen a kid in Gawd's age. Pretty, ain't she? Wot's
yer name, pretty?"

"I'm Ellaline."

"Nice name. Who'm I? Eh?"

"You're the Old Bastard."

The laughter would have been a shout if he had had a shout
in him. It broke up into a fit of coughing and then into a series
of gasps that brought the nurse running. "Get away from me,
y'bitch! I ain't laughed for a 'undred years. Come 'ere,
Ellaline!"

He put out a spider hand and very gingerly she took it, for
politeness' sake. She had expected only to look and leave but
the ancestor was giving her a welcome. She was not sure how
she felt about touching him; he was awful, really awful, but
not at all like her vidpuppet mock-up, more like something left
lying around and stirred up by a cleaning robot. But he was
happy to see her and that made a difference; it made all her
planning and cunning *right*.

He said, "You ain't one o'mine, are yer?"

Close to, his breath was nasty and his accent was even
more gutterbum that Jimmy Johnston's. "I'm your six times
great-granddaughter. Or maybe it's five times; I get the
counting muddled."

"And you come to see me, eh? Wot dju come for?"

"I wanted to look at a really old person. They don't tell us anything about old, you know."

The skull wobbled on its drawn stalk of neck. "I bet they don't. They don't even think on it. They got a few years extra and they're all frightened of dying! When we 'ad three score an' ten we didn't worry. Well, some did, like the 'ellfire brigade, but ordin'ry people didn't worry. Well, now you seen me!"

"Will I get like you some day?"

The nurse took in a horrified breath. Agnes looked interested. Perkins grinned uncertainly.

The skull nodded. "Maybe, but prettier."

Somehow that seemed quite funny and they giggled together, young tinkle and rusty gate.

He asked her, "You in one o' them regnums they talk about?"

"Yes. I'm Liberated Reaction."

"Wot's that one?"

She didn't quite know what it was because nobody had ever got round to explaining just what the libbers were about. She said, feeling inadequate, "We say liberated things — like shit and fuck."

The old eyes widened; the flesh wrinkled them almost out of sight. The pale mouth opened wide as the inadequate lungs strove to provide air for the laughing fit of a long lifetime. A dreadful cackle rattled out of the spasming throat and the thin shoulders shook uncontrollably. The spider hands beat on the blanket in ribald joy. The laughter became a volley of helpless noises while the head bobbed on its scrawny stick.

It all stopped at once.

Old Jock Higgins, the Old Bastard, had been overjoyed to see his five times great-granddaughter. Tickled to death, in fact.

On the way home Ellaline asked, "Can't the doctors fix him?"

Agnes sighed over a hopeless case. "No, dear; nobody can fix death."

173

Ellaline pondered. "He was nice," she said.

Even hardboiled Agnes found that horrifying but Perkins nearly ran the flipper down an embankment, he was laughing so hard.

There was no hiding the facts. The death of the Oldest Inhabitant Ever was news and the terrified nurse talked like a runaway printout, showering blame.

Agnes was at once ostracised, officially, by all neo-Victorians but seemed unmoved by the ban and unaware of the neo-Victorians. More seriously, Perkins was sacked in an hysterical scene that left Marianne prostrate. Agnes promptly hired him, mainly to spite Marianne, but kept him on her staff for the rest of his life.

Ellaline escaped scot free. Her mother went into a state of nervous collapse (for public consumption) from which she emerged with grim lips and a courageous determination to put the past behind her. For punishment, she sent Ellaline to boarding school, which Ellaline enjoyed immensely.

A few years later, Perkins's passing thoughts about Ellaline came true (in the garage one afternoon) and they entered on a love affair which scandalised the regna. With him thirty-four and her nineteen it was reckoned May and December — but it lasted until Perkins died in his mid-sixties, accounting himself the luckiest man who ever shacked up with an ageless rich bitch who didn't care that he got older. (He loved her very much, but the gossip discounted that.) They started a craze; it became chic for regnum folk to have servant-class lovers; it made such a painless preparation for a proper marriage later on.

Ellaline lived to be one year older than Old Jock. As she lay tranquilly waiting to die she said, "Now I'll find out. They never could explain it to me properly but now I'll see for myself."

Nonsense. The darkness closed in and her brain ceased to function and she knew no more about it than anyone else ever did.

Things Fall Apart

PHILIPPA C. MADDERN

Wardour came to Leong's private viewing clad in strict black and silver, his thick silver-rope necklace encircling the black collar of his shirt and his face grey with illness. As he walked through the door there was not so much a silence as a momentary hush preceding an outbreak of louder and more extravagant conversation, the corner of every eye upon him, in hope of either amusement or approval. He saw with foreboding that young Danny Considine, having snatched an untasted glass of champagne from his companion's hand, was rushing to offer it with much-practised artlessness.

"My dear, you look *marvellous*. Quite *en grande tenue*," said Danny as soon as he was within earshot.

Wardour looked at him as if assessing his authenticity, waved aside the wine, took up the nearest glass of chilled herb tea, and replied, "Surely the current phrase is 'tarted up like the president's robot'." Danny produced a creditable laugh. Wardour turned away to the exhibition. He never, in public, accorded patrons precedence over art, saying that he earned his fee with books, programs, and advice on art purchases, and anything more was subject to further negotiation. Lazarini, the principal patron present, thought it dignified and cultured to submit to this treatment, and went on talking kindly to the artist. Two of Wardour's old friends greeted him quietly as he passed, but only Danny, chattering desperately, accompanied him. Wardour kindly refrained from dispensing with him.

A predictable show, he thought. Here were the two mandatory social-realism set pieces, displaying hunched and smelly citizens, government-clothed, against a background of government housing, munching government handouts, and staring blankly across what Leong evidently imagined to be a government parkland. There were several bad slick portraits of patrons and their patronal enterprises; and a selection of excellent imaginative works presumably done in Leong's spare time. As Wardour halted, peering short-sightedly at each of these, he heard the talk at his back not precisely directed towards him, but swivelling, like a loudspeaker, to follow his progress.

"Five million if you count the government holding." "Won't they abstain?" "They'll be bleeding-well squeezed out of CoBia if they do." "Good. Good."

"... knew he'd been ill, but I just assumed it was aids." "No, definitely leukaemia, his patron's doctor says so." "But surely — you know — gene-washing?" "At his age? They wouldn't do it."

"And he said ..." "Yes, I was there ..." (*Ha ha ha*) "Who?" (Deep voice, imitating someone else.) "I'll have the whisky" (*Ha ha ha ha*) "And afterwards at the house ..." (*Ha ha ha*) "Yes I know —" (*Ha ha ha ha ha*).

Wardour dodged back and forth in front of a holo of two entwined athletes. There was something odd on the left face. Then looking more closely, he saw that Leong had suspended a series of magnifiers to enlarge one segment of one flawless profile of one beautiful boy. As he came closer he could see, as through an undiminishing tunnel, first the exquisite golden surface of his skin, then its individual pores and flakes, then each of its cells, then the nuclei, and hints of molecules and proteins. He watched the cells swim and shiver under the magnifier. A crowd of vague black fuzzy things was infiltrating cells in the upper right quadrant of the circle. He could see the cells begin to split and collapse, consumed by disease. His body shook with sympathy, as if each drop of his blood jumped in terror at the sight of its own death. He clutched his shuddering glass more firmly and swung round so abruptly that his sleeve whisked a plate clear out of the hand of the man standing next to him.

Wardour opened his mouth to apologise and left it open in astonishment; for the young man, quick as thought, dropped to one knee, caught the tumbling plate elegantly on the tips of his fingers, and tilting back his head, grinned in shy triumph at him. Then he climbed back to his feet, and resumed the appearance of a nondescript onlooker in overalls holding his crumb-covered plate.

Enchanted by such insouciant skill, Wardour exclaimed, "You're a juggler! A performing artist! Just what Lazarini needs. Shall I introduce you?"

The young man retreated even further, if that were possible, into his protective imitation of the ordinary. "Actually, I'm a scientist," he said; and then, as if making a gallant attempt to help out the conversation, "A biochemist." Wardour waited. The young man turned round to Danny. "Well aren't you going to introduce us?"

This surprised Wardour greatly; usually Danny's companions were even worse than himself. Yet here was Danny, with relentless charm, explaining that Patrick was a *brilliant* scientist, and an old school friend of his, and *what* good fortune that he and Wardour should have met. Patrick was apparently struck dumb by this, though the mention of Wardour's name raised no trace of comprehension in him. Wardour, really curious to hear the opinion of so surprising a person, said to him, "What do you think of this then?"

"The exhibition?"

Wardour nodded. Patrick looked perplexed. He ran his hand over his furry cropped hair, carefully, as if stroking a nervous cat, and said at last, "It's a wank, I reckon. Well, most of it. This one here's okay, with the viruses. They do that sort of thing, you know." (He sounded reproachful of the moral state of viruses.) "And a couple of others. But all those portraits — I don't know. If they were experiments I wouldn't do them."

"Quite right," said Wardour, immensely cheered; but Patrick just said, "I think your patron's trying to get hold of you."

Sure enough, Lazarini was approaching with Leong in tow, evidently bent on introducing the new artist to the established critic. Wardour collected his concentration onto Leong, and began in his best public style. There was no point in attempting private conversation; inevitably it would become a lecture delivered to Leong by Wardour in a glare of attention from the rest of the party. Already heads were turning, and conversations stopping short in anticipation of the performance.

By the time Wardour had dissected her showing into its three parts, almost nobody except the patrons were talking. After a brisk passage of arms against social realism ("If you must attempt to portray people who are, effectually, as unknown to you as chimpanzees, surely you should do so either as comic genre, abstraction, or allegory"), he proceeded to what he called "the only serious part of the exhibit. You agree with me?" Before his fascinated audience, he laid out his array of comments like sharp and shining crystals. "In holo four, you take the easy way. Why? Where you opt for the complex, as in holo seven, you reward your viewers if they pay attention. Thus you integrate them in your work. They add meaning to it by their perception, and it contributes to their perception. This is why we come back to it again and again (look at the floor in front, that tells its own tale)." Obediently, that part of the crowd nearest to it leaned over to inspect the scuffed floor at the feet of the gilded decaying youth in holo seven, and nodded wisely. So quiet was the hall that one could hear Danny's voice from the back, vibrant with champagne and venom.

"Of course it's all right if you've *got* a patron, you can say what you like *then*, about *anyone*, Peter included, not that I dislike him at all, I'm very fond of Peter, but you *must* admit that in *this* instance he's behaved like the most *arrogant*, *windy*, *pissy*, self-*satisfied* little *bastard* who ever ..."

"And I mustn't forget the portraits," said Wardour plaintively. "Why are they so bad?" He paused, but Leong would not venture on an answer. "It's not good enough, after all, to say that we don't like the patrons; Goya's portrait of the family of Charles V is not a product of liking, but it is a masterpiece. Nor is it useful to say that an artist must be free from all external constraint to do good work. The Van Eycks, Rembrandt, Michelangelo, produced some of their best art on commission. I see no reason why we shouldn't regain the knack. After all, it is no credit to oneself or one's patrons . . ." (for the first time his eye sought Lazarini in the crowd) "in fact it is shameful and disgusting — to flatter them with words and dishonour them with bad painting."

Lazarini politely interrupted a *sotto voce* conversation on currency regulations to nod back. Wardour said to Leong, "Thank you. A good exhibition. I enjoyed it," and turned away. Patrick was nowhere to be seen. Behind him, a steady shuffle had started towards holo seven. Resisting the temptation to scan the room, he made his way to the door. The voices pursued him out as the door slid shut.

". . . if the government fell?" "No chance." "Yes, *wonderful*, social realists, patrons and artists all in one hit." "No, Helen says definitely leukaemia." "But surely — gene-washing?"

He felt appallingly tired and very angry. Surely they knew, these people? How could they ignore, how could they be so blind or careless as not to see the bills for their own children's gene-reconstruction? How did they think that those huge sums of money could be met by most of the population? He knew, he, crafty Wardour, who had seen his name six thousandth on a queue at the government hospital, who had seen what was coming, and sweated out the accounting part of a Fine Arts and Economics degree, who had bluffed and weaselled and dazzled his way into the pay of the first patrons. He knew, what excuse was there for the others to be blind? It would have been better if he had had aids. Some workers still got it, some of the companies put money into improving the treatment for it.

Nobody bothered to market cures for leukaemia for those who couldn't pay for them. A blood transfusion tomorrow. Virotherapy the week after. Death coming soon, as sure as water runs downhill.

There was a bus phone at the end of the foyer, he knew. Better than begging a lift in one of his patron's cars. At the thought of the bus, the malignant hallway extended itself a further twenty metres again in front of him. Was it really possible to stagger so far? Or would he end up crawling over that shiny grey marble desert? But no. Here he was, walking upright, chatting urbanely to Matthew, who had come out after him, once (long ago) a lover, now an old if not a close friend, and the expanse of floor was diminishing steadily in front of them.

"Not an uncommonly bad exhibition, but the standard of public criticism continues to appal me," he told Matthew. And then prompted to a confidence he hardly understood himself, said, "I heard only one decent comment, and that was from a young man who is apparently a scientist. Patrick, or some such name. I don't know where he came from."

"Patrick Teague," said Matthew unerringly. As one of Lazarini's businessmen, his acquaintance was wide. He glanced curiously at Wardour, who, to his own annoyance, found himself saying, "He came with young Considine, I see. Rather a curious partnership, surely."

"No, it's the other way round," said Matthew. "He and Teague were at school together. Teague does some work for the gallery, I believe — scaffolding, hanging, something like that. They all get complimentary tickets, and of course Considine edged his way in on it. That boy's nothing but a leech."

"So unlike the rest of us," murmured Wardour drily, as a burst of pain grabbed his spine.

Matthew hitched his eyebrows in a resigned way and said "How's work? Do you get any time off?"

"I find work very soothing," said Wardour, and normally it would have been true; not only did the subject matter delight him, but there was the added joy of secrecy. No one knew, not Matthew, not even Lazarini, the treasure he was unearthing from the dingy bundles of Lazarini's last manuscript purchases. Yet tonight his own critical ear detected the echo of a lie in his voice. For a moment he thought with longing, not of parchment and gold leaf and lapis lazuli, but of Patrick's close dark hair and quiet well-trained body. He thought of waking in the night, in the dream-ridden darkness, of turning over and finding the smooth warmth of someone else there, and of going to sleep again, comforted. But, but, the boy hardly knew him, probably would hate condescension from an elderly notable, but there was no time, no time to do even a tenth of the things he had planned. Not a twentieth. "Very soothing," he repeated firmly as the bus arrived to take him home.

Home. Two rooms in a tied block of flats. No room even for Patrick, even if . . . And yet there was an obscure comfort still in his desk, his well-designed study chair, his terminal, his books and fiches, and the vellum pages which were arguably — no, certainly — the last unfinished work of Renee of Anjou, King of Sicily and Jerusalem. His patron had bought them by money without knowing of their existence. He, Wardour, alone understood what they were. Truly, they were his own privacy; to turn to the smooth white vellum sheets, to spread out his coloured fiches of comparative illuminations was as good as a journey back home to childhood. Even the colours had a long familiarity to him — the women's robes as blue as the sky above the curve of a water tank, the reds as deep as old tin roofs, the wheatfield golds. Only one page had its full two columns of text, but it was enough. He knew the pictures had been meant to illustrate the tale of the journey of the esquire Ame, the esquire Soul, from birth to salvation. He could show which was the first scene, the birth of Soul, with Reason and Knowledge as midwives. He had the last of the series, unfinished but unmistakably the picture of the justified soul standing at the entrance to the glorious blaze of the Heavenly City. He had only to identify and order the inner pages; only a few months' work. Surely death could be staved off so long? The page of text must be early in the story. It told of the battle between Soul and the dragon Anger. Anger was a young man's sin in Renee of Anjou's time. What about the rest? Was there a picture for every cardinal sin, or did the fight against the others appear in the wounded figures in the background of the dragon picture? (There was a fat beheaded figure which might be Avarice, the greed of the soul or simply the more commonplace Gluttony.) In another picture, Soul stood in the centre of a forest, reading from a book; but the pages of the book were blank. What was it? What was the meaning of the illustration with Soul sitting his horse and looking at a lion curled in a hollow in the ground? Was the dark castle to which Soul came, armed and visored, in another page, the Keep of Despair? The artist had painted rooms seen through the windows of the castle. In one was a hanged man — Judas? A woman sat, savage and brooding, in the gateway of the castle. Could she be linked typologically to Dürer's *Melancholia*?

The hours passed; Wardour had forgotten even to be tired, and had only once remembered Patrick.

Because she was so nearly not employed at all, Sanova worked in an office opening onto the foyer of the building. It was a poor area. Very little light came in, and that cold and dusty. For some reason, it seemed to Sanova like looking out of a beleaguered castle. Today, the feeling was especially strong. She leaned her elbows on her knees, and pondered how on earth she could present her research as in any way essential to the work of Consolidated Biochemicals.

If Bob would only agree to call it Defence Systems Efficiency ... but he wouldn't, too many people clamouring to squeeze under that umbrella already. Then what was a study of replicability relevant to? The answer, unfortunately, was either nothing, or almost everything. Even if she could prove that certain scientific experiments were not replicable — not just hard to test, like evolution, but not replicable, so that one could repeat the experiment exactly, and still not have the same result — would the company care? Or would they simply pay to shut her up?

At this point Patrick walked past, and in his polite way, stopped to say hello and could he do anything for her?

"Nothing at all. Why?" said Sanova, surprised. For Patrick, though phenomenally even tempered, was rarely forthcoming. Their conversations were usually confined to exchanges of information about their work. Patrick studied viruses, and had what were held to be brilliant but eccentric beliefs about the self-determination of virus behaviour. Since this led him into extra-scientific models of explanation, he and Sanova had a good deal in common. But Patrick was, in an unconcerned way, successful. His disease-control plans seemed to work, and there was a general feeling in CoBia that a lot of money could be made out of and by him. Sanova, clinging to the very edge of lukewarm managerial favour, would have hated him had he not been so patently unimpressed with his prospects. He continued to take on odd jobs in the city, in the underground, in art galleries, as the moods took him; and to stroll round other people's offices to see what was going on, stopping now and then to chat with someone and juggle deftly with their pens and paperclips, as he was doing now with three dead batteries from Sanova's desk top.

Now he said simply, "You look like despair. What's wrong?"

"Oh, it's only budgets coming up again. I suppose it'll be okay." Sanova was unable to prevent herself sounding both dreary and pathetic.

"Why? They won't dump you."

"They certainly might."

"Not a chance. They need their bright young scholars."

"I'm neither very bright nor very young."

Patrick rubbed his hair up backwards, and frowned. He said at last, "You make too little of yourself. You could ask for more than you get, and they'd probably give it to you. They don't respect people who don't ask. That's why I ask for the world all the time, and look what happens. I can't get them off my back, offering to get things for me."

Sanova, controlling her irritation with difficulty, said, "Well what would you do then? Who would you ask?"

"Anyone. Marketing Research. They do contingency maths, they'd be falling over backwards to get you. Or go out and get a patron, there's lots of them out there. I tell you, I went to a private viewing on the weekend, and there were three patrons I could have had for the picking up. Anyone could, I mean. Well there were two, anyway. I think the other one was a critic or something, but he was a good bloke, he'd help you all right. And you don't have to stick to science, come to that. You could do other things."

"Like juggling, I suppose."

"Yeah, it's a good living, juggling," said Patrick, impervious to disbelief. "I made a lot of money over the weekend, juggling down in the Dorms."

Sanova, horrified, said, "You don't juggle for money down there? They haven't got enough to live on anyway."

"Why not? They don't have to pay me if they don't want to."

"But you don't need it."

Patrick looked mildly irritated. "Sure, but that's not the point. They wouldn't want to watch if they didn't pay. It's like your lectures. You lecture down there, don't you? And you get paid? So what's the difference?"

"But the lecture's really useful. It — it gives them something they wouldn't get otherwise. I . . . "She hesitated before Patrick's patent scepticism. He said, kindly changing the subject, "Want me to introduce you to a patron? Herds of them in the galleries. Just waiting to be picked up. Like a lot of little lap dogs. Woof woof." He held his hands up, paw fashion, under his chin, and let his tongue hang out winsomely. Unwillingly, Sanova smiled at him and said, "You really think market research might do something?"

"Sure. Try Alice. She's good. Do you know her?"

"Well ... yes, sort of. I doubt if she'd remember me."
"You just try," said Patrick tolerantly, and walked off.

Ame sat his horse in the shadow of the forest. Ivy curled at its margins, entwined with solemn flowers; silent birds perched in its curly tendrils. Before him, the green hillside sloped away, drawing him towards, towards whatever it was, what place, what bright city whose white towers and wide light-filled streets he had never seen, and yet longed for always. His horse Cors cropped at the grass. Cors could be a willing ally; together they had fought the dragon Ire. He could be wilful; given a chance, he would take his master to the whorehouse or the tavern. Now he seemed undecided, and Ame himself was strangely unable to fathom the way. The city over the hilltop was his destination — but what of the forest? Its twisted paths might be as good a way to the city as any — better, indeed, than the straight green way before him. The forest was more than a random collection of trees. The paths were more than random. Each track was there because someone had chosen to follow it. Each tree was as much the same as, and as much different from, its neighbour, as the words of an unknown language, arranged in curling sentences by the purposeful paths. It was a language he could learn, he was certain of it. In his mind he saw the wood as a book, and himself the reader. He saw himself following its cryptic paragraphs, which might tell him — who knew? — the way to his perfect city. He was sure he should go through the forest.

And yet — the hillside. Looking more closely, he saw that it was not a simple sweep of turf. There was a spot of colour in one of the shallow grassy hollows to his right. It was a smooth tawny gold, like ripe wheat. It filled the hollow with a solid mass of velvety fur. As he looked, a fierce frowning yellow eye opened in it. It was a lion.

He might have been afraid of the lion; it was a huge, fearsome, dangerous beast. Yet he felt sure that it was not his enemy. It stared at him, unblinking and unafraid. "We two will fight together," it seemed to say, just as the dragon had spoken to him in his own voice, saying, "You will kill me or I will kill you." The lion stretched one huge golden paw towards him, claws extended, indolent and luxurious. Cors saw it and gazed intently, excitedly, at it; but did not plunge and snort as he had at the dragon, though the dragon had faced them with just such cruel spiked claws. Cors too felt the lion was a friend. "Whom shall we fight?" asked Ame silently of the golden beast. But it shut its eye, and never answered.

He sat at the edge of the forest, trapped. He thought he saw that the lion and the dragon belonged together, in one class of beings — the deadly, bestial fighter, who spoke to him from inside his own head. That being so, he should ride to meet the lion and take the adventure. But then how would he ever come to the forest and read his way through it? Or would the lion come with him through the wood? One glance at it was enough to tell him it would not. It was too bold, too bright, to track those labyrinthine paths. There might be beasts who would guide him there — peacocks to lecture from every tree, the wise white deer with the crucifix between its antlers to light the way — but the lion would not be there.

The wood and the lion were equal ways to reach the city. He did not know how to choose, which one should come next. He could not go on. Before him in his mind, two roads opened out, as blank as two white pages.

On Tuesday evening, Sanova gave her lecture in the Ballan Dorm. She and her students met in a corner of the Barter Market. If she was lucky, and business was particularly slack, one of the stall holders would lend her a table. She could then set it on end, and draw calculations and diagrams on its peeling laminex surface. If not, she simply sat on the pavement and talked. Her students almost never had any money to spare, but they paid in kind as well as they could, and sometimes she managed to resell what they gave her for hard currency. Today, she was finishing a series of lectures on replication theory. The group in front of her, down to about seventy-five now that the less enthusiastic had dropped out, squatted dead still, following her every gesture with rigid attention. Some, she knew, would memorise the lecture entire, to take on to other markets. Others were intent from the sheer effort to comprehend; eight years in a government school was hardly adequate preparation for understanding an esoteric philosophy of science. As usual, on the completion of the lecture, she allowed the first comers, squashed together in the centre of the front row, to make comments or raise questions. They spoke in the abbreviated jargon of street debate, knowing that the rest of the crowd, impatient to get their own say in, would allow no hesitation or oratory.

"Too much evidence against you," said the first. "For one hundred, two hundred years, scientists replicate experiments. How you account for it?"

"Contrary," said the huge goitred woman on his left. "Replications can be faked, juggled. Who says experiments were done same all the time? Lack of rigorous checking could give two hundred years' quotes scientific quotes success. Anyway, suppose two hundred years' replications. Sanova's cases still the exception. Explaining exceptions often leads new understanding, example, anomaly of speed-of-light observations to Newtonian physics leads to Einstein, right?"

"Support second commentator, both points. Besides, Sanova's theory worth testing. What if causation dependent on analogical, not logical sequences, as in medieval correspondence theory? Example, experiment done under astrological sign Taurus might not be replicable under Virgo, get me? Worth trying."

"Objection, third commentator — basically says only that up till now scientists concentrate some variables, ignore others, example astrological sign. Doesn't constitute different scientific method, only extension of method.

"Amendment fourth commentator's objection. Only goes to show that notions of cause determine sorts of variables tested. For sure Sanova suggests new variables to test, she's on about new notions of cause. Logical and it corresponds, right? So pro-Sanova."

"Okay, new objection for Sanova. Replication science predicts, example tachyons predicted before found in fact. Does non-replication science predict? If not, what bloody good's it to us? You tell us when the lights'll be on next week, that'd be good science, eh?" The speaker cocked his bright-eyed, withered little face over his shoulder and grinned at the audience, who laughed at him. He was an old hand; anyone who ever went to street lectures knew him. Jocular and serious comments floated over the mass of heads towards him.

"Come on Harry, you don't want to predict the lights, you want to predict the dogs." "So who wants to predict tachyons. That any more use to us?" "Dumb talk. 'f we were only interested our stomachs, wouldn't be here. Sanova wouldn't be here. Be licking a patron's bum instead."

Sanova grinned back at Harry, and said loudly, "It's a good objection, in that maybe non-replicatory science can't predict. But then it's becoming increasingly clear that replicating science predicts only in very narrow limits. Maybe prediction isn't a good way of understanding the world, get me?" Over the heads of the crowd, she saw a group of young people with gloves and padded jackets and sticks bearing down on them, and added wryly, "But if it is, I predict the lights are going to be cut about one second from now."

Her students needed no time. They had already followed her gaze, and the Clubbers got a scatter of good-humoured abuse as they came up. "Can't you do better than that?" yelled one backbencher. "Over in Melton they have lights seven nights a week."

"Not our fault," said one of the Clubbers. "We squared it with the Melton bastards. Power station shut down at Portland. You better get moving."

Reluctantly, they got to their feet. Several came up to shake hands with Sanova, and pay their dues of home-grown vegies, bottles of government orange juice, sheets of capsules. Some asked when and where she would be lecturing next. As she moved away to the pub to ring a bus, she found Harry walking beside her. His shoes were made from pieces of plastic carton, he walked with a chronic arthritic jerk, his thin grey hair was tied back with an old piece of printer ribbon. But he grinned up at her cheerfully and shrewdly, and said, "And what about it, eh? This company of yours employ you again next year? You think?"

"I don't know," said Sanova. "You're quite right, they want predictions. If they knew what I was doing, I wouldn't see the door, they'd shove me out so fast. I asked the Market Research manager if she'll protect the project. She said she might."

"Pressure on her?"

"Yeah. Things are pretty tight." She hesitated a moment, and said, "A guy upstairs suicided the other week, because he couldn't get his group any more money to work on, and no one else would take them on. Alice — she's the Market Research woman — told me to try for government grants as well. So there you are, it might go either way."

Harry stretched his eyebrows comically up away from his eyes, as if with incredulous innocence; then closed one eyelid with a parody of cunning. "Govament!" he said. "Govament! Nah. Govament won't have any money soon. Bankrupting, they are. You listen to me. If they toss you out, you come to us. We'll look after you. You'll see."

Sanova felt a burst of affection from him, for all her hungry, dilapidated, keen-witted students. Of course they could not help. No amount of improvisatory scrounging could provide the equipment to test the limits of replicability in any fashion that would hold water. But they meant the offer, all the same. She smiled at Harry, and patted his arm. She said, "Yes, I'll remember."

Harry smiled back. They were standing at the door of the pub. "Got some cash to buy me a drink?" he asked hopefully. Sanova gave him all but her bus fare.

She went on down the street to ring for the bus. Already the lights were cutting out in some of the side alleys. The phone booth, when she reached it, was fortunately still functional, though the slime on its floor and the smell of it showed clearly that its main use was as a public urinal. Sanova balanced distastefully on the driest patch of the floor, and waited for the bus signal to come through. Another light went out. Soon it would be dangerous to stay around alone, especially with a purse in hand. And Alice, though she had been kind enough, had not rung back ... all very well for Patrick to be so unconcerned, he really did not care whether CoBia employed him or not. *What shall I do*? she thought.

Because of the virotherapy, Wardour missed two of his patron's weekly drinks parties, and he was too proud to ask whether anyone had seen Patrick or not. When he arrived at the third, he was given no chance to look out for him. A furore of unexplained origin was taking place, and Danny Considine again rushed to meet him. "Wardour, have you heard the news? The government's fallen."

Wardour would have replied "Again?", but had no time. Two of his fellows came and swept him into the centre of a serious discussion, presided over by Lazarini. It appeared that the problem was not that the government had fallen, but that no party or combination of parties could be persuaded to take over the departed government's huge debts and increasing obligations. What would happen if this state of affairs were to continue, was the theme of the second patron's pontifications. What would happen to the Dorms, the Schools, the Hospitals? "I predict," said he, confidently ominous, "that there'll be anarchy, simple anarchy. Unless CoBia can put pressure on the New Liberals ..."

"Anarchy?" said Wardour, as of a new and interesting word.

"In the Dorms, of course, in the Dorms. Among the unemployed," said the patron kindly.

"But my dear fellow (no, no sherry thanks; tea if there is some) my dear fellow, you speak as if people *like* anarchy, *want* anarchy, are only waiting for a chance to *exercise* it. Where did you pick up such a ridiculous idea? Now I know *nothing* about politics, nothing at all, but surely we can all see that some of the best brains of the last hundred years have *tried*, have attempted diligently to persuade people of the virtues of anarchy, and got absolutely nowhere. People will set up *any* sort of order rather than have none. It may not be the sort of order which we like, but order of some sort in the Dorms there will be. Now tell me — do you seriously think the so-called government has in fact been running the Dorms for the last twenty years or so? Hm? Of course not. As I hear it, almost all institutions are now run of the Dorms by the Dorms for the Dorms — especially when it comes to law and order. So I really can't see that a lack of government will make so much difference.''

There was a hush. The patron said, "Er yes. Well," and appeared to lose all sense of direction. Matthew said, "You really are wonderful, Wardour. You make it sound so much less important than the authenticity of one of your medieval manuscripts.''

"So it is," said Wardour happily, thinking of his unknown treasure. Lazarini laughed heartily and buffeted him painfully on the upper arm. The group split up, some attending the patron in another low-voiced doom discussion, others with Wardour, or chatting idly. Wardour prattled artlessly about sequence and symbolism in manuscripts, trying not to look across his listeners' shoulders as new arrivals came in the door. But Matthew had implied the boy was not a client of Lazarini, and he was undoubtedly right ... "The dragon of Wrath, for instance, very interesting, is matched, I would hypothesise, by the Lion of Righteous Rage, neither precisely *heavenly*, if you see what I mean, but one considerably better than the other. Really, such a complicated view of the world. Everything with its counterparts in the various spheres.'' Someone quoted psychotherapy on rage and libido; someone else mentioned Dante. Wardour listened gracefully, but he felt immeasurably lonely. None of them, he thought confusedly, really knew what had happened. Governments, all governments, gone; a change that had never been seen, a world as it had not existed for what? Ten thousand years? And all they could think of was their own

191

safety. Perhaps they still thought they had safety to preserve. Surely Patrick would not say such stupid things, if one could ask him? And then suddenly he wondered if he were not so sad, so immensely miserable, because he, Wardour, would never see the new world, would die before he could observe it, he who had always loved new things, while the cowards, who were afraid of it, would live and never know what had been given them. Everything would go on; but he would not be there.

"Very plausible," he said. "Now Lawrence would say . . ."

He left the party early, as was increasingly his habit, and went downstairs intending to do no more than glance at the latest extension to Lazarini's gallery. Lazarini, for obscure reasons probably connected with the fall of the government, was anxious to have it opened to selected visitors as soon as possible. Lazarini's decorator, an unimaginative woman, immediately buttonholed him for detailed instructions on the lighting of various exhibits. Exasperated as he was by this triviality, Wardour was constrained to stand talking with her, and marking-up the hanging diagram in detail. As he did so, someone walked by carrying a load of glass plates; and as if his nose or his ears telegraphed to his unconscious eyes, he looked up, and saw Patrick. Patrick was wearing the same overalls as before, as if he had no other style of dress. He carried the heavy brittle sheets unconcernedly, whistling softly the while, and set them down gently and precisely in their place. As he came back, he turned aside and stood patiently, evidently waiting for some further order or explanation from the decorator. She ignored him, and Wardour, who had previously set her down as simply pompous, was now furious with her as a snob. Pointedly, he stopped talking and waited, hand on keyboard. She turned to Patrick with bad grace and asked him what he wanted.

"Nothing actually," said Patrick in his light carefree voice. "It's the blokes downstairs. They've got another job to go to, and they say if they're not given parking room they'll take the whole load back to the warehouse. They're getting stroppy."

The director, with an air of self-righteous disgust and a hasty apology to Wardour, bustled off. Wardour and Patrick turned to watch her out of sight, shoulder to shoulder as if they were in collusion. Patrick said contentedly, "Thought that would get her off your back."

Wardour gaped at him. "My dear boy, how did you know? That I, er, that . . ." He had not been reduced to stammering since boyhood.

Patrick looked surprised. "Well, you did want her to stop going on about all that crap, didn't you?"

Dumbly, Wardour nodded. Patrick said cheerfully, "Well, I'd better get going. And I guess you want to get home." They turned together and ambled towards the door, Wardour, for the first time in his remembered life, with more will than power to speak. The doorway loomed ahead. He would have to turn one way, down the marble entrance corridor, and Patrick would go the other, to the loading bay, and there was nothing he could think of to say. At the last minute, desperately, he said, "This government bankruptcy — I trust it won't affect your prospects at all? I presume science is still safe in the hands of business?"

Patrick stopped, considering. "I think so," he said at last. "I expect there'll be lots of refugees crowding in, but I think CoBia'll keep me. They may want someone a bit keener, that's all. You know, run round after the project manager and look eager. I'm no good at that sort of thing. But I'll manage."

"If there's anything I can do — a recommendation . . . ?" said Wardour, and cursed himself for sounding so eager, like that classic figure of fun, the ancient lecher. But Patrick smiled at him, and reached out to touch his arm. "That's good of you," he said. "That's nice. But I'll be okay, I don't care a lot what I do." He nodded goodbye and turned away.

Mercy, in her severe blue gown, was talking. "Forgiveness of all these you ask of me, and I will give you. Freely and unstintingly you are forgiven all your sins. For I, Mercy, have watched you in all your journey, have longed after you as a mother after her child. I watched you in your battle with Ire; I saw you lead Luxuria on a leash, as a tamed lion. You wandered in the thickets of worldly knowledge, and I saw you. You turned away from the poor man in his need, and I wept for you ..."

Ame, his knees sore from the stony ground at Mercy's feet, felt a sudden alarm. What poor man? The other adventures he remembered, but what was this? Should he have seen something? Had he or Mercy got it wrong, and if so, how?

"Now at this time when you must be torn for a little while from the body which you have mastered, ask of me, and my sister Grace, and you shall have entrance to the holy city ..."

Ame looked round anxiously, but was relieved to see Cors stuffing himself with grass as usual. If a poor man was still to be found, he might need Cors. But how was he to explain this to Mercy, who apparently did not see the need at all? Could this indeed be Mercy, who stood before him as blind as Justice, never knowing that something was wrong, that he could not rise from his knees, that he was trapped again in a hiatus of indecision?

He closed his eyes against the aching of his legs and pressed his hands together to endure.

When Sanova got into work the next day, there was a notice on the terminal to contact the Marketing Manager. Sanova's stomach jumped. She had heard of the fall of the government on the bus news, and expected no good things of it. It was possible that Alice had known it was impending when she suggested government grants, in which case it had been no suggestion, but a clear warning. But if not? She picked up the phone, and got the queue message. After several agonising minutes, Alice's voice said impatiently, "Yes, who's there?"

"Sanova. You asked me to call."

"Sanova, Sanova, oh yes, published a paper on reliability theory. Look, we can't get you in. This government crash will overload us ten applicants to each place."

Sanova said nothing. It was no worse than she had

expected. Alice paused, and went on, "I have got a suggestion. It's not much, but it's worth trying. You know Wardour?"

"Who?"

"Wardour. Art critic, journalist. Big name. Client of Lazarini's. He's dying, or so they say. Aids probably, he's as gay as a gamer, but that's beside the point. There'll be a client vacancy. Lazarini's a generous patron. I can put a word in for you if you like."

"Please. Please do. Thank you," said Sanova. Alice had switched on to the next call before she finished. She put down the phone and was immediately stabbed through by a piercing blow of guilt. Be a client? Never go down to the street lectures? Leave brave Harry and fat Martha and all the rest just when the government money which gave them all their margin between desperation and livelihood was gone too? Never; and she had done it.

She went slowly back to her desk, and sat staring at the offprint on it. She had requested it some time ago. It was unpromisingly entitled "Some notes towards a Critique of the Theory of Experimental Practice." Unwillingly, she began to cry.

When Wardour came at last to hospital, even Lazarini visited him. He had been given a single room. He had a console and desk beside his bed, but complained that the keys were too stiff to be used. It was a standard console. Only Matthew told him that there was nothing wrong with it.

In the intervals of typing, he arranged and rearranged his folder of illuminations. He was almost sure they were right, almost certain that the figure dividing his cloak with the beggar was, unlikely as it seemed, Ame rather than St Martin. He was dressed in Ame's colours; and the beggar, oddly enough, had a twisted face a little like the juggler's in the feast scene. And all the while he pored over the paintings, he was nerving himself to ask a favour of Lazarini. He had never done it. Illogically it seemed to him worse than ordinary clientage, to take gifts and beg for more. But (he sometimes thought) there would be no shame to bother him after he was dead. And it was for Patrick. And he had, in his hand, a gift for Lazarini which would sell for millions.

When Lazarini arrived, Wardour was sitting propped up with the folder of illuminations in front of him. He said, without preamble, "These are yours. I had hoped to give them to you in a proper order, with a sufficient commentary. But I shan't have time. You'd better take them as they are." He held them out, open to the page of the feast of the humours and elements, white and green and gold and red and blue. Behind the high chair, where Ame sat, half lord and half subject of his strange guests, a jester with cropped hair and a twisted face juggled forever with five coloured balls. Lazarini took it carefully, real delight on his face.

"What do you mean mine? I haven't seen this, have I?"

"Possibly not. It was in the Sikoyo collection you bought — in fragments, not as you see it here. I admit, I may have been wrong to keep my counsel all this while, but it was with the best intentions. It's certainly Renee of Anjou. A hitherto unknown work. It's worth millions to you, of course, even if you choose to sell it now."

Lazarini said nothing, turning the leaves carefully, by their edges, with his clean fingers. He noticed that Wardour's hands were covered with tiny blood blisters. There were slight smears of blood on the turned-back sheet, but none on the vellum pages. Wardour had used a cloth to handle the manuscript. There was a long silence. When he reached the end, Wardour said carelessly, "I hope you like it?"

"Like it! Well, yes, I — you old bastard," said Lazarini, and laughed. "You stupid amazing old bastard, just shut up and let me look at this again."

Satisfied, Wardour watched him scrutinise the manuscript, closely, giving little grunts of appreciation. "He pretends to know nothing but the value, but it's a pose," thought Wardour, as if seeing the man for the first time. He waited, tensing himself for the right moment. Now, in a minute, in a minute more, he could get a job for Patrick — if he were careful. Lazarini looked up, and Wardour said, "So where will you sell it, do you think?"

But Lazarini for once did not answer. He smiled at Wardour, looking almost shy. He said at last, "I won't sell this. I can't do that, it's your life's work. What do you want done with it?" And then, the old habit of command reasserting itself, "No, don't tell me — I know. I'll set up an institute — with a gallery and school — I've been meaning to do something like that. I'll call it after you. We'll have every good young artist in the country trained there, and we'll have this manuscript there on display all the time. How about it?" He reached out and took Wardour's hand.

There was silence. Wardour was too moved and grief-stricken to speak. He saw Lazarini's face lightened and eager with rare affection and generosity, and knew that he had lost, that he could never now throw back that offer and ask another favour. His throat swelled; he supposed it was a fair appearance of incredulous gratitude. He managed to shake Lazarini's hand and croak, "And scientists. We'll get a few good scientists as well." But that was all he could do.

In the morning, Sanova, bleary with crying, read on the message-screen, "Contacted Lazarini. Reckon you're in. Alice." Wardour closed his folder and died, haemorrhaging. Harry took an overdose, reckoning correctly that his family could no longer afford to feed him. Ame stood on the threshold of a new city, white and gold under a new heaven, and heard the eternal music call him in.

Thy Sting

D A M I E N   B R O D E R I C K

Stop me if you've been this one before ...

See, there's a Catholic, a Buddhist and a Communist. They're sitting at a bloody enormous conference table, members of their staffs on every side, shaven monks in saffron robes, Opus Dei operatives gliding suave as barracudas, jowly apparatchiks muttering into tiny Japanese discorders, and everyone except the Catholic terribly grim and serious.

So the Catholic says, "I've got some good news and some bad news," pushing back his satin skullcap and propping his elbows on the table.

"Let's hear the good news first, your Holiness," says the Dalai Lama with a little shudder, because for months now they've all had their scouts out, ever since James the brother of Christ turned up in the Leningrad clinic (if you could believe the Russians about anything, let alone that), and then Mary three days ago in Chile, a pious peasant selling tea-towels of herself as the Virgin of Guadelupe.

"The good news is that we've found Him, thanks to your Chinese pals."

You know that kind of silence in a room. So finally:

"I would not have thought *you'd* find that good news," says the Communist, a lean academic type in his mid-thirties, just a trace of guttural Georgian there in his voice. As well as being front-runner for both Physics and Medicine Nobels for his discovery (though there are whispers) of Gravitino-induced Intron Recovery, he's the sole known current reincarnation of Josef Stalin (there are whispers about that, too), a universal genius utterly without fear but not altogether innocent of humour. He grins with great pleasure. Thin lips and no moustache.

"The Pope is a notable ironist," the Tibetan remarks irritably, and pushes his round glasses up on his small Mongolian nose. "You're sure it's a valid Jesus Christ?"

"No doubt about it. We've got a ream of validated cross-indexed material from His brother and His mother."

"I hope you don't think it indelicate of me to ask, but who was His, uh —"

"Mary Mag —"

". . . genetic partner?"

"— dalene, of course."

"Oh. You're not surprised?"

"We've had documents under lock and key for upwards of sixteen centuries," the Pope says.

"How many children at demise?" Stalin asks acutely, taking a pocket calculator from the outstretched hand of an assistant.

"Unknown. We have a Primogenitary Line Revenant, from slightly less than one year into His ministry." The Pope gives a rueful chuckle. "He may have been tempted in the desert but evidently He kept His legs crossed until remarkably late in the piece."

The Russian glares, scandalised. Five years at the close of the nineteeth century in the Tiflis Theological Seminary rises in his blood to darken his face, to sharpen a repugnance for blasphemy he learned in that century, that lifetime, from his doting mother.

And the Dalai Lama just broods on the Angutarra Nikaya: "*There is one who, having been one becomes many, appears and vanishes, unhindered he goes through walls, he dives in and out of the earth as if it were water.*" He sits back in his chair, clearly at a loss. "You accept this claim, then?"

"Looks watertight, Padmasambhava."

"Hmm. And the bad news?"

"I withdraw that remark. You would certainly consider it in poor taste."

"Certainly we have gone beyond taste, for good or ill," growls the revenant of J. V. Dzhugashvili. "What is the balance of your news?"

"It's the old gag. Embarrassing. Enough to make you believe in prophecy."

"Gag?"

The Pope sighs. "The bad news is, She's black."

"Oh God," cries the Dalai Lama, who until three months ago has truly believed himself the lineal descendant of his saintly predecessors and now can't deny that for a hundred generations he's been no greater than a clod in the fields. "Oh God," cries the Dalai Lama, who knows his Hegel and his Marx at least as well as the frowning Russian across the table from him, "the first time as tragedy," cries the sad little Dalai Lama, "and the second time as farce!"

And there's these other three people, see, sheltering from the sun under a rag strung on a stick and a length of ratty rope in the middle of an almost motionless sea of human misery in hottest bloody driest darkest Africa. There's a white man, a black man and a yellow man.

I tell a lie. The yellow man is a swarthy good-looking fellow from the Beijing Television Centre, a poet who specialises in science reporting. That bit is true. But the white man is actually a nun, and she's not exactly white, being a quadroon from Miami named Sister Concepción Ortiz. And the black man is really a skeletal adolescent girl. The adults argue while she lies perfectly still, flat on her back in the scant shade, eyes huge and passive in a face like a skull.

"Keep your stinking hands off this child," the nun screams. "Bloodsuckers! Liars! Goddam *creeps*!"

The handsome man is sweating. The ground is foul with sludge and the sun drives up wavering sheets of humidity. Here they all are, poor bastards, twenty or thirty thousand of them and more arriving every day, perishing from thirst and hunger as the wobbling world, God's spinning top, drives the scorched Sahara farther and ever farther into the heartland of Africa, and the appalling random thunderstorms spill damfuls of useless water into the eroded dust, into the trampled, pissed-in, shat-in mud. "We saved her life," he explains patiently, his Yale American classier than Concepción's.

"Listen, buster, what makes you think *life* is what's important here?" Her arm embraces the filthy muddy plain of numb, silent, doomed human refuse. "You're trying to kill their *souls*, you bastards."

"You're an educated woman," he begins again. "How can you ..."

"Pitiful. You're pitiful. Reductionist crap. You think that's science?" The child's head is capped with a crown of wires, transmitting gravitino-induced data to a briefcase of microprocessors in the cooler cabin of the Chinese's Toyota where the Intron tech is drowsing. "Why not just cut the top off and stir her brains with a stick?"

"You're defending a paradigm that's dead and gone, Sister. Your trendy holism doesn't have a single valid response to Intron Recall. So you abuse us wicked communists for saving a child's life."

"*Fuck* off." She is quite beside herself. "Let me tell you, I've marched against corporations that send their stinking drugs here for testing, and what you're doing is exactly as bad. If it's so safe, get the hell back to the re-education camps in Taiwan and burn out a few brains there, instead." Then Concepción sits down in the mud, shaking her head and weeping, and holds the black child's hand against her breast.

"Sister, we are taking the child into Addis Ababa under your religious superior's express instructions. I have shown you the documents. Please stand aside and let me get her into the vehicle."

"Those pricks." She clutches the child to her. "You're

insane," she tells the man. "Lysenko and all that commie crap. My God."

"No. You know better than that. The surplus DNA in the genome was not even dreamt of in Lysenko's ..."

"You can't inherit someone else's memories," the nun says through gritted teeth. "That's voodoo, not science. There's not enough DNA."

"Quantum non-locality," the Chinese intones tiredly. "Bell Theorem connectivity. Reverse transcriptase Intron coding. You've seen our videodisks, Concepción." His tone sharpens. "It's this child, of course. You can swallow Popes and birth control and heaven and hell and miracles and virgin births, but you can't face the one fragment of truth that makes it all such a sham."

"Shut up." She puts the child's arm aside and walks toward the Toyota. The journalist follows her, throws open the tailgate. They hear snores.

"She's a reincarnation of His, Sister, and that's it. We have all the preliminary probes on disk. You've seen the Academy's provisional evaluation."

"Bullshit. A phoney juggler? A first-century cardsharp? A political opportunist with his hand in the till? You think a fraud like that could create a world faith that's still alive after two thousand years? A user of whores." She leans against the stinging hot metal, eyes squinting. "I mean, your own so-called theory doesn't hold up. This is a girl, haven't you noticed? I thought the memories were supposed to be passed down along with the sex chromosome."

"He was special," the journalist says. "He was ... larger than that."

"What?" For the first time Concepción looks at him and sees a human face. "*You're* a Christian?"

He shrugs. "Help me move her."

"Jesus really fathered a child?"

"How else could His *karman* have passed into the gene pool?"

Concepción walks back blindly to the small patch of shade. The girl is sitting forward, regarding her. The crown of electronic sensors has been brushed into the mud. The child's gaze is alert, penetrating, and something more. It takes the nun a moment to identify that terrible glee.

"You are both wrong," Jesus tells them, and rises to Her feet, floats and bobs above the foul mud like a feather of light. "You are both right. Come, follow Me."

The journalist utters a loud cry and runs for his portapak.

Concepción's heart clutches. She stumbles, one arm outstretched, mud sucking at her shoes, and rises, then pops free from the embrace of the ruined earth to scamper, like a besotted apostle on the wind-whipped surface of an ancient lake, in her Saviour's unmarked train.

My Lady Tongue

L U C Y   S U S S E X

Honeycomb, my honey, sweet Honey Coombe. I love her so much I daubed her name on the biggest white wall in the ghetto and round it a six-foot heart. The paint was shocking pink, and it dribbled, when I so wanted my ideogram to be perfect! She passed by that wall every day, but unfortunately so did others, and that was how the trouble started.

"Vandalism!" That was the Neighbourhood Watch, our ghetto guards. I was minding my own business, thinking of Honey, but cat curious I followed the groups of womyn drifting towards the clamour. It was only when I was in the main square that I realised the offence was mine. Ah well, I'd brazen it out — I'm nothing if not brazen.

There was a crowd in the square, which included the off-duty Watch and most of the powers-that-be in Womyn Only. One of the most dignified of these Elders was actually atop a stepladder inspecting my splash.

"Honeycomb," she announced to the groundlings as if every womyn Jill of them couldn't already read. "Possibly male reference to our genitals?"

"Ishtar!" cried the Watch Chief. "They got in this far?" There was a horrified mumble from the masses.

"Tsk tsk. Sleeping on the job," I said, just loudly enough for the Watch to hear and not pinpoint me. Zoska, who'd reared me, came forward trailing her youngest.

205

"Not quite down to their usual standard, is it?" she said. "Bar the colour."

It was strident, but that's my style.

"They go in for dribbling cocks usually, not dribbling hearts."

Some of the hearers drew in their breaths hard, and she snapped: "Don't be silly, this isn't the Hive."

"You think it's a Sister?" asked the Watch Chief, catching on at last.

Zoska nodded her coif of plaits and I cursed silently: if she got much warmer things would be hot for me.

"Our vandal," said Zoska, "loves Honeycomb."

"There aren't any Sisters of that name," said the Ladder-climber. "Unless you mean Marthe's daughter Honey ..."

Their heads followed one direction and I thought I saw my sweeting, so I waved my floppy hat at her. But it was only her grim mamma and I knew I was for it.

"I own up! I did it, I did it!" I shouted, jumping up and down.

"Thought so," said Zoska.

Marthe was looking black and I was beginning to realise why.

"Sister Raffy," said the Chief, "Womyn Only supports artistic expression but isn't this over the top?"

"Shucks Officer, I'm in love."

"Honeycomb," said Marthe as though that sweet name was wormwood in her mouth. "Is that your name for her?"

I nodded, thinking oh oh! My darling's name was Honey Marthe, the mother's name affixed to the daughter's, as is ghetto custom. Me, I'm Raphael Grania, but I only answer to Raffy. Coombe had been Honey's father, a sperm donor anonymous except in the genetic profile of his daughter. Hardcore dykes like Marthe (who never ventured from the ghetto nor indeed much from the Hive, our inner sanctum) detested the profiles — but kept them in case of genetic disorders. Honey had found the document, and discovered her humourless mother had made an accidental pun. I had laughed at that, at Marthe, but now I had made a laughing stock of her, and worse. It was bad taste to remind Womyn Only that its girl children were not spontaneously generated.

Me and my big paintbrush. There was a long, really nasty silence during which I mentally gave myself a hundred lashes, and crossed miles of paving on my kneebones.

"You'll never call her that again," said Marthe and strode off followed by a curious knot of Elders. The crowd was staring and Zoska had piggybacked her child and was pushing towards me. I didn't need comfort now, just action! So I pretended not to see her and nipped around the corner and over a couple of back gardens, shortcutting to Honey's home. It was empty; and I stood outside and thought of the hydroponic flowers I had thrown through her window. Then I embarked on a long and increasingly desperate tour of our trysting places. I found nobody waiting, alas! and at the last the Watch Chief found me. She was embarrassed but stern.

"Marthe and Honey are in the Hive, from which the Elders have banned you until further notice."

I lay down by *our* fountain and imitated it for a while. Then I recovered and went to see Zoska.

"Ninny," she said.

We sat in the sunny brick courtyard behind her little house, she at her embroidery frame and Basienka, who had accompanied her to the meeting, wandering around the confined space in her enigmatic two-year-old's way.

"Oh, I agree absolutely. Now what do I do?"

"Go to Bozena at Haven, until the fuss dies down."

Haven was the refuge we dykes were building in the country. I had scouted the site and normally would go there gladly.

"Can't leave Honey." Puck puck puck went the needle into the stiff linen cloth. "I get soppy just thinking about her."

"Creamy you mean," said Zoska. "I know you."

"No, this is the real thing. I'm so sentimental I could die."

Zoska sighed.

"You're old enough to be her mother."

"Not quite. Honey may be sixteen, but I — as you ought to remember — had a late menarche."

She did the sums with her lips.

"So you did. I was confusing you with Boz."

"Quite a party we had for it," I said, hopping over a wall in my mind into memory lane.

"Was it ever! You tore up the poem Grania had written for the occasion and when she created lit out with Boz. The pair of you didn't come back until six the next morning, when you burst into my bedroom shouting you were in love with each other. I haven't had intoxicants at a menarche party since. Won't have it at hers either."

She grinned at Basienka.

"Look at her. Aren't I clever? Forty-eight years and three months I was when I bore her. Broke the ghetto record."

I recollected that Zoska had begun the career of mothering with Bozena and had had thirty-two years at it since. Some daughters were hers; others came from Sisters who like Grania preferred not to have the rearing of their young.

She looked at me, reading my face.

"You and Boz may have had your adventures with Haven, but I've reared seven fine womyn. Mind you, it's early days with Basienka and with Urszula I'm not sure."

I stirred, perceiving how my least favourite sister might help my purpose.

"You could use Urszula as an example to Marthe. She's not much older than Honey, she's taken up with Bea, who's my age ..."

"I've got enough chickens to take chances with them. Marthe's only got one."

"Let me finish. And Urszula's leaving the ghetto!"

"Oh Ishtar, don't even think of saying that to Marthe!"

"Why not? Honey wants to."

"After she's been reared hardcore? To go among *men*? Raffy, she really must love you."

"I want to swear committal."

She reached into the basket between us for a new skein of wool, the colours jewel bright against her fingers.

"Wow, Raffy settling down at last. Okay, I'll talk to Marthe."

She snipped off a length of wool viciously.

"It won't be easy."

Her gaze was like a mirror, in which my scarecrow image — in old camouflage duds from Haven (worn to annoy the hardcores, who never went Outside), lurid pink shirt, embroidered scarf and old hat — was reflected with censure.

"Raffy, you're disreputable. You'll have to smarten up if I'm to get anywhere with Marthe and while I'm at it also stop teasing the Elders and getting into fights with the Watch. You're the last match Marthe wants for Honey."

"I'm the daughter of a famous poet."

"Yes, and Grania denounces you in verse for being undutiful."

"We never ever got on."

"So I got the rearing of you, half my luck. Raffy, I can't win Marthe without Grania's help. You'll have to make up with her."

"I'll put a girdle round about the earth in forty minutes!"

"What's that? What do you mean?"

"It's poetry. Shakespeare, a man. I mean, I'll do it."

She was looking puzzled and I got up to stretch my skinny legs in the courtyard, puzzled myself. I keep my Shakespeare well hid in Womyn Only, because of what it means to me: lost time with Benedict, a man. Swashbuckling Raffy might have had a child, a son even, and not by donor but by the old way, which Shakespeare writes about a lot.

There was no telling what a hardcore dyke would do if she knew her daughter was marrying tainted flesh. But Marthe would never hear of it, would she?

In my perambulations I nearly tripped over Basienka, who looked up from trying to unpick a wool flower on the skirt of the little peasant dress all Zoska's daughters, even tatty Raffy, wore. On her face was the same knowing smile as the Cumaean

Sibyl, whose painting adorns a wall in the Hive, and I was suddenly afraid. Marthe could discover Raffy's little secret, from Grania, who might tell her if we two were unreconciled.

I looked away from Basienka, to Zoska.

"Can you talk to Marthe? I'll do Grania."

She nodded her silver-brown head, and I took leave of her. Grania lived outside Womyn Only, in a small brick house with a studied bohemian air. There was a hammock on the front verandah with a huge hole in it; the garden was a careful mixture of weeds and colour-clashing flowers; the brass nameplate said "Poet's Corner". Before I could knock the door was opened by Bea, lover of my foster-sister Urszula. She carried a carton of books for her shop, my mother's literary children, new branded with her squiggly signature.

"Hi Raffy, surprise to see you ..."

"Here?" I asked dangerously.

She looked embarrassed.

"I'll get out of your way. Raffy ... do you really want Marthe for a mum-in-law?"

"Anything for Honey."

She walked down the pathway with my brothers and sisters. I waved, then went noisily inside. Grania was in her visitor's chair, a monster of carved mahogany chosen to diminish the bulk of the womyn within it. From my mother I had my height, but I blessed her donor for a lithe figure, for his genes dominated over those which would have made me resemble a hippo. She batted not an eyelid as I sauntered in.

"Come to your mummikins, lambie-pie," she said icily. It was the standard greeting and as usual I kept my distance, leaning against a wall of this book-lined grotto, with its troll-queen enthroned.

"What, no fond greeting?"

Go cautiously, I thought.

"Did you ask Bea about me?"

"Of course. She said you were in trouble, big trouble if you come and visit me. There was mention of a sweet young thing locked away from your wickedness. Then she spied your approach and bolted, leaving me in a state of gossipus interruptus.''

"I shall bring you to climax."

"This sounds like the tale of your lost month. The one time you confided in me."

I stared at her.

"Mother, we are of one mind. I want you to recall the incident.''

She grinned evilly.

"How could I forget Raphael's *True Confessions*?"

My lost time had been thirteen years back, before Haven even, but it was vivid to me. When I dipped into the past with Zoska I had half seen the brickwork and moss beneath my feet strewn with coloured streamers and crushed paper cups. Now, instead of books I could see pollution-bleached grass, weird trees and eroded hills with knob rocks sticking out. She's very visual, Honey's Raffy.

I had been Outside both ghetto and City, sussing out a site for Haven in the countryside. When I remember, the mind's eye comes through first, then later the body with what my past self was feeling. I had been happy, despite the desolation, which was coldly beautiful, and the dangers. The country had unmarked pollution dumps, which had already claimed one scout, wild dogs, and of course the bogey of man.

Ah, who cared! I was wearing camouflage clothes that were weatherproof; I had survival rations, weapons, mini-communicator, compass, heat detector, Auntie Cobley and all. The paraphernalia fitted neatly into a five kilo pack on my shoulders that left me unencumbered, feeling free. There was a wild wind blowing, early spring sunlight and Raffy who had lived behind walls was madly in love with wide open spaces.

This was my first solo voyage. Previously I had gone with senior members of the Watch, who were supposed to restrain young hotheads like Boz and me, and then with Boz. That trip had been a mistake, for in the excitement we had revived our first love, only to quarrel so bitterly we resolved: never again. We were too alike, and I crave opposites, Honey.

I was walking through a narrow valley peaceful even though bisected by a service road, when I heard a droning roar, steadily increasing in volume. Diving into the nearest cover, a ditch curtained with green weed, I checked the heat sensor, which registered zero. My fears of a behemoth mutant vanished and I peered through the green to see a robotruck on the road, making its slow thunder from a macrofarm somewhere. False alarm; but nonetheless I left the road and went cross-country, moving swiftly until I came to a patch of burnt-out ground.

I started to weep then, and my future self, standing in Grania's study, sought for a reason. There was a memory within the memory and it was red, the colour of the fire that had engulfed a house on the edge of the ghetto. Five womyn had been inside and there were more dead, Watch members who had surprised the arsonists. "Men did it," Zoska had explained to little Urszula, who had only stared at her uncomprehendingly.

After the fire had been doused there had been more red, with a torchlit meeting in the main square I was later to defile with my "honeycomb". The Elders had argued and argued what to do and slowly a consensus was reached. We were easily attacked within our enclosure, we needed to go beyond the city, found a city of our own. And so the Haven movement began, and changed the lives of Boz and me. We had been feckless ghetto girls, too wild for the Watch and too hardcore to find work in the straight world. Now we had a goal in life.

Standing amongst charcoal and singed trees, I wept for the dead, until it occured to me that were it not for them I would still be cooped up in Zoska's living room. There was a site for me to look at; I went on.

Our Haven was defined by a list of desiderata, a majority of which had to be ticked before the Elders would approve the site. My destination had already accrued some ticks, if we were to believe the intermediary feminists who had investigated the site in the guise of a macrofarm consortium. They had liked it. Yet the site needed to be seen with a dyke's eyes, and secretly. The memory of the incinerated house still burnt.

I spent a day at the prospective site, being thorough. Womyn Only looked at many locations, finding some too marshy, too polluted, too grim et cetera. I was writing the report in my head as I trudged: "Eminently suitable for our *queendom*, our *newfoundland*" — words Grania had used when she heard of my vocation, laughing all the while — "except . . ." It was insufficiently secluded, being too close to the farm I had seen the truck trundling towards earlier. And this farm, as the intermediaries had discovered, was not staffed entirely by robots.

I inked in the last mental full stop of my report and turned to go, when the late afternoon light caught a spot of colour on a distant hillside. When I pulled out my viewfinder I saw a scrawny blossom tree in its spring best. The flowers were chalky pink, beautiful.

I glanced at the sun and again at the tree, estimating it was a kilometre away. Why not? I could take a pressed flower home for Zoska to copy and maybe another for a young lady of the Watch I had my eye on. What I had not expected, though, was the macrofarm's fence between me and tree, impenetrable even for a Scout equipped to the eyeballs. I followed it hopefully and came at last to a spot where an animal had burrowed beneath it. There was just room for Raffy, but not if she were humpbacked: I had to discard the pack in order to squeeze through.

The detour had eaten at the daylight and the hill was dusked over by the time I arrived at the tree. Feeling uneasy, I decided not to stay long and reached for a blossom. There was a growl and automatically I jumped into the branches as a low shaggy shape came up the slope towards me. It was a feral dog and it was followed by its brethren.

They clustered snarling around the base of the tree and I climbed higher. Hormones from the macrofarm had affected this tree's growth: it was some seven metres high, with sturdy branches. I sat in the highest of these, watching the dogs leap upward, snapping teeth on air and scrabbling their paws on the bark before falling to earth again. I was well out of reach, but I cursed, the dogs replying in their language. Any idiot would have checked the heat sensor for these pests, or considered that they might have dug under the fence. Any idiot, but not Raffy.

Packless I was not quite defenceless, wearing under my camo shirt a weapon as unphallic as a dyke could make it. I took out the gun and shot experimentally at the dog chieftain, remembering my target practice with the Scouts. It was close: there was a smell of singed hair and the pack ran off a little, yelping. I gloated until I registered another smell, that of singed tree. The shot had nicked a lower bough, had almost cut it through.

Rather than whittle my sanctuary away I stopped, and the dogs settled under the tree for a long wait. I considered my options: the gun had a limited number of charges and the waning light would not improve my aim. Better to wait until the morning. I ate a couple of blossoms and found them tasteless, then had the joy of a half-eaten lolly Urszula had dropped in my pocket during the farewell. Lest I fall in sleep, I buckled my belt around flesh and tree trunk. The sun set and like the dogs I waited.

In the darkness maybe I slept, for when I awoke suddenly it was moonrise and all the landscape silvery. There was a pawing and moaning at the foot of the tree, as the dogs milled around something strange — a metal canister. As I watched it emitted white mist; the dogs sniffed at it and whined. I could smell chemicals now, stupefying, and below the dogs were staggering like drunks. I pulled my scarf over my face for a filter, feeling weak and glad of the belt that bound me.

Walking among the fallen, twitching forms was a figure oddly distorted around the face. It stopped and stared upwards at my form outlined against branches and sky.

"Here, catch!" and it threw a package to me expertly. The gift was a mask like the mask, I saw now, of the giver. I pulled it over my head and breathed freely again.

"You can come down now."

For the first time I noticed the lower timbre: a man's voice. Was I going from frying pan to firing squad? I began to pick at my self-made bonds watching *him* all the while. The canister had disgorged its drug and he was walking from dog to dog, pressing a rod against each head. There was a faint click, then death.

A deep-voiced thank you, I decided, then scram! I rebuckled my belt and clambered down, too fast, for in the haste I put foot to the half-severed branch. It cracked beneath me and I fell in a shower of pink flowers made silver. With a splintering crash, bough, Raffy and all hit earth, just missing the hillock of a dead dog.

"Are you all right?"

He was bending over me now, and I heard him draw his breath in deep. I looked and noticed my leg caught between wood and ground. Funny, it never used to bend that way.

"If you don't mind me saying so, that's a godawful break. I'll have to take you back to the farm."

He was fumbling in a pocket of his coat.

"Can't have you screaming blue murder all the way there . . . sorry about this, mate."

His hand emerged from the pocket with another canister, and simultaneously he reached forward and snapped my mask off.

"Sorry," he repeated and cracked the canister under my nose.

Much later I awoke in yellow artificial light and found myself lying on a table, head propped up on foam. There was a machine covering one leg.

"Robo doctor," he said, from where he sat watching. "They gave me one 'cos I'm all alone here."

I stared at him; a smallish man with a lined, weary face, not young, not particularly muscled, and not threatening at the moment, although you never could trust them.

"Well, say something! Think you'll give yourself away? I can tell you're a woman."

"Womyn."

"And that you're one of those."

"I'm Raph-ael."

"That's a man's name, an archangel's."

"My mother says angels don't have gender, so there."

"Your mum knows her theology, Raphael. I'm Benedict. That means blessings, and I don't mean you harm. I even left your toy with you."

Sure enough, my right hand had been folded around the gun. I lifted both cautiously.

"Don't burn me," he said, and I lowered my hand.

"We aren't all beasts," he said seriously, and at that moment the machine on my leg thrummed. He got up to inspect it, and satisfied, lifted it off. Revealed were my camo pants cut off at mid-thigh and the rest encased in pale, stiff plastic.

"Like I said, bad break, and you'll find bruises and cuts too. To get you down to my transport I had to hook your belt onto the branch and drag it behind me like a peacock's tail."

Our gaze met.

"You're bigger than me, in case you hadn't noticed."

Perhaps he expected me to smirk. I merely changed the subject: "Can I have some water? That mist dehydrates."

"I'll make some coffee, grow it myself. Ambrosia!"

I looked puzzled, and he added: "Food of the gods."

"Goddesses."

He disappeared from my view, and I got up on one elbow to see where I was. From the curving plastic walls I guessed I was inside a housing module, but the high-tech was offset by an incredible mess. These was furniture, mainly in disrepair, plants in pots, odd bits of machinery, some half dismantled, tools, rusty wire, music tapes, collections of coloured stones — clutter everywhere. Vaguely I wondered how Benedict had managed to bring me in here, then realised with a grimace that he must have carried me.

When he returned from the small cook-unit set against one wall he handed me a cup, taking care our flesh never touched in the transaction.

"How did you find me?"

"I'm the caretaker, I know what goes on down the farm. The dogs showed up on the heat sensor when they broke in and so did you. When all the blips were grouped round the old cherry I could kill two jobs at once: get the pack and see who you were. From the wavelength I knew it was a human."

"Homo sapiens."

He put his cup down on the table hard. "Raphael, I've been talking to you fifteen minutes and this is the third time you've corrected me!"

"It offends my sensibilities."

"And being corrected offends mine!"

We glared at each other and he sighed.

"Sorry, I'm not used to *people* much. Maybe I'll leave you and your leg alone for now."

He went over to a packing case and dragged out a blanket, which he draped carefully on the table beside me.

"I sleep in the next module. If you want something, scream."

He shuffled away, following some invisible path that led him to the door without falling over anything. Pausing at the threshold, he put his hand to a knob in the plastic and the yellow glare dimmed down to nightlight.

"Thanks for the rescue," I said, and threw the blanket over my head before he could respond.

Daylight shining through the translucent plastic woke me, that and a pain in my groin.

"Benedict!"

He appeared in the doorway, in a change of clothes, but unshaven.

"I wanna piss!"

"Oh gawd," he said, looking from door to table and at the mess in between. I flung off the blanket and slid to a one-legged stop on the floor, forcing the issue.

He bent down and rose with a large broom, which he used to clear a haphazard path from me to the exit. Experimentally

I hopped, and nearly went face first into a robot of some kind, its sharp guts exposed for maintenance. As I wobbled, he restored my balance with a hand to my sleeve.

"Can you lean on me, perhaps?"

Once Boz and I had gone out of the ghetto to visit Bea, now Urszula's Bea, and a man had grabbed at me. After we had rubbed his face in a mud puddle it had vaguely registered that his flesh felt no different from a womyn's. Then, as now.

Benedict lived in three small modules, living, sleeping and bathroom, all detached from each other and set in a circle. Although the day was overcast and chill it felt good to be outside, so afterwards I let go of him and sat on the little grass courtyard between the ovals of plastic. He brought coffee and insta-bread from the module and we breakfasted.

"Raphael ..."

Only Grania called me that, and now Benedict. After his outburst I did not want to correct him again, to say: *Just Raffy*.

"What's to be done with you?"

"I'll contact the Sisters. There's a communicator in my pack."

"Pack, where?" and I said: "By the hole under the fence."

He groaned.

"Knew I'd have to fix it sometime. Okay, I'll kill two jobs again: get your handbag and seal the fence."

It was starting to drizzle, so he helped me inside again, then left. I very soon got bored silly in the crowded room and gazing around spotted a fat old book. After one glance I dropped it — full of strange words. Then I thought to clean my gun and found that Benedict had removed the charges when I was unconscious.

When he came back I threw it at him, shouting: "Pig!"

The impact left a white mark on his face, but he stood still as the gun clattered to the floor.

"How was I to know you wouldn't fry me for laying hands on you?"

"I don't care! Pig!"

His gaze flitted about the room.

"You've been at my Shakespeare."

I recalled the name on the old book.

"I'd have ripped it to shreds if I'd known you valued it."

He lunged forward and grabbed the volume. "For that I'd have killed you."

I had never cared for poetry, thanks to Grania, and so was struck mum by his feeling.

"You've never heard of Bill," he said sadly and opened the book. Seeing him distracted, I snatched at the pack, but he deftly kicked my good leg from under me. I fell heavily, breath and pride knocked out of me. While I lay, he began quietly to read:

"O! She doth teach the torches to burn bright.
It seems she hangs upon the cheek of night
Like a rich jewel in an Ethiop's ear;
Beauty too rich for use, for earth too dear!
So shows a snowy dove trooping with crows,
As yonder lady o'er her fellows shows.
The measure done, I'll watch her place of stand,
And, touching hers, make blessed my rude hand.
Did my heart love till now? forswear it, sight!
For I ne'er saw true beauty till this night."

I was a captive audience, but it was words rather than a shackle of plastic that held me. Word that summoned memories: in front of me was the beautiful face of a dark girl who had come just once into the ghetto. I had made enquiries about her and found her irrevocably straight, so I kicked a wall and went on living.

(Never would a face have the same effect on me until, years later, I came back from Haven to find little Honey had grown up. But by then I knew Romeo's speech by rote.)

Benedict stopped, and spoke his own words:

"See, it's not all rapes."

I was sitting up by then; he dropped the pack into my lap and went out. I opened it, found the communicator and began to cry.

"What is it?" he asked from the doorway.

"I — can't. I've blown it, I'm better off dead."

He sat down on the arm of a laden armchair.

"Have you noticed, Raphael, that I've never asked you what you're doing out here? You lot haven't been careful enough. For months now there's been rumours on the computer of walkers in the waste, consortiums nobody's heard of waving big money, a girl dressed like you found dead in a dioxin dump . . ."

I scowled, remembering how the Scouts had ascribed the death to inexperience: "Poor thing, let her go alone too soon." Now they would say the same about Raffy.

"Stop crying. I don't care what you're up to so long as I'm left alone. And I never dob in anyone. Call the ladies!"

Maybe I trusted him, but the Sisters never would. Besides:

"I'd be a laughing stock, skiving off after flowers and having to be rescued — by an andro! They'd never let me scout again."

"So," he said. "I'm not going to tell my bosses and you're not going to tell your bossesses. What then?"

"How long before I walk?"

"Coupla months. The robo gave you a calcium accelerator, but you can't hurry *Mother* Nature."

He was looking glum and the emotion was infectious; the consequences of our silence were an unwanted guest for him and dependence on a man for me.

"I can modify a robo into transport for you," he said. "But it'll take time."

"Gimme materials and I'll make crutches."

He fished in the litter behind the chair, emerging with an all-purpose kit, its plastic grimy and dented.

"You can make one crutch from the broom — never use it anyway. I'll see what's handy for the other."

He was half out the door when I yelled at him: "Benedict! I want something else."

He turned and I tapped the gun meaningfully.

"Promise you won't burn me?"

"I promise only if you promise not to ..."

I stopped, for an extraordinary expression of grief had taken hold of his face.

"Lord, what we've done to deserve this, and rightly too!"

He took the charges from his coat pocket and rolled them across the floor to me, where they were stopped by my leg in its plastic chitin. I picked them up, counted them, slotted them into their pods — and looked up to see that Benedict had gone.

Good, because I needed to consider the strange situation we had fallen into. An analogy came to mind: Edge City, when two wildly differing ghetto factions united against the middle ground. Just because their interests coincided did not mean opportunities were lost for mischief to each other; I should remember that. He had several Edges on me: mobility and his computer, wherever it was, with which he could summon his bosses if the guest proved irksome. On the other hand I had the Edges of a gun and my communicator, for a last-resort SOS.

Thinking of a Mayday caused me to remember that I had not given my daily position report to the ghetto. I glanced at my watch, noting I was several hours late. If I didn't send the Scouts off on a wild-gorse chase they would go straight to my last location, just south of the site, and from there track me to the macrofarm. Loss of face for me: but of life for Benedict, who despite his hospitality would be killed out of hand.

I unfolded my map, looking for a labyrinth or tangle-wood, and found a marsh, probably once a sewage farm. It was off-course; perfect. I fed its coordinates into the flute, a coding device that unravelled information into its component yarns and sent it across space, to be knit up only at the other end. "Chased by wild dogs," I added for explanation, and flicked the communicator to receiving mode.

A jumble of symbols appeared on the little screen, resolving first into letters, then words. "OK. Come on home." Whoever was on the other end was in a laconic mood. I had a moment of conscience, as I remembered Zoska, Boz and my other foster sisters, even despised Grania — then I turned the communicator off.

"The rest is silence," I said, as I returned the communicator to my pack.

Benedict spoke from the doorway, and I jumped:

"Do you know where that comes from?"

"How long have you been there?"

"Only long enough to hear you quote Bill."

He came in lugging a collection of staves.

"Any of these do?"

"Yeah, the longest," and we set to woodwork. Our hands dipped in and out of the kitbox, never coinciding.

After a while he returned to the quotation:

"Where'd you hear that?"

"Probably my mother."

"The authority on angels?"

"Yeah, I've got two mothers." He blinked. "One gave birth to me, the other reared me."

"So which knows Bill?"

"My blood mother, Grania Erato."

"Poetry woman, eh?"

Now I blinked, then I remembered that he read.

"You know her?"

He shook his head.

"I only read one book. See Raphael, I decided long ago that a man, begging your pardon, didn't have time to read everything. There's too many people writing and nearly all of them are mediocre. There ought to be a pogrom — they hide the really good writers with their verbiage. So I just stuck with the very best."

He gestured at the book.

"Before you flare up at me again, I'm not saying your mum's no good. I never read her ... I'm restricted in my reading."

"But how do you know she writes verse?"

"Erato's the muse of love poetry."

222

"How pretentious," I said without thinking, and bit my lip, too late.

He looked at me, reading more than I wished him to, so I bent over the crutch and worked like a machine. After a pause, he followed suit. Even when we broke briefly for more bread and coffee, we did not speak — until the crutches were finished.

"Yeay!"

I pulled myself up to standing and fitted the pads under my arms. Suddenly Raffy metamorphosed from crawling caterpillar to a mummy-long-legs, with limbs of wood, plastic and flesh. It was fleet, in a lurching fashion, for with three long steps I was down Benedict's pathway and outside, being buffeted by the late afternoon wind.

"Whee!"

He had followed me outside protectively.

"Don't overdo it. Years ago I was on those things and took days getting used to them. Don't think because you're muscled like a racehorse that you won't be sore."

Just for that, I left the courtyard, hopping through the gaps between the modules to the farm proper. It consisted of more modules, but giant, in row after row with tidy concrete paths in between. I lolloped to the nearest and stared through the plastic opaqued by my breath, like a child at a shop window. There were many green plants, and the glint of steel as a robot gardener rolled up and down.

I glanced behind me and saw Benedict watching like a guardian angel. Irritated by his solicitude I swung away from the wall and went for a long walk along concrete, walled in always by plastic. He did not follow, perhaps expecting a clout over the head with a crutch.

When I returned, doused in sweat and radiating heat like a boiler, I found the courtyard littered with Benedict's junk. Dust blew like a mist from the door of the living module.

I sat down with a thump on the packing case and at the noise he came out, wearing a faded red scarf over his grizzled hair.

"You want your broom back for the spring-cleaning?"

He scowled. "I'm making space. If you're living here you'll need territory of your own. For *my* sanity I'm making a moiety of the living room."

"Need help?"

He stared at me. "Move furniture when you've buggered yourself with the most strenuous walk you could manage? Braggadacian!"

He disappeared inside again and I, feeling parched, went to the bathroom to get a drink without disturbing him. There was a mirror there, overlooked previously, and it reflected the new face like a stranger. I saw a girl weary and strained, with twigs in her brown hair and smears from bark on her face. The man's glass told me what I had not noticed in his gaze: this girl was attractive.

The water splashed into my hands and I longed for a bath, but only cleaned my face. To strip, and to have him sneak up behind me ...

When I went out it was sunset and I shivered at the memory of dogs and flowers. I sat on the crate again and watched lights come on inside the living module. It resembled a giant phosphorescent slug.

"You can come in now, Raphael."

Within, a low wall had been built of odds and ends; on one side was Benedict's clutter, on the other was an area cleared of all save a mattress with my pack and blanket set neatly upon it.

"I'll make the wall higher, give you privacy, promise. I'm just out of energy now."

"It's not urgent," I lied politely.

He grunted and dodged effortlessly to the cook-unit, where a saucepan bubbled. I looked for the table and found it pushed against the wall, at the end of the path. There were two chairs by it; I sat down and noticed the Shakespeare on the table, like a second guest for dinner.

Benedict brought stewpot, cutlery and crockery to the table.

"Let good digestion wait on appetite!"

"I suppose that's in your book too," I said.

"Bill says something about everything."

Chit-chat was forgotten then, as we ate like a pair of wild beasts. When the meal was over I reached for the book.

"What are you doing?" he asked suspiciously.

"Seeing what he says about the likes of me ... *them*, as you put it. What's this, *The Taming of the* ..."

"I doubt you'll find it there," he said and pulled the book from me. "How 'bout this: 'Would it not grieve a woman to be overmastered with a piece of valiant dust? to make account of her life to a clod of wayward marl?' That's feminist at least."

"Nice. Who is she?"

"Lass called Beatrice. A bit like you: fierce."

I twitched the book into my grasp again, accidentally losing the place. In front of me was a list of names followed by their speeches and I looked for Beatrice.

"Phooey. Here she's saying: 'I love you with so much of my heart that none is left to protest' to a clod named ..."

"Benedick," he finished. Picking up the book he walked to the door.

"Goodnight," he said without turning.

"Goodnight."

I fidgeted for a while then shoved the robot against the door and went to sleep. In the morning I was awakened by the sound of an electric motor. Moving, I found my muscles sore (prophetic Benedict!), but pushed the robot aside and swung out. The courtyard was empty but through the gap I could see Benedict atop a squat vehicle with fat rubber wheels. He zoomed it down a pathway and out of sight.

Tied to the largest bit of the courtyard junk was a note:

"Off to check fences. Back late today. Place yours."

I stood there like a tripod, listening to the motor fade out of earshot. How lovely to be alone again! Then my solitude was interrupted by the tock of rain — within moments my hair was soaked and drops trickled down my neck. I laughed, throwing my head back to drink rain, and went to the bathroom module to finish what the cloudburst had begun. Only the mirror marred my mood; its big round eye seemed prurient so I made it stare at the wall.

Showered, I went searching for Benedict's computer and found the console behind a filing cabinet that looked as if the robot had kicked it in a pet. Raffy was never a hacker, except for a romantic summer with the ghetto's computer whiz, yet the sight revived memories. Benedict was no hacker either, for log-on instructions were taped to the keyboard. There was no password, but I guessed "Shakespeare" and guessed right.

The screen lit up with a list of options and I chose "Security" and after that "Heat Sensor". An infra-red picture of the farm covered the screen, with the small blips of wildlife and one big blip moving slowly around the perimeter. It would appear Benedict was truthful. I returned to the original list and took the option "Maintenance". This killed the curious kitten for diagram after confusing diagram of the giant modules appeared. The care involved indicated that the green crop I had glimpsed so briefly was highly lucrative. What was it? Best not ask. The seclusion of the farm and the fact that the intermediaries had not been able to discover the names of its owners argued a need for secrecy.

Benedict returned after dark, to the lukewarm half of a meal I had concocted from various odd edibles found around the cook-unit. He devoured it, then looked closely at me.

"Good, you had a bath. Thought if I went away you would — you were starting to pong."

I was silent, and he gazed around the module. After my hacking I had got sick of having to weave through his mess like a drunkard, so had added the more manoeuvrable furniture to the wall.

"And you made space! I can work in here."

"What on?"

"Robo-digger. To modify for *your* transport."

"I've got the wood legs."

He shook his head.

"Very soon you'll find them restricting."

He spread a plastic groundsheet on the floor and wheeled in the digger, which — shovel apart — was the baby of his transport. I opened my mouth and he said, raising his voice an octave:

"Need help?" Then, in his normal pitch, "No thanks Raphael, unless you're an expert on robotics."

I shook my head, reluctantly. He grinned, then saw my expression and pulled the corners of his mouth down.

"Why don't you talk to me while I work?"

"About what?"

"The ghetto. See, I'm curious — it's natural with something that excludes you. Years ago, before your wall went up, I walked through the ghetto fringes. Dirty looks galore, but nobody beat me up. I suppose being a little tich saved me."

I agreed silently.

"What did you see, Benedict?"

"Nothing much, just no men."

I snorted and he blushed rosy pink.

"I was only there five minutes, girl."

I gazed at him, gauging what information to give and what to withhold. At Bea's house I had met straight women who would politely, deviously, direct the conversation to my lifestyle. All I need do was think of the most unsound of them, add a dash of caution, and I would have a recipe for Benedict.

"Why are you staring at me?" he asked.

Just for a moment, the image of a woman had flickered on his face.

"It's just a place where womyn live. We have the wall, and beyond that are 'suburbs' where feminists and dykes who don't mind mixing" — like Bea and Grania — "live. The Watch, that's our Police, call them the first line of defence. Softcores live just inside the wall, hardcores further in."

"What's them?"

"Degrees of ideological rigidity."

"And what are you?"

"Guess," I said coldly.

"In between, I'd say."

Correct, but he needn't know that. He waited, then ventured: "What of your economy?"

"The suburbans pay tithes from their work in the andro's world." Grania had been bankrolling the ghetto for decades, to name one prominent instance. "There's also workshops, factories, where goods are made to sell Outside."

"Like what?"

"I'm not going to tell you."

"Knitting," he fished, half-seriously. I smiled at his little joke and also at the thought of the systems that my old hacker love marketed to a lot of blissful ignoramuses.

"The ideal is self-sufficiency," I said, imagining the walled Haven in the country, our City of Womyn.

"In more ways than one," he muttered. "I've heard talk of a Hive."

Loose lips! I thought, but continued, trying not to let the exchange become an Edge Game.

"It's the centre, for us. To stay there long is to forget that your kind exist. Call it an editing device."

Any mention of andros was forbidden in our temple to the Gyn principle, which caused some bizarre conversations. Once Urszula, being a brat, had asked Zoska in front of hardcores where babies came from. ("Yes Mama, but what makes the baby grow in your belly? Why aren't I growing one now?") She had got a flustered answer about cabbages and my accompanying raucous laughter got me thrown out of the Hive for the very first time. It had been "unseemly", in this quiet place decorated with murals of Ishtar, Athena and Joan of Arc sans Ur-Nammu, Zeus and the English clerics. I could feel uplifted, even refreshed in the Hive but ultimately it was claustrophobic. All restrictions annoy Raffy.

Benedict should not hear criticisms, but neither could I

voice vague platitudes. I clammed up. The cessation obviously irritated him, for he began to quote his Bill, half to himself, a quarter to the digger and a quarter to me. I listened until we parted for the night.

In the morning it rained again, and Benedict's robotics were interrupted by the visit of a truck. He dealt with it, returned, and worked with a mixture of care and haste. By a happy coincidence the sun poked out moments after the contraption was finished. He pushed it out into the courtyard and through a gap to the start of a sloping path.

"Hop on."

He took the crutches, slotting them into a niche at the back of the transport.

"Oh, so that's what it's for."

"That, by your hand, is direction and this is speed. This starts the motor."

I forestalled him and switched it on myself. As the machine purred he grinned at his handiwork. Seeing him off guard I put my hand hard on the speed button.

"Hey, wait! Whoa!"

"Wowee!"

The machine shot down the path straight for one of the giant modules, and I grabbed the steering just in time to execute a two-wheeled turn. To show Benedict I had mistressed the vehicle I did a circuit of the module and risked glancing behind for his reaction. He was open-mouthed like a yokel, so with a wave I disappeared around the module again.

When I had explored on crutches I had found the farm monotonous; riding, it was the same, although I passed a processing plant and the road for the trucks, which relieved the uniformity. There was more fun in being Raffy the speed maniac, careering around like a pinball. Pride cometh before a crash, of course, and I was sobered by a near collision with a robot gardener.

"Roadhog!" I shouted at its featureless metal carapace, largely to cover the pain from my leg, which had been jarred.

Then I continued down the path and found I was free of modules, in open, tussocked country. Still adventurous, I rode to the fence and back, but at an invalid's pace.

It was late when I puttered nervously up to Benedict's home, and to my relief he was not waiting outside. I parked the transport and became a stick insect again.

He was sitting at the console.

"Have a nice time?"

"Yes, thank you."

"I watched your blip until it slowed down. Then I did some hacking."

I poled to where I could see the screen, which resembled the old samplers displayed in the Hive: across the screen was verse, Grania's verse:

"Battersea blues couldn't keep me apart
I got to play songs in a grimy gutter
With you along — your clutter.

There's leaves in your hair, have you
been dancing with your old man again?
Walk on the wind of September evening
Don't come down until I've finished playing.

Lend me a mood, oh no
I'm not wistful, not jealous.
I have the music and you have the heart
Battersea blues couldn't keep me apart."

"She was very young when she wrote that," I said. "She still had her father's name."

"So I saw."

"You didn't get far with her verse."

"On the contrary. I accessed the biography first, which was mainly a list of prizes, then the contents page of the *Collected Works*. There were lots of poems about R. and Raphael, but I thought you'd thump me if I read them. So I accessed the cheapest poem about anything else."

"Thanks."

"Amazing! She's said thank you to me twice in one conversation."

There was a round scrap of plastic temptingly near; I leaned on one crutch and savagely batted it across the module with the other. It hit the wall with a satisfying clunk.

"I live in glass. Anything she hears about me goes into her verse! Vampire!"

"The parent feeds the child and then feeds off him ... her."

I stared at him.

"You're not unique," he said. "With me it was my father."

"My father was 10cc of sticky fluid," I said viciously. He ignored the goad.

"Lucky you."

He switched off the console.

"Dad was a drunk. Only good thing he did was desert the family. Trouble was he kept coming back."

I too had been incompletely deserted.

"Mum was all right," he said. "Earth mother type."

"Like my foster mother."

"That's right," he recalled. "You said you had two."

"She says the world's oldest profession isn't whoring, it's motherhood. That's what she does."

"She good at it?"

I laughed. "You think so, on the evidence of me?"

"I meant, is she respected for it?"

"It's high status in the ghetto."

Zoska had been nominated as an Elder, but had dodged the election by beginning Basienka.

"That's how it should be," he said.

Both of us had become embarrassed by the confessions, and so gravitated to the table, where there was a bowl of fresh greens.

"Grow it myself," he said proudly. "One of the perks of the job."

"That and being alone," I said, and he nodded, a little too emphatically. We sat and ate, crushing crisp leaves between our teeth. The crunching made me aggressive, revived my daredevil high with the transport. Foolhardy as ever, I decided on an Edge Game. If Benedict was in a confessing mood, he might give information valuable to the ghetto and my curiosity.

I waved a strip of bok choi: "You grow other greens in the modules."

"You noticed?"

This was not a good sign, but I persisted: "I don't know botany, but they're like no plants I've seen."

"They're intoxicants. The only other perk of the job."

I had not expected him to fold so easily. Careful, a biochemical sensor warned.

"They come from what used to be the Amazon rainforest. Got saved from extinction when a scientist et one and had a nice time. They're still only quasi-legal, like the other substances that relax society's rules a little. That's why this farm is far from awkward questions."

He paused. "Except when asked by Raphaels. You want to try some?"

We were both on the razor's edge now. His suggestion had caught me off-guard, but to signal that might be dangerous. I had to answer quickly.

"Sure."

He went out and I grinned like a wedge of cheese. Free intoxicant!

Benedict was gone a long time and returned, not with the expected green sheaf, but carrying a small box.

"Could have got raw stuff, just pull it off the vine, but it's rough. This is processed, ready for the truck."

He opened the box, to reveal grey crystals, more intoxicant than I had ever seen before. I nodded warily, thinking about dosages — in the ghetto only Boz had had a stronger head than Raffy for the drug. He set the box on the table and to my surprise ignited the crystals. A soft grey smoke, reminiscent of Zoska's old homespun shawl, drifted upwards.

"This is freebasing. Extravagant, but the best."

I attempted the worldly-wise expression of a drug savant, and obviously failed, for he continued:

"This extract's euphoric. Other types make people concentrate, make 'em sexy, send 'em to sleep ... the many words that describe emotions, they're all covered by the drug. It's a universal, like Bill."

The smoke swirled round me, like the three witches on a panel in the Hive.

"Weird sisters," he said, and I goggled: did the drug cause telepathy?

"From the book," he explained. "Want to hear it?"

"Yes."

He read from his memory, speech after fantastical speech, and I savoured them. All, except for the initial extract from *Macbeth*, were descants on the theme of heterosexual love, which might have been oppressive had not the language transcended gender. I heard the love-talk of men and women, and interpreted it as that of womyn.

He stopped, dried out, and an eerie silence descended. The room was a ball of smoke and we were silhouettes to each other. Feeling nervous, I moved closer to him, and he turned his head.

"Did that upset you?"

"No."

"Very sexist. I'm sorry. I forgot with you it was girl and girl."

"It's much like the other," I said, recalling the language.

"Really? You've tried?"

I was feeling pleasantly confused.

"No, although Grania said I'd try anything except incest and folk dancing."

He had never seemed threatening; that was his advantage, or Edge. Perhaps to convince myself he was still there, in this witches' brew, or perhaps for Raffy's damned curiosity, I reached out and touched him. His chest was as hard as that of a prepubescent girl.

"Is this an advance?" he said, cautiously flattered.

It was now. Raffy is also tactile.

He put his hand reverently over mine — they were almost the same size.

"Who'd have thought it? An old man like me."

Actually he was younger than Grania. Our other hands were grappled now.

"I'm out of practice," he said, and glanced around. The smoke had cleared a little.

"Not on that hard little mattress," I said.

We stood up, and I teetered as I tried to fit the crutches.

"Are we ever stoned!" he said. "You'll never make it out the door."

He tried to lift me but got hopelessly tangled with a crutch, and nearly fell over himself.

"Any suggestions?"

"Pig-back," I said muzzily.

He laughed: "Yeah, appropriate for a pig."

He knelt in front of me and I stood on my good leg, tucking the crutches under one arm.

"Hupsy-daisy," he said, and I rode him out the door to the sleeping module.

I awoke, again to daylight diffused through module plastic, and looked into the face of Benedict. Asleep, he looked like something the cat had dragged in: a little beat-up mouse.

As if on cue he opened his eyes.

"Raphael, that was sweet."

I rolled over on my back, to get the weight off my cast and also to escape his sooky expression. There, above me, was flesh, holos of naked women, all breasts, buttocks, thighs, taped to the module ceiling. They had a look of vacuous unreality suggesting the counterfeit; if not, they were like no womyn I had ever seen.

It had been dark in here last night. Intentionally? He saw my expression and groaned like a creaky door. I shot up and began to extract my clothes from the mess around his bed, swearing under my breath. Pulling on a garment I overbalanced and fell on top of him; he lay still beneath me. I scrambled up again and finished dressing. Then I found my crutches at the foot of the bed and poled furiously for the living module. There was a box of grey ash on the table and I knocked it to the floor, before grabbing my pack and heading for my transport.

He was standing in the courtyard, wrapped in a blanket.

"Raphael!" he shouted. "I'm only human and I mean a man!"

"That's no excuse!"

I started the motor and sped away, making a grand exit. Moments later I remembered my gun: should I return and use it? No. I never wanted to see him again.

My intent had been to follow the roboroad to the gate, the weak spot in most defences. However in my haste I had made a wrong turning and was as lost among identical paths and modules as an ant on a draughtsboard. The sun was out; I estimated east and headed that way. The maze of modules ended and I continued towards the fence, thinking to circumnavigate to the farm entrance. Idly I noticed the tracks of a larger transport on the grass before me. Then there was a cherry bough, its flowers withered and dry, and beyond it, up a steep slope, the rock-a-bye-Raffy tree.

I pulled out the communicator and held it in my hand like a shell. It was no use, for the same restrictions still applied. If I returned to the ghetto on a stolen transport questions would still be asked about my leg. For expediency's sake I would have to return and make peace with Benedict.

I drove along the fence to the gate, as planned, and found it open. Was this an invitation to leave? If so, I refused it and took the road back to Benedict.

He was waiting outside this time, looking worried.

"Why didn't you go?"

Dismounting, I tapped the cast with a crutch, in answer: it made a dull sound, like a prison door slamming.

"Yes, but after what we did? I did?"

His tone was guilty and something occured to me: he had mentioned that the drug could make people "sexy".

"Benedict, was there aphrodisiac in that blend?"

"A little," he said sheepishly, a repentant ram. "Didn't think it'd work."

I struck him with a crutch, not hard, but sufficient to send him reeling back against the nearest piece of junk. He hit it at an angle, gashing his scalp. Blood dribbled down like water into his eyes.

"I can't see! Raphael, help!"

He was crouched on the ground, both hands over the wound. There was no way I could lift him.

"Stand up!" I said like the Watch Chief and he obeyed.

"Easy. I'm here."

He reached one blood-sticky hand out to the voice. I anchored the crutches and took hold of it.

"Inside," he said. "Doctor!"

Now I had the problem of getting him to the living module, for while he clasped me as though drowning I could not use the crutches. They required both hands. A sudden gust of wind flapped my scarf, left untied in the hasty dressing, and I had an idea.

"Benedict, let go!"

Very slowly, he complied.

"Now take this," I said, and brushed one fringed end of the scarf against his fingers. He took it, and I wrapped the other end around one crutch handgrip. Carefully I swung into the module, leading him by an embroidered tether.

"The lame leading the blind," he said.

Inside I sat him down at the table and found the doctor unit. When I activated it, the optical sensors swivelled and it made a clicking noise, tsk, tsk, tsk. Metal hands shot out of the body and began to minister. Within minutes the blood had been cleaned from him and the hair shaved from around the gash, which was staunched with a dab of sealant. The robot went into inert mode and I switched it off.

He opened his eyes and stared down at an anthill of spilt ash. Absently he smoothed it with the side of his hand.

"Raphael ..."

"Yes?"

He doodled in the ash with a forefinger, then erased the design.

"Don't hit me again, but I'm not protected against fertility. Are you?"

I sat down too, feeling sick to my boots.

"Of course not. And I'm at full moon."

He sighed, and as if his head was suddenly too heavy, rested his cheek on the ashy hand. Realising too late, he withdrew the hand and stared at it glumly.

"Next it'll be sackcloth."

I made no reply.

"Say something. Laugh at slapstick old me."

"The doctor," I said incoherently.

"They programmed it for a man on his own, no gynecology. I've heard that jumping with your legs in splints ..."

"Very funny."

"Well, surely the ghetto has herbal remedies."

"No need."

"No, I suppose not."

"I'm *not* speaking to you," and with that I retired behind the wall of China, or rather of junk, and huddled under the blanket. After a pause he went out, and I heard the noise of his transport, moving away.

He did not come into the living module the rest of that day, nor did I go out — thus we avoided each other. The following day the pattern was reversed: I took the little transport out around the farm while he was a stay-at-home. In this way we had the necessary illusion of being alone. If our paths crossed the junctions were marked by a chilling silence.

The routine was finally aborted one rainy morning, as we breakfasted — he on fresh-brewed coffee and I on food-concentrate from the pack. An electronic whine crossed the wall.

"The heat sensor!" he said, and dashed to the console. I followed in seven-league strides.

"What is it?"

He jabbed a stubby finger at the screen.

"Figures, just north. Your mates?"

I leaned closer to stare at the sexless blobs. The marsh had been north of the farm.

"Relax, this isn't the dyke cavalry. They're just being curious."

(Taking a look at the farm and also the site, but I couldn't say that.)

He frowned.

"Don't think much of their tracking. You and the tree were on the other side."

"I gave them a position reading for the marsh centre."

"Gulper? They could have been killed looking for you there."

After all that had happened since I had crawled under the fence, I should have been immune to shock. Yet that jarred me. With my luck it would probably be Boz.

"Well, I didn't know it was dangerous. If I hadn't they'd have burst in here thinking I'd been kidnapped for a sex slave — which is partly true."

He winced.

"Take the cart and catch up with them."

They would come back and kill you, I thought, but only said: "I'd be pitied for the rest of my life."

"A fate worse than death," he said drily.

"And what if I were carrying?"

We had agonised silently about that question for three days now, but to voice it hurt not at all. He took the cue quickly.

"Any reason you might not?"

"I never tried. And you?"

"The ladies all took precautions. I never got close to one so she'd stop using them and have my baby ... have a child with me."

I rocked on the crutches and considered.

"What are our options?"

"One — nothing's cooking. Two, there is, but you want to stop it."

That option was tricky: the knowledge lay outside the ghetto and I would have to consult with feminists, who might blab.

"Three, you don't."

"It might be a boy!" I cried. How unpleasant, to have the enemy growing inside me.

"Can't see him being reared by manhaters," he said.

"I suppose you'd want to keep him."

"I just remember," he said reasonably, "the one nice thing my dad did with me, which was fishing. Sitting by a stream, if I can find one unpolluted, teaching a small me . . ."

"Small you!"

He looked at me.

"He might take after his tearaway mum."

There was a pause while I tried to imagine a male Raffy.

"You'd not let me keep a girl?" he said.

I shrugged, recalling Grania's poems about father-daughter incest. On the other hand, the idea of returning to the ghetto with a female infant, claiming to have found her in bullrushes — the idea was preposterous.

"Look Benedict, aren't we counting chickens before they're hatched? There might be nothing in the eggshell."

"True," he said dubiously, and we left it at that. At least we were talking again, but the cautious camaraderie was gone. In the days that followed we ate together, did odd jobs around the farm together, but were emotionally apart. The book remained a common ground but we read it to ourselves separately.

Time passed in this waiting game. One day he put in hours at the terminal, while I hogged the book, enjoying the three witches and disagreeing with their images in the Hive (not evil enough). Sensing from his absorption that this was no farm matter, I sneaked up behind him, as quietly as a Woodeny could.

He was searching scientific literature, combining the terms "calcium accelerator" and "embryology".

"Raphael, quit reading over my shoulder," he said mildly.

"Tell me what you found first."

"See for yourself," and he dodged past me. I sat down at the terminal and saw that he had accessed several articles, full-text. One dealt with white mice, the other with monotremes.

"What about people?"

"I tried that," he said from the other side of the room. "No research reports."

The door of the module slammed and I began to read the articles. The monotreme one was inconclusive and the white mice had eaten their young — not an encouraging prognosis.

I glanced back and saw that Benedict had snaffled the Shakespeare. Ah, well, it was his turn for it. To complete the reversal I began hacking myself, first checking the account to which the searches were credited. It worried me that Benedict's bosses might smell a lady rat if their employee ticked up searches unconnected with their product. However, the account was private, its searches — until recently — solely of the database Shaklit.

I returned to the original enquiry and discarded "embryology" to concentrate on the drug that was healing my leg. After an hour I knew that in the young and healthy the period of accelerated cure could be as short as one month. I patted the cast thoughtfully; it would be rushing things, but if Option One occurred I could be away much sooner than Benedict expected. A quick getaway was desirable — he was starting to look sooky again.

He made one more attempt to discuss our possible parent-hood:

"Have you decided yet?"

"On what?"

"Options Two or Three?"

"Oh Ishtar, it might well be neither!"

I stormed off, more bluster, for I was late and I think he

knew it. Of course, the upsets I had experienced this month would have disturbed the cycle of a she-elephant ...

One pale spring dawn I woke up very early and found it was Remembrance day, as in Grania's famous poem. Her words had never bobbed up in my mind much before, but now I was thinking in a mixture of Grania and Bill. I activated the Doctor and addressed it to my leg. It whirred, clicked again, shone lights, prodded me here and there — and then it extruded a nozzle which sprayed the cast with pink mist. The plastic melted away as I watched, leaving not even a discarded cocoon to mark my change. The leg underneath was scaly and looked strange; I cautiously tried exercises then shuffled up and down. It was whole.

Much of my silence had been put to the devising of contingency plans, and I knew what to do. I laid the crutches aside and *walked* to the console, where I instructed the gates to open. Then I shouldered my pack and left, pausing only to streak blood on the door of the sleeping module: my explanation.

He must have slept late that morning, for I had escaped the farm and was following the road through thickets of yellow gorse before he came after me. Hearing the motor, I moved to the roadside. Prickly leaves brushed my bare new leg — if I hid there I would be scratched raw. Instead I pulled out the gun, hating to use it.

Benedict was astride the little transport and for the first time I noticed, as he must have before, that riders of the converted digger looked absurd. He brought it to a stop on the other side of the road, several metres from me. Now I was in sight he seemed unable to speak.

"You got the message," I finally said.

He nodded. "Raphael! Not a word goodbye."

A buzzing insect shot past my head, going from gorse bush to gorse bush and incidentally from Raffy to Benedict. He continued:

"Oh I know that you couldn't predict what I'd do. Suspicious minds! I'm not here to compel you."

"What then?"

"I'm worried. What if you meet another pack of dogs? I know you accessed CA data, and that you think the leg's sound. But you could refracture if you run on it, and this time nobody might help you."

He was right: although I had paced myself carefully over the distance, I had developed a limp.

"Do you want to guard me back to the ghetto?"

"And ruin your reputation? No girl, just take the transport."

I started to demur, but he kept speaking:

"You can ditch it near the city. There's a homing circuit and it'll make its way back down the road."

"I can't."

He looked astounded.

"How do I repay you? I've taken and given nothing in return."

"But you have."

He clambered off the transport.

"Raphael, you've not been easy to live with. I cannot endure my Lady Tongue, not lately. But I've fallen in love with her."

He stopped.

"My first love! A lesbian who won't be tamed, won't play Beatrice with Benedict."

Slowly he moved away from the vehicle.

"It's a gift to me if you take it, stops me imagining you et by dogs."

There was no real answer to this speech, not one which would satisfy him. I took one step, then two, towards the transport.

"Thank you," he said, when I got onto it.

"Thank you! Goodbye."

"Goodbye," he replied, his expression bleak. I started the motor and coasted away, glancing back now and then to see him standing there against the yellow like a spoon in mustard. A bend of the road hid him, and I never saw him again.

Now I knew how he had felt. Oh Honey! The emotional ache had become physcial — I stared at Grania, and suffered.

"How could I forget?" she said. "You limped in here like a wounded bellatrice, expecting me to shred the — quite good — elegy I'd written for you. When I didn't, you told me what you thought of me. It was a strange speech, first ghetto-gutter, then becoming arcane and archaic. 'Cacodemon' was one word used — I had not heard it outside *Richard III*. How strange to hear it from my Raphael's foul mouth. When you finished, your womynly chest panting up and down like a bellows, I remarked, quoting as is my way ..."

"'She was wont to speak plain and to the purpose ... and now is she turned orthography, her words are a very fantastical banquet — just so many strange dishes.'"

"And you turned to the bookshelf, and following the alpha-beta round, you discovered Shakes-rags and opened it."

"I said, '*Much Ado About Nothing*, Act 2, Scene 3, nyaagh!'"

"Whereupon I remarked that while missing, presumed dead, you had attended classes on Shakespeare."

"And I told you the whole story."

"Which made me wonder why you, so secretive —"

"Because you write about me!"

"... should spiel the most profound experience of your life. Raphael, I know a dare when I see one. You were daring me to write that Raphael Grania had fornicated with an andro. Being contrary, a trait you have inherited, I didn't."

"Would you, now?"

"It's stale bread news. Haven's half-completed and I doubt anyone would murder that poor man for slipping you a mickey thirteen years ago. The hardcores wouldn't like it, but you dislike them."

"I intend to marry into them."

This time she did blink.

"Oh, the sweet young thing. What's her name?"

"Honey Marthe."

"Is she pretty?"

"Very. And with a mother like a meataxe."

She put her pink hands to her mouth. "So that's why you want my silence!"

"I want a vow of it."

"On one condition."

"What?"

"Raphael, on that night you withheld information from your dear mamma. You never said what you thought of the heterosexual act."

I considered.

"Very well, but you must swear first."

"On something sacred. I know you."

Feeling foolish, as she no doubt intended, I knelt down by the chair and she put her heavy hand on my head. An opportunity for caress, I realised.

"I swear, on Raphael, not to tattle."

I stood up.

"That promise covers what I shall tell you."

She nodded.

"Spit it out, this byte, this titbit."

I was silent, thinking of words.

"Mumchance! I see I must interrogate you. Was it pleasurable?"

"Of course. But not the real thing. Hence Honey."

She stored the information away.

"Well, my heretic, we both lose by this transaction, you some privacy, I for not being able to put this grain through the art mill."

"Crushing me," I said, continuing the conceit.

"You exaggerate, nothing could do that. I know being muse-food, muesli, was irksome, but it cracked your indifference wonderfully. Naughty of me, but fun — you always bit."

"No more."

"No, if we are to be at peace. Allow me at least an epithalamium."

"You do that. Make it good."

Interview concluded, I strolled down the hall and out. The garden summoned memories of other flowers, but I brushed them away. Benedict, my apologies ...

I returned to the ghetto, encountering the on-duty Watch at the gate. Considering my scuffles with that body, they were friendly, which made me suspect some support. This inkling and the news of Grania I wanted to share with Zoska, but when I returned to her little house, she was out. From Basienka's room came a voice singing lullabies, probably Urszula bullied into babysitting. Not wanting questions, I raided the larder, mouse-quiet, and went to bed. Sated physically but not emotionally, I slept.

In the morning Basienka awakened me by crawling into my bed with a huge rag doll.

"You want breakfast, kid?"

She considered it like a duchess.

"Yes."

"Well, we'll make some for everyone."

We brewed coffee, chopped fruit and toasted bread rolls, then I carried the tray into the bedroom. Zoska was weeping.

"What is it? Row with your lover again?"

In answer she waved her hand at the little radio beside the bed, which received only the ghetto's weak FM signal. I listened, to an Elder talking excitedly about —

"Parthenogenesis! They've done it at last!"

Zoska blew her nose loudly.

"And it's too late for me. Curse the biological clock!"

With exquisite timing, Basienka plonked herself in her mother's lap. Zoska hugged her.

"Still, you two will benefit. No more seed and egg, just egg and egg."

"Omelette."

"Don't be facetious, you dreadful child. Other dreadful child, don't spill my coffee!"

Complete independence, I thought, as she fussed over Basienka. It had been the inevitable consequence of the Sisters' path, an ideal from the beginnings of the ghetto. Just because

I had once been friendly with a man did not mean I regretted this innovation, that cast my kind adrift from his. Benedict, I was a Sister first, and there was no changing it.

"How did it go last night?" asked Zoska, munching fruit.

"All fixed."

"Good girl."

"How about you?"

"I talked my head off, first to Marthe, then I had tea with the Scouts and dropped in on the softcore leaders. On the way home I was met by the faction of hardcores at odds with Marthe. We're getting an Edge City."

"There's still the Elders."

"A Scout talked on the flute with Boz, and she sent the Elders a rocket, saying Marthe was behaving like a heavy father. I thought that too, but it takes the Head of Haven to say it and remain unscathed."

She gestured at the radio.

"But this news has done it."

I finished my coffee and lounged back.

"Sure it's wonderful, but how does it affect Raffy 'n' Honey?"

"Well it's like I'm fighting with the baby and the sky rains honey apples. Instant end to hostilities as we gorge."

"Honey apple," said Basienka.

"Silly," I said. "Now you'll have to get her one."

"Honey apple."

"Later, sweet tooth," said Zoska. "Talking of H-O-N-E-Y I saw her."

I sat up straight, rocking the bed.

"What she say, what she say?"

"She loves you."

I jumped off the bed and capered around it, followed by the imitative Basienka.

"She got Marthe out of the room to tell me that. Not as submissive as I thought."

"My bad influence."

246

"No doubt. But I still think you'll be doing the fighting when that girl leaves the ghetto."

"What if I take her to Haven?"

"A good compromise."

She paused.

"Is it as utopic as Boz claims?"

"We're working on it," I said.

"You do that. I'll stay at home, old imperfect ghetto, in case Haven goes ..."

"Dystopic?"

"Dystopic. Forget I said that. I just realised I'm being thrown out with the bathwater. Still, it's the best way to get Marthe out of your hair, which now I think of it —"

She put her head on one side.

"— needs a cut."

She hopped out of bed.

"Let me bully you for the last time."

First she made me wash in the little bathroom cluttered with water-toys, then combed down my damp mop and trimmed it. With an air of relish, she next produced respectable clothes, bought in between the visits of the day before. There were grey pants, grey shirt, smart black boots and a stiff, sobersides hat. As I admired my well-behaved self in the bedroom mirror, I noticed her sidling out the door with my old gaudy rags.

"What are you doing?"

"Throwing these out."

"Including the scarf, your handiwork?"

She pulled it out and inspected it.

"No! But it's filthy, I'll get you another."

She rummaged in her workbasket and withdrew a strip of linen embroidered with pink cherry blossoms. I wondered vaguely if there was a cosmic conspiracy to remind me of Benedict — Zoska had never seen the flowers, the dogs had prevented me plucking one for her. Smiling wryly, I put the scarf on.

247

"You look very eligible," she said and kissed me.

"Honey apple," said the repeating machine.

"Come on," I said. "Let's buy one for her."

Outside the little street was bustling with womyn, some carrying flowers and all smiling.

"What's this?" I said to nobody in particular and a passing softcore replied:

"Party in the main square. To celebrate!"

We strolled towards square and Hive, infected by the festive mood. A junior Scout dashed by, came to a dead stop, twirled round and gaped at me. Recovering, she ran off in the opposite direction and returned with two giggling girlfriends, and the Watch Chief.

"Lay off," I said, embarrassed.

"Well," said the Chief, "you are nicely turned out."

"For the books," I muttered.

"Doesn't she look fine?" said Zoska.

"My word yes. Almost unrecognisable."

I clenched my fists behind my back, momentarily regretting that all my rowdiness must be past. To my annoyance, the Watch Chief fell into step with us, chatting to Zoska about weddings:

"I cried and cried when my eldest . . ."

"Honey apple," said the tireless Basienka.

"Soon, when we reach the square," I said. The Watch Cheif bent close to me:

"We whitewashed your graffiti."

"Censorship."

"It benefits you. Marthe was turning cartwheels every time she passed it."

"What a sight. Well, thank you."

But she was not finished yet. "One of my lasses let in Bea this morning with a message for Marthe. From Grania."

She eyed me, awaiting the reaction.

"How nice," I said blithely. Maybe it was the festival ambience, but I felt as if I was riding the crest of a wave, which would not suddenly dump me in a welter of foam and sand. We were nearly at the square now, its proximity marked by music, the whiff of intoxicant, and thankfully for the little girl clasping my hand, a sticky-sweet smell.

"There you are, persistent child," said Zoska. "Raffy, do you want one?"

"Not in these clothes."

The Watch Chief had already, incongruously, been tempted by the confection.

In a procession of four, and attracting more womyn in our wake, hardcores, softcores, stray lovers, friends and the curious, we crossed the square to the Hive, our sunken fortress. The girl on guard was unexpectedly confronted by her superior, sticky.

"Tell Marthe she has visitors," said the Chief.

We waited, the crowd jostling and muttering around us. After a suitable delay, the door at the foot of the ramp opened and Marthe, flanked by the two hardcore Elders, ascended.

"Greetings, Raphael Grania," she said formally.

"Greetings, Marthe Maria," I replied, tit for tat.

I saw her gaze roll down my attire, but being as good an actor as Grania, she made no verbal or physical comment.

"I have received a verse letter from Grania Erato. It commends our alliance."

Behind me, I heard Zoska intake breath in gleeful surprise and then let it out slowly, as if she would have liked to whoop. Several of the rowdier Scouts actually cheered, and this was picked up by the young, the noisy and the disaffected. It was in the end an impressive sound, threatening even. Marthe suddenly looked, and I think felt, vulnerable.

"I am, of course, honoured to communicate with the great poet."

And mediocre parent, I thought.

"Having long admired her verse, I am pleased — my words can't express how much — to be given a holograph sample of it."

And to be the subject of it, I thought. Vanity! I could tell her it was no pleasure.

"For some reason," she added, her tone changing, "it's called '*To a Fellow Widow Twankey*'."

She looked flustered; the crowd, equally puzzled, was silent.

"I never understand all her allusions," I said quickly, well-knowing Grania's dangerous humour. "Marthe Maria! Has my mother's intervention changed your mind?"

She regained a little of her dark composure.

"The Elders have informed me that in a day of such celebration, Hive cannot be off-limits. In view of that, the letter, and other factors ..."

She looked pointedly at someone behind me, from the opposite faction of hardcores, I presumed.

"I have no choice but to withdraw the prohibition."

Zoska hugged me, releasing Basienka, who for some time had been tugging at her mother's hand. Seizing the opportunity, she ran down the ramp and through the slit of door held open by the Watchgirl. There were stairs behind that door — Zoska looked over my shoulder and screamed. The guard started and let the door clang shut.

There was a moment of agony and then the door opened slowly again. My Honey came out cradling my foster-sister.

Beautiful Honeycomb! I wanted to shout it, but that would have ruined everything. Instead I stood silent as a doll, watching Basienka offer Honey some of her apple. Honey, smiling, took a bite and the crowd went "Ooh!"

"Little scene-stealer," muttered Zoska. She walked halfway down the ramp and collected the baby. Marthe took *her* baby by the hand for a moment: goodbye. Then we faced each other, with no womyn between us.

"Get a move on," yelled somebody.

So, shyly, we met at the top of the ramp and kissed. The ghetto cheered and we parted, half-embarrassed by the noise. Her lips had tasted sweet from the candied fruit.

"Honeymouth," I said.

"Yes, that is her name," said her mother. "Honey Marthe."

And I laughed, and Honey laughed, and it was all right.

On the Turn

LEANNE FRAHM

The wind met them head-on with an almost overpowering gust as they tramped their way through the last of the scrub and topped the final dune. It was deceptive. In the hollows, there had been no hint of the blast moaning overhead, no hint of a breeze on the highway, or when the car had turned at right angles onto the dusty pocked road that led to the beach. They had travelled between fields of sugarcane, three-quarters grown, that scarcely moved, between great loops of electricity lines on which anxious-looking nankeen kestrels and querulous butcher birds alternated, studying the fields below them intently for signs of tiny prey movements.

Saph had liked the trip. She knew birds pretty well, most of them, and had enjoyed the sudden intimate glimpses of small feral lives as they went, the noise of the car disturbing the quiet. Once, as they had rounded a bend, a small goanna had reared up with a look of astonished terror and had run waddling into the ditch, legs pumping comically at right angles to its body, almost tripping itself. Saph had laughed; Reg had grinned at her pleasure.

Then they were past the canefields, into flat greyish country, sparsely treed, where gaunt cattle were browsing on tufts of brittle grass. "Look at them," Saph had said mournfully. Reg had glanced at the herd, his hands still firm and assured on the wheel.

"They're drought cattle," he had said. "Brought in to the coast for agistment. They'll fatten up soon, soon enough to be nice and plump for the abattoirs.'' Saph had been silent; she enjoyed steak.

The cattle place had given way to muddy lagoons, sprouting water weeds and reeds, where a few black ducks were paddling industriously and white egrets were poised as if caught and preserved in amber. The road had become worse, and Reg had steered the car carefully between the ruts and hummocks until they could go no further, and had come to a halt in a little cleared patch where the solid ground became soft and sandy.

"Here we are," Reg had said.

They had alighted from the car, and Reg had apportioned the gear between them, carefully retaining his precious rods. It had been still in the clearing, but Saph had heard the muffled roar of waves. The beach wouldn't be far. They had walked along a faint trail that four-wheel drives had made, flattening the dry grass, letting the sand plump up and spill over it. Then they had climbed over the dunes.

And met the wind. It was blowing straight in from the sea with an implacable, unvarying determination. Reg looked dissatisfied. "No good casting into that lot," he said. "It'll blow the sinker right back in your face." He eyed the direction, and looked up and down the beach on which they stood. It stretched from a remote rocky point on their left to a place not far away to their right where mangrove thickets abruptly blocked its golden infinity.

"We can try the creek," he decided. Saph nodded; it was Reg's decision to make. He was the fisherman.

It was a pleasant walk, despite the gale lashing sideways at them, forcing Saph to stagger from time to time. The night tide had been high, and had left the sand compacted and firm to walk on. She found a huge whelk in their path, the slug coursing aimlessly across the drying sand, dragging its conical shell behind it. It could be drying up, she thought. She picked it up and it slowly withdrew into its shell, snapping its door shut, dangling strands of sand-encrusted mucus.

"Where are you going?" said Reg, loudly, because the wind was howling so.

"I'm throwing it back in the water. It's lost, and the tide's going out."

Reg snorted. "It'll last to the next one, won't it?" Saph continued to the water's edge anyway. Reg didn't know, not for sure. Better to be sure.

They reached a point where the beach rounded into a point, and mangroves grew as suddenly and as high as a wall in front of them. A narrow meandering creek issued from them, its banks sand for a little way inland, then transforming by degrees into the gelatinous mud of the mangrove swamp. "Down there a little," Reg said, pointing to a spot where the sand and mud formed an uneasy alliance that made it possible to walk comfortably. "We'll wait for the water to go down a little, and cross the creek to those mudflats over there." He waved to what was still a sheet of water on the other side of the creek's mouth where the mangroves faced the sea. "There'll be lots of lobbies there. We'll pump for them, come back here, and wait for the turn of the tide."

"Can't we fish now?" said Saph. "You've got some bait ...."

"Lobbies are better, fresh ones. And it's no good trying to fish on the falling tide. Fish just won't bite then. It's a waste of time."

Saph wondered if waiting for an incoming tide wasn't a waste of time when there was all that water there, but she said nothing. Reg knew about fish; she didn't.

Reg placed their gear on his chosen spot, flopped down beside it and pulled a paperback out of the rucksack. Saph stood watching the water in the creek. He glanced up at her. "You might as well relax. It'll be at least another half hour before the turn."

"Then why are we here now?" said Saph.

"Because I thought we could fish the surf for whiting. We can't. This is the alternative." He went back to his book.

Saph shrugged, and wandered back along the beach, examining stray shells and driftwood, kicking at clumps of drying seaweed. She liked the beach; always had. It was a place

253

somehow linked with childhood fun and parental indulgence. Of course, those beaches had always been crowded, peopled beaches, like the ones in children's storybooks, with deck-chairs and buckets and spades and other kids wailing with sand in their eyes. And sunburn cream. She glanced at her pale freckled forearm, where the sunburn cream glistened colourlessly.

This beach was different, though. Nothing moved, except the sea and a seagull far out and hovering above the rough waves. The wind was lifting fine sand and driving it into the dunes, making it look filmy and off-focus. It felt desolate, almost eerie under a bright sun that shouldn't have allowed eeriness. You probably have to get used to this sort of beach, Saph thought.

They waded through water up to Saph's thighs in crossing the creek. Saph was amazed at how shallow it was.

"And it still has further to go out?" she said.

Reg nodded. "Two o'clock it turns."

"It must get awfully low," she said. In affirmation, little sandbars and pieces of driftwood were already emerging at the edge of the creek, sending the current into new directions and complex eddies. She stopped to look at a tiny crab busily investigating a rotting tree trunk embedded in the sand, saw Reg almost across, and scampered through the water to catch up, wetting her jeans to the waist. The wind made it cold, but already the sun was heating the damp material. She could feel it hot on her rump.

Reg had walked a little way onto the mudflat as she came up to him, sinking a few inches with each step. He was examining the ground intently. She could see that it was covered with tiny holes. "These are lobby beds," he said to her. "They burrow into the mud and sand and live in the holes." Saph nodded, although she didn't even know what a lobby looked like yet. But the size of the holes indicated that they weren't very large and were therefore unintimidating.

Reg positioned the lobby pump in the middle of a particularly dense group of holes. He plunged the tube into the mud at an angle with a liquid squelch, at the same time drawing up on the plunger. He pulled the pump from the mud, pressed down on the plunger, and with a gurgle a cylinder of mud and sand squirted out at their feet. Saph stared at it. Little forms were squirming frantically in the middle of it.

"Quick!" yelled Reg. "Grab them!"

"What?" said Saph.

"Those! They're lobbies. Put them in the basket."

Saph held out the small wicker basket Reg had given her to carry. "This?" she said.

Reg grabbed it from her, and bent towards the lobbies, already almost invisible as they wormed their way back into the mud. He managed to pick up a couple, threw one back — "Too small" — and put the solitary catch in the basket.

"Now," he said, straightening. "I'm sorry, I didn't explain it properly. When I pump, you have to be ready to catch them before they dig in again. *That's*" — he pointed to the lobby in the basket — "what you have to pick up."

Saph examined the lobby curiously as it scuttled up and down in the confines of its cage. It was less than an inch long, pale orange, and looked just like a miniature prawn, except that it was armed with a pinky-white claw that was nearly as long as its body. "Does it bite?" she asked doubtfully.

"They'll nip if you're not careful," Reg said. "Now, be ready."

"All right," said Saph.

After half an hour the basket was half full. Reg seemed pleased that the beds had proved so lobby-abundant. Saph looked into the basket, glad that Reg was pleased, despite the many lobbies she'd missed, but the sight of the packed mass of little creatures heaving while the uppermost ones scurried back and forth over the bodies of the bottom layers unsettled her.

"How do you kill them?" she asked.

"*Kill* them?" Reg echoed. "You don't *kill* them. You use them for live bait."

"What — alive?" said Saph.

"Now you know why I didn't want to bring you fishing," said Reg, the exasperation that she'd known lurked beneath his calm bursting forth. "You're too soft," he added roughly, as if to emphasise that softness by contrast.

"I wanted to share it with you," Saph said, tears trembling her voice. "Marriages are for sharing, aren't they?"

His annoyance gentled, and he smiled at her. "Most things, but you weren't meant for some things, Saph."

She smiled tremulously back at him. "Now, how are you going to kill them?"

Reg snorted, and turned away, picking up the gear. Saph was left with the basket of writhing lobbies. She knew he wasn't going to kill them, even for her. She tried to imagine what it felt like, to have a huge hook sliced into your chest, feeling it worm its way down into your entrails —

"Do they die straight away?" she called above the wind.

"No!" A gust of wind trailed the word away from her, towards the land.

— Your legs and arms twitching in a mock paralysis of screeching pain ... But the thought was too uncomfortable, so she busied herself in hurrying after Reg, feeling the wind burning the other side of her face now, as they strode back towards the creek.

"What time did you say?" Saph asked, as much to make conversation as to know.

Reg didn't look up from his paperback. "Two o'clock," he said.

She threw another shell into the creek water. It was less windy here; a rise in the sandy point as it turned into the creek kept the wind mostly above them as they sat by the water's edge — or what had been the water's edge. Still, the wind howled into the massed growth of mangroves opposite their position, tossing the leaves on their stunted branches, whipping the creek waters into waves that marched inland, making it look like the tide was indeed coming in.

"It's quarter past," she said.

Reg closed his book on a finger. "They take that time at the harbour. We're quite a bit south of that, and the coast curves inland, so the tide's probably going to turn a bit later here." It was nice of him, Saph thought, to explain things so considerately to her. She threw another shell at the water.

"Don't do that," Reg said automatically. "You'll frighten the fish."

"What fish?" she said.

"The fish are there, all right, but they won't bite until the tide turns."

"Oh."

She looked closely at the surface of the water. Yes, the waves gave the impression that the water was racing in, but when you looked through the water, you could see dead leaves and sticks whirling along in the current, towards the sea. And bubbles, as if the fish below were breathing gently, gathering strength for the turn and the feeding frenzy ... And she'd placed a sea-bleached shell upright in the sand where the waves washed the bank, and now the water was several inches beyond it, still receding.

She got up, brushed the sand from her bottom, and walked to where the lobby basket sat. Reg had scooped a hole in the wet sand, and it had half-filled from seepage. He'd placed the basket in it, in the shade of the creel. "To keep them alive till we need them," he'd explained, and Saph wondered if his smile hadn't been just the littlest bit cruel as he'd looked at her, and then had dismissed the idea as unwholesome and false.

The lobbies were still milling around, although more lethargically. Some didn't seem to be moving at all, were floating limply in the water that now enveloped them within the wickerwork. Saph thought they looked forlorn, but resigned, as if they'd been brought up to expect little from their muddy lives, and this little seemed to be just about right. She sighed, and looked at the creek.

More sandbars had risen, and only one narrow channel still flowed seaward with any confidence. Some water was trapped in little pools, and it flowed nowhere; only the wind ruffled it into waves that looked as if they meant to march somewhere.

Saph said loudly, "I'm starting to fish now. I'm sick of waiting." Reg jerked his head up; he'd pulled a dead tree trunk, scoured white by many weary miles of ocean travel and deposited high on the beach by some king tide, down to a spot closer to the creek, and had been leaning back against it, reading.

"What's the time?" he said, and answered himself by glancing at his watch. "Ten past three ... Is that water still going out?"

Saph looked at a brown fragment of leaf drifting past with a hesitant swirl. "Yes."

Reg looked surprised and stood up. "Should be turning by now, surely." He stooped to pull another book from the rucksack. Saph recognised it — his *Tidal Diary 1985*. "Maybe I got the date wrong," he said, flicking through the pages. "No — no, that's right." He pushed the book back in between the first-aid kit, the torch, the spare lines, and stood staring at the creek, hands on hips, frowning.

"Well, I'm going to fish anyway," Saph repeated.

"Okay," said Reg absently. Then, "Do you want me to bait your hook?"

"No, I'll use the dead squid." It came out more forcefully than she'd meant, but that was because she had to shout against the wind. Reg shrugged, and with a final puzzled glance at the creek, went back to his reading.

Fishing was fun, she decided. It was fun to get squid juice all over her fingers, fumbling to push the flesh? skin? muscle? of the piece of squid onto the hook, and to wipe it carelessly, stinking of salt-ocean, off on her jeans. It was exhilarating to feel the line zing out as she cast, right into the middle of the channel, and pleasant to sit quietly holding the rod with her fingers over the line as Reg had taught her, to feel when the fish bit. She felt at peace with all the silence around her, with the sluggishly ebbing water, even with the wind moaning and whipping the mangroves opposite.

Overhead two brahminy kites were sailing, pausing head-on into the wind sometimes — how could they not be blown away, she wondered, when they hovered so motionlessly — mewling with a sound like a new baby that came strangely from those relentless tearing beaks. The gull had been joined by some others, and they spent most of their time strutting up and down on the beach behind her with a curious mixture of aloofness and supplication now that they saw she was fishing, and that there might therefore be scraps of bait. Smart birds, she thought with a grin. A couple of terns — two different species, she could tell, but which, she couldn't identify — glided out over the rumpled sand that marked the mouth of the creek, disdaining the pouty beggarship of the gulls. She watched them soar against the hot blue sky.

From where she sat, the sandbars exposed by the falling tide seemed to stretch to the horizon. Only a fuzzy white and grey-green line beyond the yellow of the sand proved that there was still an ocean out there. She wondered about the tides. The moon pulled the high tide after it, she knew, and left the low tide eternally hurrying behind it, round and round, up and down. She tried to picture it, but instead of a globe she could only see a teacup slopping brown liquid from side to side, until it slurped over the rim and ran down the side, leaving a muddy brown stain on the white china surface.

The line tugged under her fingers. She jerked her hands up, more from fright than experience. The water was so shallow that the sinker exploded into the air on her jerk and sailed towards the beach, drawing a silver-flashing shape with it. She turned the reel inexpertly, crying out to Reg. "A fish! Look! I've caught a fish!"

He dropped his book and came over to her, seizing the line and pulling the dangling tackle and its burden towards him. He laughed. "It's a bit small," he said.

"What is it?" she asked.

"A little perch." He grabbed it with his thumb and finger round the body, well back from the gasping gills. "Careful, it's got nice little spikes there." He took the hook in the fingers of his other hand. "You've hooked it nicely," he said. Saph felt the glow of his compliment fade as she stared at the mouth of the little fish. It was gaping open, and she could see that the hook had pierced the flesh on the inside, behind the jaw and the tiny teeth, and had come out on the other side, through the pulsating white skin above its throat. She thought of a hook jabbed through *her* jaw, coming out in *her* throat, and almost gagged with the imagined pain.

"It's far too little," Reg was saying. He deftly twisted the hook, withdrawing it from the mouth of the flapping fish, and tossed it back into the water. It disappeared with a silver flicker. "Want more bait?" he said, then looked up at her.

"Saph," he said, almost angrily, she could sense.

"I'm sorry," she said.

"You wanted to fish," he said, turning the statement into an accusation.

"I didn't think — I didn't realise ..." It was impossible to tell him how the pain felt. Fish didn't feel, he would say. Not like us, he'd point out. She turned away from him.

"Well, then," he said, with a forced jollity. "I almost dozed off then."

He looked at his watch. "Ten to four ..." Saph barely heard his mutter in the wind. He glanced at her quickly, then walked to the edge of the trickle of water that ran from the creek, still on the ebb. Saph had not seen him look like this before; Reg never looked bewildered.

"What's wrong?" she asked.

He was frowning again, a hard set to his face. "The tide should have turned well and truly by now," he said. "There's something wrong somewhere. Either the diary or ..." He couldn't seem to think what else could be wrong. "Well, we've been here so long that even if the time was wrong, it must turn any minute."

"Yes," said Saph. "There's hardly any water left to come out."

He grinned at her. "That's one way of putting it. We'll give it a bit longer."

Saph was suddenly tired of the fishing trip. The afternoon sun was slanting across the mangroves now, more golden than the white hotness of noon, but out over the sea and sandbars the wind seemed to have sucked the colour from the sunlight, making it grey and oppressive. The last of the afternoon's comfort was lowering with the sun, and Saph wanted to follow that sun home. Besides, she knew she wouldn't be fishing again, ever.

"It's getting late," she said. "Can't we go home now? Even when the tide comes in, it'll take a long time to start filling up the creek and we'd be here for ages."

"I came here to fish," Reg said. His face was stony; sometimes he could be very obstinate. Saph recognised that this was a sometimes, and sat down by the creek, putting the rod behind her where she couldn't see the hook.

The mudskippers were out in force. They could skip practically right across the creek now. All the bed was exposed except for a thread of water, oily-looking and black in the heavy shadows of the mangroves. The tiny mottled fish hopped around, leaping into puddles and awkwardly out again, having a great old time, Saph thought, with so much air available to them. They'd get sick of it though; they'd need the water to come in and dampen everything down again.

She looked at the shell she had erected so hopefully as a marker for the tide. It was a long way behind her now; she'd followed the water right down, heedless of the spreading muddy stain on the seat of her jeans, so she could watch the 'skippers and the tiny black crabs with the huge threatening claws they waved in a sort of crustacean semaphore, whether signalling "Attack" or "Truce" or "Hi beautiful" she didn't know. The wicker basket of lobbies was beside her. Its original Reg-made pool had dried up, and loose sand had begun to blow over it. As she'd moved forwards, she'd made new puddles for it at each stop, pushing the sand and mud to one side, and putting the basket into the water that gathered. It was little use, though. Most of them looked dead — motionless, at least. Still . . .

She glanced back at Reg. He was not reading now. He was sitting on the log, staring at the dark strip of moving water that was the creek, concentrating on it as if to turn the current by force of will. He looked angry — no, more than angry — but she had to try.

"Can we go home now?"

"Not yet," he said.

She turned back to the water. The setting sun threw a final effulgence that glimmered briefly on the stream, turning it momentarily from black to blood-red. She shivered. The wind seemed even stronger.

The wind-grey had seeped across the unending sandbars, across the beach and reached them in the creek. There was little light, only a suffocating dimness that strained the eyes more than blackness. The mudskippers and crabs had retired to their mud homes, seeking moisture deep within the ooze. Saph had watched the last of them pop into their burrows with a final flick of tail or wave of claw. The birds had long since gone, crooning and calling, to faraway nests. Saph looked at the creek. There was no thread of water now, only unconnected pools, small isolated lakes left in the depressions in the sand whose surfaces shuddered in the wind.

"It's stopped," she called loudly without turning her head. There was no reply from Reg. She stood up and faced him. "It's stopped," she repeated.

He was a pale shape against the paler sand, leaning against the driftwood and staring into the mangroves across the creek bed, his arms huddled across his chest.

"I'll wait," he said.

Saph bent down to the basket, opened the lid, and upended it in one of the shallow pools. One or two lobbies stirred; the rest lay like a child's sandcastle, a cake of dead bait, gradually dissolving into the water.

She left the basket where it lay, on the mud, and walked back to where Reg sat. She felt sorry for him, but she said firmly, "I'm going now. I know an end when I see it."

"I'll *wait*!" yelled Reg, making her jump.

She turned away and began walking back along the beach towards the car, with more difficulty now that the sand was dry. The wind buffeted her, blowing faster now that it was coming over smooth sandbars instead of rough water.

She noticed in the gloom another large whelk at her feet, began to pick it up, then realised that there was no water handy to put it into. "You should have kept up," she said out loud. It made her chest hurt to think of the millions of little things, like the mudskippers and the crabs, who hadn't kept up, who were unaware of the end that Reg stubbornly didn't believe in yet.

She looked back towards the invisible creek. "It's not coming back," she called, but the wind picked up her words and sprayed them uselessly across the night, and she continued to trudge along the long empty beach.